TWINS to QUINTS

The Complete Manual for Parents of Multiple Birth Children

Compiled by

National Organization of Mothers of Twins Clubs, Inc.

Edited by Rebecca E. Moskwinski, M.D., FAAFP
Family Physician, University of Notre Dame
Notre Dame, Indiana

HARPETH HOUSE PUBLISHING

Nashville, Tennessee

This is a Harpeth House Book
Published by Harpeth House Publishing

Library of Congress Cataloguing-In-Publication Data

National Organization of Mothers Of Twins Clubs, Inc.
Twins to Quints: The Complete Manual For Parents of Multiple Birth Children/National
Organization of Mothers of Twins Clubs, Inc.

p   cm.
ISBN: 0-9705692-3-8
1. Twins
2. Multiple Births
1.Title

Manufactured in the United States of America

First Edition

TWINS to QUINTS

This book is dedicated to all multiples

and their families.

They inspire us, teach us, humble us,

and were the driving force

behind this book.

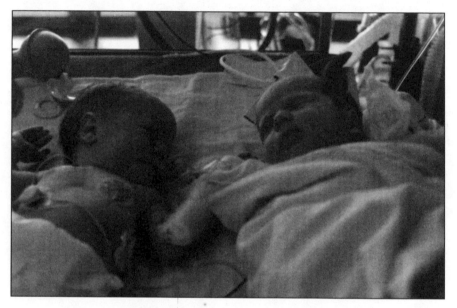

Multiple birth children — a team from the start.

CONTENTS

In the NICU
Coming Home
Making Adjustments, Planning Ahead
Basic Equipment
Breast-Feeding
Bottle Feeding
Daily Routine
Out and About
Facing the Public
Multiple Development
Multiple Joy

CONTRIBUTORS

Patti Beemer
Adopting

Edna Coburn
Bereavement

Mary Moore Davis
Set or Individuals, Disability

Margie Downey
Founder and Senior Editor of *Home School Families of Twins*
Home schooling

Martha Eicker
Middle School Educator
School Age, Stay at Home, Set or Individuals

Elitha Farmer
Bereavement

Susan F. Grammer, BS
Science Writer, *Biotechwrite: Biomedical and Science Communications*,
Houston, Texas
Working Parents

J. Susan Griffith, MD
University of Kentucky Health Services, Family Physician
Single Parenting

Jill M. Heink
Supertwins

Allen Helvajian
Just for Dads

Christy Helvajian
Stay at Home

Kathy Hornsby
NICU Staff Nurse
NICU

Marie Jansen
Bereavement

Donna May Lyons
Freelance Writer and Stay-at-home mom to Ashleigh, Amanda, and DJ
Stay at Home

Rebecca Moskwinski, MD, FAAFP
University of Notre Dame Health Services, Family Physician and Team
Physician
Pregnancy, How Could this Happen, Preparations, Infancy, Toddler,
Disabilities

Lisa Pilon
Independent Breast-feeding Advocate, veteran of Jessica, Christopher
and Nicholas
Breast-feeding

Toni Simoneaud
Stay at home

Linda J. Simpson
Computing Resource Specialist
Adult Twins

Mary Beth Snelson, RN, BSN
Staff Labor and Delivery Nurse
Labor and Delivery

Dale Willenberg, CRNA, MHS
Clinical Nurse Anesthetist, Maury Regional Hospital
Labor and Delivery

Kelly Willenberg, RN, BSN
Clinical Director of Clinical Trials Office, Vanderbilt-Ingram Cancer Center
Labor and Delivery

CONTRIBUTORS TO QUICK TIPS

Adcock, Mary (Hutchinson Area MOMs, Hutchinson, Kans.)
Alvis, Jennifer (Albuquerque MOTC, Albuquerque, N.M.)
Anderson, April (Fair Haven, N.J.)
Aucoin, Darlene (Acadiana MOM, Port Barre, La.)
Beemer, Patti (Colorado Springs MOM, Colorado Springs, Colo.)
Bennett, Susan (Napa Valley MOTC, Napa, Calif.)
Berube, Nancy K. (Cape Fear MOTC, Cape Fear, N.C.)
Bingham, Sherry (Edmond MOMs, Edmond, Okla.)
Black, Shannon (Kalamazoo, Mich.)
Brumfield, Elizabeth (South Palm Beach County POMC, South Palm Beach,
   Fla.)
Burke, Alice (Waterbury MOTC, New Britain, Conn.)
Campbell, Cheri (Northern Virginia POMS, Alexandria, Va.)
Carroll, Patti (Eugene, Ore.)
Castelot, Laurel (Southside MOTC, Greenwood, Ind.)
Chaisson, Valerie (Albany, N.Y.)
Chrisman-Keller, Marianna (Mid-Peninsula POMC, Calif.)
Ciardi, Debbie (Rare Pair, Norman, Okla.)
Clauss, Patti (Duvall, Wash.)
Cluff, Monica (Valley Twins Club, Buellton, Calif.)
Coburn, Edna (Tucson, Ariz.)
Cowden, Lisa (MOMs Society, Littleton, Colo.)
Dautremont, Kathleen (Des Moines MOMs, Des Moines, Ia.)
Davis, Mary Moore (MOMC, Jackson, Miss.)
DeVore, Jennifer (West Los Angeles MOTs, Calif.)
Downey, Margie (North Dallas MOTC, Dallas, Tex.)
Duglenski, Daria (Waterbury Area MOTC, Waterbury, Conn.)
Dziurzynski, Karen (Hamburg, N.Y.)
Eagleson, Christie (Mobile, Ala.)
Edelman, Pam (Osceola, Ind.)
Edgington, Teresa (NEMOTC, Cincinnati, O.)
Eicker, Martha (Twice as Nice MOMs, Chicago, Ill.)
Elder, Susan (Capital District MOTC, Wynantskill, N.Y.)
Eliseev, Christine (Arlington MOM, Arlington, Tex.)
Emerson, Chandra (Bluegrass MOT&M, Cynthiana, Ky.)
Fresco, Caryn (Tidewater MOM, Virginia Beach, Va.)
Fulmer, Chris (South Dade POMC, Homestead, Fla.)
Gaitto-Lemmon, Chris (Northeast & Westchester MOTC, Cincinnati, O.)
Galle-Mattia, Denyel (Westside Suburban MOTC, Spencerport, N.Y.)

Gatewood, Karen (Levittown, Pa.)
Gomez, Bobbi (East Quogue, N.Y.)
Gonzalez, Tasha (Ossining, N.Y.)
Grammer, Susan (MOMs of Houston, Houston, Tex.)
Gratz, Liz (Coastside MOTC, South San Francisco, Calif.)
Griggs, Mary (Michiana POMC, Mishawaka, Ind.)
Grossbaum, Debra (West Suburban Chapter, Dover, Mass.)
Guthrie, Michelle (Belleville, N.Y.)
Hames, Becky (San Diego, Calif.)
Hanold, Lori (Bay Area MOMs, Odessa, Fla.)
Hazelton, Kathy (Naugatuck, Conn.)
Heink, Jill (Lexington, Ky.)
Helsley, Susan (Winchester, Va.)
Hinrichs, Anita (Albuquerque MOTC, Albuquerque, N.M.)
Hoff, Kim (Pairs and Spairs, Newman Lake, Wash.)
Hottel-Burkhart, Nancy (Kingdom of Morocco)
Hsu, Amy (Rockville, Md.)
Hurwitz, Janet L. (MOT&T, Valley Forge, Pa.)
Inniss, L.K. Buckner (Alpharetta, Ga.)
Izard, Margaret (Katy Area POMs, Houston, Tex.)
Jeffway, Celeste (Hampshire County MOTC, Northampton, Mass.)
Joe, Camilla (Gemini Crickets POM, San Jose, Calif.)
Jones, Diana (Bay Area MOMs, Baldwin City, Tex.)
Kapinos, Tina (Buffalo Grove, Ill.)
Kaufman, Beth (Montgomery County POMs, Bethesda, Md.)
Keller, Dawn (Thompson Station, Tenn.)
Kellogg, Diane (Richmond, Va.)
King, Sharon (Chester County MOT&T, West Chester, Pa.)
Knox, Karen (MOTC of Rockland County, N.Y.)
Landrigan, Donna (Farmington, N.Y.)
Levison, Heidi (Coastside MOTC, Brisbane, Calif.)
Lothringer, Lisa M. (Southeast Suburban MOTC, Carleton, Mich.)
Lovaglio, Susan (Rockland County MOTC, N.Y.)
Lyon, Patti (Albuquerque MOTC, Albuquerque, N.M.)
Mackey, Melissa (Capital Area MOTC, Lansing, Mich.)
Marinack, Donna (Shawano Lake Area MOTC, Shawano Lake, Wis.)
Mason, Cheryl (Murfreesboro POTC, Murfreesboro, Tenn.)
McKinney, Lisa (Mesquite, Tex.)
Meinders, Florence (Pella, Ia.)
Mervosh, Laura (Nassau County MOTC, Westbury, N.Y.)
Michael, Shannon (Bothell, Wash.)
Mickler, Michelle (Rantoul, Ill.)
Miller, Donna (Greenville MOMs, Greenville, S.C.)
Mitchell, Ann Marie (POTATO, Nashville, Tenn.)

Moskwinski, Becky (Michiana POMC, Granger, Ind.)
Noble, Dyhanna (Billerica, Mass.)
Noyes, Barbara (MOTC of Rockland County, Blauvelt, N.Y.)
Olson, Shanna (Aurora, Colo.)
Pawlik, Jennifer (Desert Sky MOM, Chandler, Ariz.)
Phelan, Lohri (Pomona Valley MOTC, Double Deal MOMs, Anaheim, Calif.)
Plunkett, Larrie (Wailuku, Hi.)
Rabinowitz, Robin (Nassau County MOTC, Merrick, N.Y.)
Ricci, Kathie (Berkshire County MOT, Lee, Mass.)
Rohling, Colleen (Cedar Rapids, Ia.)
Rokicsak, Maria Patrick (MOTC of Rockland County, N.Y.)
Rooks, Joy Duncan (Wetumpka, Ala.)
Roy, Melody (Gold Country MOMs, Auburn, Calif.)
Russell, Tina (Twin City MOMs, Winston-Salem, N.C.)
Rustchak, Natasha L. (Tidewater MOMs, Norfolk, Va.)
Rydland, Danine (Martinsburg, W.Va.)
Sageev, Lisa (Cranford, N.J.)
Samick, Susanna (Bellaire Area MOM, Tex.)
Sampedro, Kelly A. (Camden County MOTC, Camden, N.J.)
Sciarrone, Kelly (Bi-County MOMs, Shoreham, N.Y.)
Sherlock, Sandy (Chico MOMs, Calif.)
Sikes, Deanna (Houston, Tex.)
Simpson, Linda (Valley MOTC, Kent, Wash.)
Singy, Andrea (Colorado Springs MOM, Colorado Springs, Colo.)
Slayter, Ann (Twins Family Club, Corvallis, Ore.)
Smith, Penny (Cape Fear MOTC, Cape Fear, N.C.)
Smith, Melissa K. (Double Delight MOTC, Windsor, Ill.)
Sovia, Julie (MOTC of Rockland County, Orangeburg, N.Y.)
Spangler, Deidre & Dan (Webster, Mass.)
Susi, Carolyn (Greater Portland MOTC, Gorham, Me.)
Teeple, Lisa (POTATO, Whites Creek, Tenn.)
Thomas, Carol (Oviedo, Fla.)
Thompson, Jennifer (High Bridge, N.J.)
Tier, Kelly (Saddleback MOMs, Lake Forest, Calif.)
Urbowicz, Kris (Abilene, Tex.)
Vaughn, Jane (Central Jersey MOM, Bordentown, N.J.)
Viggiano, Karen (South Hills of Pittsburgh MOM, Pittsburgh, Pa.)
Wallace, Sheron (Colorado Springs MOM, Colorado Springs, Colo.)
Watson, Olivia (Great Valley POM, Tracy, Calif.)
Willenberg, Kelly (Columbia, Tenn.)
Wilwart, Jennifer (BAMOMs, Tampa, Fla.)
Winn, Nancy L. (North Dallas MOTC, Plano, Tex.)
Woodruff, Marie (Ocean County MOTC, Toms River, N.J.)
Zick, Grace (Nassau County MOTC, Baldwin, N.Y.)

These boys are on their way up

FOREWORD

FIFTEEN YEARS OF "MULTIPLES" has taught me that no parent knows exactly what the arrival of multiple birth children will truly do to their family's life. Yet, one by one, we assume the responsibility of the "wonder" of multiples without much preparation, learning as we go. Parenting multiple birth children is much more complex than parenting single birth children. Most muddle their way through, sometimes not having adequate information to guide them through the ups and downs of this challenging, but rewarding job we all endure.

A multiple birth is a vulnerable situation, whether it's by natural circumstance or adoption. Parents are placed in an unknown situation where fear and confusion makes most of us anxious and stressed. Lives are disrupted, marriages change, and multiples make us different people. None of us truly understands the multiple bond among twins, triplets, and even higher order births and how this affects our parenting. Yet, day to day, we raise our multiples to be independent thinking adults ready to face the challenges life gives them. From day one as a parent of multiples, I sometimes needed answers and depended on my multiple birth parent counterparts to guide me through the awkward moments. Thankfully, I was a member of a parents of multiples club for the necessary support. I hope you are, too.

Being a mother of multiples has given me more to study and explore in the psychology unique to multiples. I suggest you read our manual to parenting multiple birth children and find answers to many of your every day questions. This book will help you to better understand this inexplicable web that no parent of multiples truly knows how to maneuver.

As President of NOMOTC at the turn of the millennium, I want all parents to have fun with their multiples, interact with them in a positive way, and remember that those vulnerable moments are sometimes theirs alone as multiples. Join a parents of multiples club, share situations with others who are going through what you are experiencing, and relish this informative book written to give you all of the information you need on the mysterious bond of a multiple relationship and the unique aspects of parenting multiple birth children.

Kelly M. Willenberg, RN, BSN
NOMOTC President
1999-2001

ACKNOWLEDGEMENT

IN ANY BOOK OF THIS NATURE, there are many hands contributing to the final project. In attempting to name some of them, inevitably there will be someone who is missed. For that, I apologize.

Initially, thanks to Dr. J. Susan Griffith who first broached the topic of writing this book at a NOMOTC Board Meeting. Though we had talked of it many times, she had the foresight to get the project off the ground. Thanks to the sitting president of our organization at that time, Martha Eicker, who gave the go-ahead for the project and the Board of Directors at that time for agreeing to move forward. The following presidents, Nancy L. Winn and Kelly Willenberg, kept the book project viable through the many years it took to write it.

A special thanks to Martha Eicker who helped me edit the chapters and saw the entire manuscript. Her tireless devotion to this book and friendship have been priceless. Also, thanks to Mary Adcock, who read the entire manuscript and gave some great suggestions and edits.

Grateful acknowledgement goes to the current Board of Directors, Patti Beemer, Nancy L. Winn, Mary Adcock, Trish Michalkowski, Brenda Roser, Patrice Sullivan, Pam Krell, Misty Fry, Edna Coburn, Christy Helvajian, Pam Edelman, Kelly Willenberg, and executive secretary Dawn Keller for their help and passion for this project.

The final project would not have been possible without the help of Ellen Johnson, a twin and a friend, who helped us negotiate the muddy waters of the publishing process. Her patience and fortitude and the donation of a considerable amount of time were instrumental in making the book a success.

Thanks to Wendell Rawls and Jack Hurst, who saw what we were trying to do and made it their passion as well. Their cheerfulness, calm demeanor, belief in our work, and most of all their patience with our occasional craziness has been the glue holding this project together, and for that I am extremely grateful.

Finally, to my family – my husband Jerome, my twins Lindsay and Bridget (who got me into this mess) and their sibs Nick, Ted, Kelsey and Molly – for their patience with my long hours at the computer and their support. The question "Are you still writing that book?" was an endless one; the process probably seemed to consume me for most of some of their lives. I love you all very much. And to my Lord, Jesus Christ, my strength and my inspiration, who watches over me and keeps me grounded.

— *Rebecca Moskwinski*

A WORD ABOUT ABBREVIATIONS

Within our organization, there are some common abbreviations we employ for frequently-used words and club names. Here are some you will find throughout this book:

HOM - Higher Order Multiple
MOMs - Mothers of Multiples
MOTC - Mothers of Twins Club
MOT&T - Mothers of Twins and Triplets
NOMOTC - National Organization of Mothers of Twins Clubs, Inc.
POMC - Parents of Multiples Club
POMs - Parents of Multiples
POTC - Parents of Twins Club

We had tried to conceive for about three years but never required any
fertility drugs. When it finally happened we were very excited. Being in
the medical field, however, I knew I was getting larger than predicted for
my dates. At 18 weeks I was finally scheduled for an ultrasound. (I had
already been listening for more than one heartbeat.) My husband is six
feet three inches tall, and I really just assumed it was going to be a big
baby. As soon as the technician put the transducer on my abdomen there
were two round circles, and I knew immediately what was going on! I kept
saying, "I knew it!" My poor husband just sat there in shocked silence,
although later on he was as excited as I was. I must have called everyone I
knew that night, even long distance, to tell them the news! We kept track
of my expanding abdomen monthly. I got so large that I could hardly walk
around; the whole lower half of my body swelled up, and I outgrew my
maternity clothes, which was very depressing. I remember I kept having
the strangest dreams that one baby was normal but the other one wasn't or
that I would forget and leave them places. It was fascinating and
frightening at the same time.

Rebecca Moskwinski, Granger, Ind.

1

"I'm Going to Have WHAT?"
THE TWIN PREGNANCY

Multiple pregnancy brings with it many mixed emotions — elation, fear, depression, shock, joy, pride — sometimes all at the same time. In very few cases is it expected. No woman "sets out" to have multiples.

DIAGNOSIS

Chances are good that you will suspect the multiple pregnancy before your health care provider does. However, if it is your first pregnancy you may not have anything to compare it to.

SIGNS OF MULTIPLE PREGNANCY

Some of the signs that mothers notice are: being larger than expected; feeling movement and kicks in all areas of the abdomen, rather than only on one side; an earlier onset of morning sickness and severe bouts with it; and sometimes just a sense that something is different.

Your doctor may detect other signs — such as a larger size of the uterus than expected, based on your due date. Your serum alpha-fetoprotein (AFP) level may be elevated. He or she may hear two heartbeats during one of your prenatal exams.

ULTRASOUND EXAMS

When your doctor suspects a multiple birth, an ultrasound exam may be ordered. Ultrasound exams use sound waves to form an image of tissue in the body. It has been proven to be a very safe test for prenatal diagnosis. New advances in ultrasound technique can detect even small abnormalities.

Ultrasound exams are generally painless. You will be instructed to drink several ounces of fluids and take the exam with a full bladder. This helps to separate the bladder tissue from the tissues in the uterus (womb) to make the image clearer, especially in early pregnancy. The technician will put a lubricating jelly on your abdomen and slide a wand-like object (the transducer) over your belly to get the image. Sometimes the pictures are obvious, but the technician may not inform you of the results until the doctor is notified. It is always exciting to catch those first glimpses of the babies and see their hearts beating! Suddenly the pregnancy is more real.

Sometimes ultrasound exams are used several times during the pregnancy to follow the babies' growth and help determine whether the pregnancy is proceeding as it should. Because of the safety and widespread availability of ultrasound exams, no multiple pregnancy should go undiagnosed.

Before the advent of ultrasound exams, the diagnosis of a multiple pregnancy was difficult and unsatisfactory. In the 1950s only 50 percent of multiple births were diagnosed before delivery. At that time, diagnosis was made by measuring the size of the uterus, noting an excess of weight gain, hearing two separate heartbeats, and sometimes by taking an x-ray exam later in pregnancy.

When ultrasound exams came on the scene, diagnosis improved. However, in 1975 one quarter of multiple births still were discovered only after labor had begun. A review of the database of the National Organization of Mothers of Twins Clubs from 1991 shows that 78 percent of multiple births were diagnosed in the second trimester and 83 percent were diagnosed by the time of delivery.

Sometimes, very early in pregnancy (before six weeks gestation), multiples may be discovered, but then later only one fetus is seen. This *vanishing twin* phenomenon will be discussed in chapter 3, but because of it a true estimate of the number of babies present cannot be made until after seven weeks of pregnancy. The use of vaginal (as opposed to abdominal) ultrasound can enhance the diagnosis in very early pregnancy.

MULTIPLE PREGNANCY AND RISK

While a multiple pregnancy is considered a high-risk pregnancy, the majority of twins and triplets have no major handicaps. Though the multiples may be small at birth, studies show that by the time the children reach school age they have caught up with single-born children developmentally and physically. The low birth weight multiple actually has a better survival rate than the low birth weight singleton. Low birth weight multiples also have the same mean IQ scores as singleton children. For support and reassurance, meeting and networking with other mothers of multiples while you are still pregnant can be a source of support, reassurance, and positive feedback. Make contact with a parents-of-multiples club early in your pregnancy.

Another point to remember is that you have a hand in helping to keep your babies healthy. Proper prenatal care, rest, and nutrition, as well as a positive attitude, will go a long way toward increasing the chances of having healthy multiples.

PRENATAL CARE

From the moment the diagnosis of multiples is made, early prenatal care is a must. Though the vast majority of multiples are healthy at birth, there can be an eight to 10 times increase in the risk of problems surrounding the birth compared to singleton pregnancies. Premature (or preterm) birth is the leading cause of neonatal death in multiple pregnancies. Because of this, it is important that a health care provider is chosen who has some experience in multiple births. Higher order multiple births should be managed by a perinatal specialist at a hospital with a high-level Neonatal Intensive Care Unit (NICU).

CHOOSING A HEALTH CARE PROVIDER

It is important to be comfortable with your health care provider. You should make sure that you and the provider share similar philosophies with regard to the type of anesthesia and delivery. Be sure to know ahead of time what the options are. It may be disappointing to discover that the type of delivery that you dreamed of (such as a home delivery) may not be possible with multiples. Be willing to compromise for the health of the babies. Working together with the health care provider should make possible a good birthing experience that is safe for the babies, still leaving room for other options should the unexpected occur. (See Chapter 5.)

Because of the possibility of early delivery, you should become familiar with the NICU and the routine there. Doing this ahead of time may help prevent anxiety or concern should it become necessary to have the babies stay there for a time. For some women, the sight of the tiny babies and machines may be frightening.

Lamaze classes or childbirth preparation classes should be taken early, while you are still comfortable, at approximately 25 weeks (when you will be close to term size) or sooner. Some hospitals have special childbirth preparation classes designed for expectant parents of multiples. You should also attend a Caesarean section preparation class or make sure it is part of your regular class. It is most helpful to deal with childbirth educators who are familiar with the unique aspects of a multiple pregnancy.

BODY CHANGES

There are many remarkable changes in your body when you become pregnant. Some are sources of fascination, and others are sources of discomfort. A multiple pregnancy will exaggerate the normal changes of pregnancy.

WEIGHT GAIN

Increased weight gain is the most obvious change. You will notice a higher than expected gain in the first trimester compared with a singleton pregnancy. Though many women are distressed with the gains, they are crucial to the development of the babies and the ability to carry them to term.

LIGHTHEADEDNESS

The blood pressure usually will decrease, especially in the middle part of pregnancy. This will make you more prone to lightheadedness or fainting. Lying on your back is to be discouraged, as this puts more pressure on the blood vessels and leads to a lowering of blood pressure. This lowering of blood pressure can decrease the blood flow to the placentas, which are the babies' life-lines and sole sources of nutrition and oxygen. The best position for lying down is on your left side, as this increases blood flow to the uterus.

SWELLING

The growing size of the uterus by the third trimester puts pressure on the blood vessels carrying blood back from the lower part of the body. This can cause a backup of blood and body fluids, leading to swelling in the feet, legs, and the vulva.

ANEMIA

The volume of blood will increase markedly. This can lead to a decrease in red blood cells (anemia) because of the higher requirement for iron to make the red blood cells. Some women will have a small heart murmur during pregnancy due to the increase in flow of blood through the heart.

Do not buy your entire maternity wardrobe in the beginning of your pregnancy! After being pregnant with a singleton and then conceiving twins, I figured I would be a bit larger around the middle. However, I did not realize that I would be in and out of my singleton maternity clothes by my seventh month! If this is your first pregnancy, buy your clothing as needed. Invest in a really good maternity girdle, which holds everything in and helps you carry the load. Women's sized clothing is usually cheaper than maternity sizes, especially in shirts.
Kelly Sciarrone, Bi-County MOMs, Shoreham, N.Y

INCREASED URINATION/INFECTIONS

The kidneys will become enlarged due to the increased flow of blood. Since they are filtering more blood each hour, most women will have to use the bathroom more frequently, even in the early stages of pregnancy. In the later stages, the urge to urinate will be made worse by the enlarged uterus and babies' body parts pressing against the bladder.

The tube leading from the kidney, called the ureter, can increase in size as well. This can cause urine to back up or back wash into the ureters and kidneys, making a kidney infection more likely. This kidney infection, called pyelonephritis, can be serious in pregnancy and will usually require antibiotics and hospitalization. Additionally, it can lead to premature labor. You will also be more prone to a lower urinary tract infection, also called a bladder infection or cystitis. Cystitis symptoms may not be as typical in pregnancy, and any cystitis should be treated promptly to avoid the possibility of pyelonephritis.

STOMACH PROBLEMS

The gastrointestinal (GI) tract can be affected by pregnancy. The movement of the GI tract is slowed, and the stomach also empties more slowly. This is due to the increased level of the hormone progesterone. This causes common symptoms such as heartburn, hemorrhoids, and constipation. You may also be more prone to gallbladder disease due to enlargement of the gallbladder and decreased tone. The liver undergoes no changes, but certain of the liver enzyme blood levels do change. The intestines are pushed higher in the abdomen due to crowding by the uterus. This can make conditions such as appendicitis very difficult for the doctor to diagnose because the pain would not strike the usual location.

BREATHING

You may breathe faster when you are pregnant. In the later stages of pregnancy, when the lungs are pushed upward with the diaphragm, you may become short of breath more easily. The chest diameter can expand.

BREASTS

Breast tissue undergoes changes due to hormonal stimulation, and the enlargement of the breasts may be rapid enough to cause stretch marks. Women who have inverted nipples may need to wear a special breast cup which everts the nipples to prevent breast-feeding problems.

BLOOD SUGAR

Blood levels of sugar (glucose) and insulin are lower, but there is not an increase in diabetes in pregnancy, except in higher order pregnancies. A glucose tolerance test is done in the second trimester and indicates how the body is processing sugar. Diabetes of pregnancy (gestational diabetes) can be controlled by limiting the amount of sugar and fats in the diet. For more serious cases, a standard approach to diabetes is necessary, including blood sugar monitoring and insulin injections.

SKELETON

The skeleton undergoes relaxation under the influence of the hormone relaxin. This helps prepare the pelvis to stretch and allow the delivery of the babies. It can cause some discomfort over the pubic bone, called the symphysis pubis. Sometimes the combination of swelling, increased weight, and softening of the joints can cause your shoe size to change permanently. One woman went from a size six and a half to an eight!

MANAGING THE DISCOMFORTS OF PREGNANCY

Here are some helps for many of the common complaints and discomforts of pregnancy. If no relief is obtained with the suggestions or if any symptoms are particularly prolonged or severe, always consult your health care provider and follow his or her advice.

Backache: This can be severe because of the exaggerated back-swaying posture a pregnant woman uses to help support the weight of the babies. Schedule numerous rest periods. Some women find relief with counter pressure against the back. Wearing an elastic belt that presses against the lower back and swings around the front to help support the lower abdomen relieves some of the discomfort. Some find the support of a maternity girdle helpful.

Constipation: Drink plenty of fluids, eat lots of fiber, fresh fruits, and vegetables. Engage in moderate exercise. Mild bulk laxatives may be helpful.

Fatigue: This is common early in pregnancy and then again in the third trimester. You should listen to your body and schedule adequate rest periods and naps during the day. Always try to lie on your left side, never on your back. Make sure to get adequate iron in your diet, as anemia can cause increased fatigue.

Headache: Plain acetaminophen (such as Tylenol™) is safe to take in pregnancy. Avoid aspirin and aspirin products. Avoid combination products. Headache may be a sign of toxemia.

Heartburn: Eat several small meals a day instead of three large meals. Wait two hours after eating before lying down. Antacids are safe to take, but avoid salicylated products for nausea and diarrhea (such as Pepto Bismol™), as they can be associated with birth defects.

Hemorrhoids: Use cool compresses of witch hazel and sitz baths (sitting in a tub of warm water). Over-the-counter preparations for hemorrhoids are generally safe, but avoid any products with cortisone in them. Avoid standing still or sitting for long periods of time. Prop your feet up. When constipation is a problem, laxatives may help avoid straining, which can worsen hemorrhoids.

Leg Cramps: These may be caused by a lack of calcium or an imbalance between calcium and phosphorus. Stretching the cramping muscle can often relieve it quickly, and massage can help. Increasing the intake of milk and dairy products may improve the symptoms. The health care provider may prescribe an additional calcium supplement. Check before adding any supplement to your diet.

Leg Numbness: This may be due to pressure on a nerve from the extra weight. Resting on the left side and off the feet may help. The health care provider may prescribe a dietary supplement to promote better nerve action.

Morning sickness: This can be more severe in a multiple pregnancy. Eating dry cereal or crackers before arising from bed can help. Eat ginger (soda, tea, or ginger snaps). Suck on hard candy. Combine salty and tart foods. Taste and smell are enhanced in pregnancy and can lead to previously tolerated smells and tastes becoming offensive. Avoid the foods and smells that seem to cause nausea. Avoid drinking large amounts of fluids with meals. Frequent

When preparing for the birth of the babies, I found it of most importance to accept all of the help others offered. I made schedules in advance of times when dinners being dropped off would be most appreciated. I also prepared meals and froze them in advance. This was made easy by duplicating some of our favorite recipes and wrapping one and putting it away. I must admit, though, we did seem to dip into them while still pregnant, especially after working all day!
Teresa Edgington, NEMOTC, Cincinnati, OH.

smaller meals are better. Add a vitamin B6 supplement (25 mg three times a day). Try wearing a brand of elastic band worn on the wrist that is specifically made for treating nausea. Severe, prolonged vomiting associated with weight loss may require hospitalization.

Skin rash/itching: There are several known skin rashes that can occur in conjunction with pregnancy. Itching can be caused by the accumulation of bile salts in the skin under the influence of the hormone estrogen. This is most common in the third trimester. Ointments and soothing baths are helpful. Consult your health care provider for other treatment.

Stretch marks: Contrary to popular belief, there is no cream that can prevent stretch marks. The marks are due to the underlying loss of tone in the deeper (dermal) layer of the skin and also are influenced by the hormone levels. There is no harm in keeping the area moisturized, and this will often relieve the itching that sometimes occurs as the skin becomes stretched.

Swelling/edema: Scheduled rest periods – at least three times a day – can help. Elevate the feet above the level of the heart. Use support hose, especially if you are prone to varicose veins. Be sure to remove rings at the first sign of swelling of the hands. Swelling of the hands and face may also be a sign of toxemia, a serious condition.

Urinary frequency: Frequent urination can be common in the first weeks of pregnancy and then again in later pregnancy when the uterus presses on the bladder. There is no prevention, but if it is associated with any burning, pain, or cloudiness in the urine, see your health care provider.

Varicose veins: Schedule plenty of time off your feet. Use support hose. There are many maternity brands available — or use Queen size.

DIET AND NUTRITION

Your diet is very important during your pregnancy. A steady weight gain is key to maintaining your babies' nutrition. Certain foods should be avoided, while other food substances should be increased. Basically, a balanced diet free of junk food is the most sensible.

FOOD REQUIREMENTS

Multiple pregnancies require approximately 3,000 calories daily. Suffice it to say, it is the *quality* of those calories that is important. Many women have a hard time eating the amount of food required. It

> Keeping snacks in a bedside cooler for snacking through the night helps not only during the night, but I found that a juice and cracker before rising in the morning helped me wake up, feel more steady (not dizzy) upon rising, and helped nausea. It was just another one of the smaller meals I had each day (small canned juices were the handiest).
>   *Laurel Castelot, Southside MOTC, Greenwood, Ind.*

sometimes helps to eat smaller amounts more often during the day, such as a snack every two to three hours.

Along with all the food, you should try to drink a lot of water, at least 60 ounces each day, as well as juice and milk. Water keeps the body hydrated, which can lower the chance of premature contractions, keep blood pressure down, and help cut down on urinary and kidney infections. Try filling up a pitcher or jug each day and drinking all of it by the end of the day.

Protein helps provide for increases in the blood volume, uterus, breasts, and placenta. Carbohydrates are a primary energy source for you and your babies, and often contain fiber and B vitamins to help with constipation. Fat storage occurs between the twentieth and thirtieth weeks of gestation. Consult the chart on page 11 for specific recommendations.

WEIGHT GAIN

The weight gain in pregnancy can be a sticky subject for many women. The issue is surrounded by many misunderstandings and old wives' tales. Certainly everyone has heard the adage "Now you're eating for two," which is often thought to mean you should eat twice as much food as normal.

However, the importance of weight gain in pregnancy has been proven in many studies. There is a positive connection between weight gain and infant birth weights, mostly in women who start out underweight or normal. The best

> In order to consume enough calories during pregnancy and while breast-feeding, leave the low fat diet behind. I ate large quantities of cheese, used margarine and peanut butter (as opposed to eating something dry), and switched to two percent milk (from skim). I ate meals four times a day and had hearty snacks in between. Despite this change in my eating habits, I lost all of my weight from the pregnancy and an additional ten pounds. (Aren't we lucky to have twins?)
>   *Jennifer Pawlik, Desert Sky MOM, Chandler, Ariz.*

outcomes occur with a total weight gain of 40 to 45 pounds. There is a greater risk of prematurity if you gain less than 13 pounds by 28 weeks. The rule of thumb is one and one fourth pounds per week. If you are expecting triplets, the goal is 36 pounds by 24 weeks and one and one fourth pounds per week after that. If you are underweight at the onset of pregnancy, you may need to gain more. Likewise, if you are overweight when pregnancy begins, you will need to gain less.

VITAMINS

Most vitamins and minerals can be obtained easily with a proper diet. However, it is standard practice for health care providers to prescribe a multivitamin supplement in pregnancy. This should not take the place of a sound diet.

FOOD REQUIREMENTS:

Protein: 60 grams daily, 11 to 15 ounces of lean meat, poultry, fish, eggs, liver, or vegetarian protein sources such as tofu, beans, and legumes.
Carbohydrates: Pregnancy does not usually require any need for additional carbohydrates, as long as the total caloric needs are met. Carbs are found in such foods as cereals and grains, breads and pastas, potatoes and squash. These foods are high in fiber, which can help prevent constipation.
Fats: Eat a normal amount. Fats carry the fat-soluble vitamins A, D, and E and are easily attained in a standard Western diet.

WATER SOLUBLE VITAMINS

Folic acid, or folate, is an essential water-soluble vitamin that helps in the growth of tissues and has a role in making DNA (an important building block). It has recently been found that having enough folate in the diet helps to prevent birth defects of the neural tube, such as spina bifida. Preventing these defects requires adequate folate before conception, and all women of childbearing age should make sure they get enough of this important vitamin. After January 1998, the addition of folic acid to grains and cereals was mandated by the United States FDA. Pregnant women are usually supplemented with four tenths to one milligram of folate daily.

Vitamin B6 requires an intake of four milligrams daily. Vitamin B12 deficiency is rare and is usually only seen in strict vegetarians. Vitamin C requires an intake of 150 milligrams daily.

Taking more than 1,000 milligrams daily can sometimes lead to scurvy in a newborn, due to conditioning of the babies to a high level of Vitamin C. Aim for two to three servings of fruits or juices — such as tomatoes, orange juice, and broccoli — per day.

FAT SOLUBLE VITAMINS

The recommendation for Vitamin A — found in spinach, kale, green beans, carrots, or yams — is unchanged from the pre-pregnancy recommendation of 800 micrograms, though some sources recommend 1,000 micrograms. Vitamin D helps to regulate calcium and phosphorus. The RDA during pregnancy is 15 micrograms daily. This is usually easily gotten by exposure to sunlight and drinking fortified milk. Vitamin E deficiency in humans is rare. The RDA is 10 milligrams. It is important not to exceed recommendations of fat soluble Vitamins A and D, because in megadoses they have been associated with congenital abnormalities.

MINERALS

Most minerals do not require supplementation and are obtained in an adequate diet. The exception to this is iron. Iron is crucial for making and maintaining red blood cells, and it is involved in other metabolic processes. A multiple pregnancy requires 50 milligrams daily. Multiple pregnancies carry a special demand for iron. The average American diet does not usually supply enough iron. Most women will require iron supplements when pregnant. Iron should be added beginning at 12 weeks. Ideally, a supplement of 30 milligrams along with enough red meat in the diet and Vitamin C (which help in iron absorption) is recommended. If you are found to be anemic (a hemoglobin value of less than 11.0 in the first or third trimester, or less than 10.5 in the second trimester) you should receive 60-120 milligrams of iron.

Iron supplements may cause common side effects such as nausea, indigestion, constipation, or diarrhea. Iron is absorbed better when not taken with food, but taking it with meals will tend to decrease the side effects. The stools will turn green or black when iron supplements are taken. Iron can be dangerous if eaten by infants or young children, even as few as three to five iron tablets, so they should be stored carefully. The babies absorb most of their iron in the third trimester, so premature infants may have fewer iron stores.

Calcium is important for the development of bones and teeth, plus it promotes healthy nerves and muscles and normal blood clotting. It has been recently shown that adequate calcium can decrease the blood pressure and prevent preeclampsia. An adequate intake also protects the mother's skeleton. While the loss of teeth in the mother due to the babies' needs for calcium is an old wives' tale, the loss of bone mass in the mother is not. Multiple pregnancy requires an intake of 1,800 milligrams daily. Sources of calcium are milk and dairy products, in five or six servings per day.

EXERCISE

If you have been physically active before your pregnancy, there is no reason to stop exercising completely. Early in the pregnancy most women can continue their usual routine. Women who remain physically active will feel better and recover faster after the pregnancy. If you have a history of preterm labor or are carrying higher order multiples, you may need to decrease your physical activity. You should not begin a new exercise program during pregnancy. Drink plenty of liquids during exercise. Always discuss the exercise program with your health care provider.

Most women do best with non-weight-bearing exercises, such as a stationary bicycle, swimming, walking, and arm exercises, especially in the later stages of pregnancy. However, moderate or high-intensity exercises are safe in healthy, well-conditioned women. An increase in joint laxity and changes in the center of gravity in later stages of pregnancy may cause problems with activities that require balance and extreme ranges of motion.

One type of exercise that helps to strengthen the pelvic floor

HOW TO DO THE KEGEL EXERCISES

- Identify the muscles you will be using. To isolate the back part of the pelvic muscles, imagine you are holding back a bowel movement by tightening the muscles around the anus.
- Try to stop and start the flow of urine, which will help you identify the front part of the pelvic muscles.
- Working from front to back, tighten the muscles while counting to four slowly, then release. Do this for two minutes, three times a day (try for at least 100 repetitions a day).
- Each week increase the number of times you do the exercise. Some women do from 30 to 300 contractions five times a day.

before delivery is called the Kegel. Named for Arnold Kegel, M.D., who developed it in the late 1940s, the exercise keeps the muscle, called the pubococcygeus (PC), toned and taut. These simple exercises can be performed throughout the day and throughout your pregnancy. They increase circulation to the genital area and will also help restore muscle tone after delivery. This exercise can be done anywhere, while reading, standing in line, driving, or watching television. No one will know what you are doing.

There are some precautions that should be taken when doing any exercising. Avoid any exercise flat on the back. Weight training or resistance exercises should be avoided. There may be a tendency to get lightheaded more easily than normal. If this happens, the intensity of the exercise should be decreased. A fetus has a limited ability to get rid of heat, so you should not exercise in hot, humid weather or if you have a fever. In addition, hot tubs and saunas should be avoided.

When I was released from the hospital I was on complete bed rest, not getting up for anything except going to the restroom. My husband would make me a cooler full of food. He would put in a sandwich with fruits and veggies and some of the "goodies" I liked to munch on. He also froze my drinks so I always had a cold drink: milk, water, or juice. He also had a stack of magazines and word games for me to do. I had all the remotes as well as the phone and blood pressure monitors within reach. He put all my busy stuff right next to the bed, which was the couch. Try to enjoy yourself, since that will be the last time you ever have days of rest and relaxation!
Deidre & Dan Spangler, Webster, Mass.

BED REST DURING PREGNANCY

Bed rest in multiple pregnancies is a controversial issue. Some studies do not show any decrease in preterm labor with strict bed rest, while others show a beneficial effect. Some researchers advocate preventive bed rest for all multiple pregnancies.

Most women are put on bed rest with any sign of premature labor. This may occur in the hospital or, more frequently, at home. Home uterine monitoring and home health care nurses can help facilitate bed rest at home. Mothers at bed rest can develop feelings of boredom, depression, guilt, and anxiety. Frequent telephone and personal contact are essential. Assistance with other children is a must. This situation can tax the most loving and supportive of husbands. There are organizations formed especially for the mother restricted to bed rest. (See Resources, Appendix A.) More commonly, the mother pregnant with multiples must schedule rest periods frequently. It is suggested that you should rest at least twice a day for 30 minutes at a time.

> I was on bed rest for mainly my whole pregnancy due to an incompetent cervix. Once the cerclage was inserted I was able to move around a little more, but what I had to remember was that it was not about me anymore, it was for the safety of two beautiful, healthy children. Because being in bed can be depressing, I had to cast out all doubts and negativity (people and thoughts). I made sure I stayed focused on the matter at hand and read uplifting articles and books, and I stayed away from trash talk shows. Well, after all that I was able to have a vaginal delivery for both Micah, six pounds four ounces (vertex), and Micailah, five pounds two ounces (breech). If you believe, you can achieve.
> *Michelle Guthrie, Belleville, N.Y.*

DRUGS/MEDICATIONS

Drugs and pregnancy do not mix. You should assume that anything you take will also be taken by your babies. No medications should be taken in pregnancy unless absolutely necessary. This applies to over-the-counter medications as well as prescriptions. This said, there are many medications that have been shown to be safe in pregnancy, such as acetaminophen, antacids, and antibiotics. Herbal remedies and home remedies should be avoided. Only a health care provider can determine whether or not any medication should be taken. Street drugs of any kind are dangerous in pregnancy. They can cause increases in fetal death and complications as well as endanger the health of the mother.

While not commonly thought of as a drug, alcohol can cause as many problems as other drugs. Many fetuses are exposed to alcohol in the prenatal period. In mothers who drink alcohol on a regular basis, the infants are at risk for the Fetal Alcohol Syndrome. The worldwide rate of this syndrome is one and nine tenths per 1,000 births. It is associated with mental retardation, growth deficiency, and peculiar-looking facial features, with increases in heart disease and joint problems. The rate of miscarriage is doubled, and the rate of stillbirth is increased. It is felt that alcohol may be the leading cause of mental retardation. Though the risks of major malformations are usually associated with daily alcohol use, any amount of alcohol consumed should be considered unsafe.

Nicotine, from smoking, has an effect on the babies' growth. In heavy cigarette smokers (20 or more daily), premature delivery is twice as frequent as in nonsmokers, and the infants weigh less than normal. Nicotine decreases blood flow to the uterus, which lowers the supply of oxygen available to the babies. There is also an increase in prematurity, stillbirth, and SIDS (Sudden Infant Death Syndrome).

PRENATAL SCREENING TESTS

Diagnosing problems before birth is becoming more common. A variety of tests can be used to detect many different kinds of abnormalities in the babies prior to birth. Circumstances in which prenatal tests should be considered are listed in the accompanying chart.

MATERNAL SERUM ALPHA-FETOPROTEIN

This is a protein that makes up a major part of the fetal blood. When there is an open neural tube defect (such as spina bifida) the amount of alpha-fetoprotein (AFP) in the amniotic fluid surrounding the baby is greatly increased. Elevated levels of AFP can indicate a poor fetal outcome including prematurity, low birth weight, and a number of other malformations. Decreased levels may be associated with Down Syndrome. Mothers must be tested between 15 and 20 weeks (and optimally between 16 and 18 weeks). This involves a blood test. The AFP level will be increased in multiple births. Other

REASONS FOR PRENATAL TESTING:

- The mother is older in age.
- The mother has had a previous child with a genetic (chromosomal) abnormality.
- One of the parents has a structural chromosome rearrangement.
- There is the possibility of genes in the parents that are associated with certain errors of metabolism (i.e., Tay Sachs disease).
- One of the parents is a carrier of a disorder that can be detected during pregnancy.
- There is a family history of a neural tube defect (such as spina bifida).

causes of high AFP levels, besides neural tube defects, are underestimation of age of the pregnancy and decreases in amniotic fluid. Sometimes the cause is unknown. When the level is above a certain critical value, an ultrasound should be performed of the fetal head and spine.

AMNIOCENTESIS AND CHORIONIC VILLUS SAMPLING

Amniocentesis involves placing a needle into the uterus and drawing out some of the amniotic fluid. It is usually done between 15 and 20 weeks. Genetic amniocentesis can detect chromosome abnormalities, biochemical disorders, neural tube defects, and other abnormalities. Ultrasound is performed to check the location of the babies and placentas. The procedure is technically more difficult in twin pregnancies and may be impossible in some higher order multiples. Newer techniques involve injecting a blue dye into the amniotic fluid after testing of the first fetus to be sure not to test the same fetus twice.

The more recent test called chorionic villus sampling involves obtaining a small portion of the placenta (chorionic villi) by drawing it out with a syringe. It can be done through the cervix or the abdomen. It does not screen for neural tube defects, however. It is more technically difficult in twin pregnancies, and there is a higher chance of cell contamination from the mother and the twin. There is also not an easy way (such as dye) to be certain that the same twin is not tested twice. The advantage is that it can be performed earlier in the pregnancy, at eight to12 weeks.

NEWER TECHNIQUES

Other techniques of prenatal screening and testing involve fetal blood sampling from the umbilical cord (percutaneous umbilical blood sampling, or PUBS); fetoscopy using fiberoptics, which allows for direct viewing of the fetus; and a test that has been developed to detect preterm labor, called the fetal fibronectin test, which will be discussed in Chapter 5.

CHECKING ON THE BABIES' HEALTH BEFORE BIRTH

Monitoring the condition of the babies will usually begin with an ultrasound exam. The growth of multiples should not be any different from the growth of singletons. If there is a difference in the growth of the multiples, or some other abnormality is detected on ultrasound, other tests will usually be performed. These include the Non-Stress Test (NST); the Contraction Stress Test (CST) or Oxytocin Challenge Test, and the Biophysical Profile (BPP).

Often, the timing of any such testing is based on the type of twin pregnancy. There is a higher chance of fetal abnormalities and problems with monochorionic (one gestational sac) placentas. If the multiples are found to be monoamniotic/monochorionic, testing with the NST will begin at 28 weeks and be repeated twice weekly. If the membranes are monochorionic/diamniotic, then NST will start at 30 to 32 weeks and be repeated weekly. If slowing of growth develops, then the frequency moves to twice weekly. In dichorionic (two gestational sacs) pregnancies, an NST will begin at 34 weeks and be repeated weekly.

NON-STRESS TEST

The NST involves the monitoring of the babies' heart rates along with fetal movements. A positive or reactive test would consist of at least two increases in fetal heart rate in twenty minutes with no slowing of heart rate. Care must be taken with this and the other tests to be sure that one is not testing the same twin twice. If this test is not positive, then attempts will be made to arouse the baby by various means, such as movement of the mother or stimulation with sound. If a test is negative, then further testing should be done.

CONTRACTION STRESS TEST

This test involves starting some contractions in the mother with medication (oxytocin) or by nipple stimulation. A normal test involves no slowing in the baby's heart rate after three contractions in

10 minutes. If the test is abnormal, this may indicate the need for delivery. There is some controversy regarding the use of this test in multiple pregnancies, due to the possible stimulation of preterm labor.

BIOPHYSICAL PROFILE

This is considered a more specific and sensitive test. The profile takes about a half-hour for each baby. It involves five different variables: fetal breathing movements, gross body movements, fetal tone, reactive fetal heart rate, and amniotic fluid volume. Each of these is given a score of two. A high score is termed "reassuring" while lower scores are termed "equivocal" and then "non-reassuring." The tests are run twice a week for better results and can generally detect whether a complication with the fetal central nervous system is present.

MEDICAL COMPLICATIONS OF MULTIPLE PREGNANCIES

Most multiple pregnancies have a good outcome. Complications can happen, however, and some parents like to be informed of any possible problem that could occur in order to be better prepared. This is the reason for discussing the possible medical complications of multiple pregnancies. It is not intended to frighten parents but to inform them.

As noted before, a multiple pregnancy is a high risk pregnancy. Identical twins have a higher chance of problems than fraternal twins, though the rate is still low, approximately two and three tenths percent for major malformations. Male-male twin pairs can be more vulnerable than female-female pairs. Twenty-five percent of twins have a one minute APGAR score less than seven. (See Chapter 5 for a discussion of APGAR scores). Keep in mind, however, that the vast majority are born healthy and without any major handicaps.

HIGH BLOOD PRESSURE

High blood pressure is more common in women with multiple pregnancies. It can occur two to three times more often than in a singleton pregnancy. It also tends to develop earlier in the pregnancy and be more severe. The treatment is similar to a singleton pregnancy.

EXCESSIVE AMNIOTIC FLUID

The accumulation of excessive amounts of amniotic fluid is called *polyhydramnios*. This can be common in twin pregnancies, especially monozygotic (in which twins develop from one fertilized egg). It occurs in approximately 12 percent of all multiple pregnancies. This can increase the chance of premature labor. It may also be associated with abnormalities of the baby's gastrointestinal or central nervous systems. Mortality rates can be as high as 41 percent, so it should be treated early.

PREECLAMPSIA

Preeclampsia, also called toxemia, is a serious condition brought on by elevated blood pressure. The cause of this condition remains unknown. Along with the rise in blood pressure, symptoms also include severe headache; blurred vision; swelling in the hands, face, and legs; severe heartburn; or pain under the rib cage. Pre-eclampsia causes the kidneys to start shutting down and spilling protein into the urine (one reason a urine sample is taken at each checkup). As the disease progresses, it may develop into eclampsia. At this stage, the mother is also in danger from the possibility of seizures, stroke, ruptured liver, clotting problems, and even death.

HELLP SYNDROME

HELLP stands for Hemolysis, Elevated Liver enzymes, and Low Platelets and is a special variation of pre-eclampsia. In HELLP the blood pressure may not be elevated, and there will be no protein in the urine. This condition, however, can cause serious complications with blood coagulation and ruptured liver. HELLP syndrome is only diagnosed by blood tests, which can make diagnosis difficult.

PREMATURE RUPTURE OF MEMBRANES

In this condition, the "bag of waters" (membranes of the amniotic sac surrounding the fetus and holding in the amniotic fluid) break before the thirty-seventh week of pregnancy. This occurs more frequently in multiple births and is associated with preterm labor and possible infection. The breakage may be due to an infection or possibly to the rapid growth of the uterus and the stretching of the cervix. In most instances, however, there is no ready explanation for why the breakage occurred. In a few rare cases the membranes can reseal, but in most cases there is no way to prevent the continued leakage of fluid. While the baby continues to make more fluid, there is a very real possibility of infection to the baby, problems with lung development, and umbilical cord accidents. The rupture may start premature labor. In recent years medical teams have had increasing success with delivering the baby that suffered the ruptured sac, while the remaining babies are left in the uterus to continue their development. This has become known as "interval birth."

TWIN-TO-TWIN TRANSFUSION SYNDROME

The risk of placenta-related problems in multiples is related to the type of placenta that forms. Twins may have either one placenta or two. When two placentas are present, they can be either separated or fused. The fetus is surrounded by amniotic fluid that is contained in membranes. These membranes consist of an outer layer, the chorion, and an inner layer, the amnion. Twins may share both (monoamniotic, monochorionic), have separate amniotic cavities within one chorion (diamniotic, monochorionic), or have all the membranes separate (diamniotic, dichorionic).

Eighteen to 36 percent of identical twins are dichorionic. Only one percent are monochorionic/monoamniotic. Two thirds of identical twins have a monochorionic placenta and share some blood circulation. When the circulation is only one-way (usually from artery to vein), then one twin will be anemic and have a loss of nutrients (donor), while the other twin (recipient) has an excess of blood and may suffer from cardiac failure, hyperbilirubinemia, and blood clots that can damage any organ in the body. This happens in approximately 15 percent of diamniotic/monochorionic twin pregnancies. It is called Twin-to-Twin Transfusion Syndrome (TTTS).

The diagnosis of TTTS is not always easy to make. Ultrasound may show unequal growth and amniotic fluid in the two sacs. Blood sampling through amniocentesis can be performed. Neither of these methods allows for precise diagnosis. Most fetuses with TTTS in the second trimester can have excess amniotic fluid leading to premature rupture of membranes and very preterm delivery.

Researchers are looking for new ways to treat this condition. Therapies in the past included digoxin (a heart medication) and medicines to halt labor. Reduction amniocentesis is the most common treatment. This therapy involves removing excess fluid, which can improve survival. It must be done frequently throughout the pregnancy. It is not known why this therapy works.

Newer therapies involve direct in-utero treatment (done on the babies while still in the uterus). Such treatments include laser coagulation of the vessels through a fetoscope, which is one of the newer promising therapies. Another approach is a "give and take" transfusion in which blood collected from the recipient is transfused into the donor. There are several support groups and foundations dealing with TTTS (See Resources, Appendix A). Parents are encouraged to seek out one of these groups if faced with this uncommon abnormality.

SIAMESE TWINS/CONJOINED TWINS

Those twins with one amnion and one chorion are at highest risk from complications. Conjoined twins are one rare complication of monoamniotic twins and are commonly called Siamese Twins. It occurs in one of 200 monozygotic pairs, and one in 33,000 births. Approximately 70 percent are female. This happens when the embryonic disc does not divide completely, usually at the 15 to 17 day stage. The twins may be connected by only small areas of skin or may have major connections of brain tissue and major organs. Survival depends on the amount and type of connection. Separation of the twins also depends on that. Sometimes the twins' organs may need to mature before separation can be done. Separation is a complex process, and many advances have been made in recent years in this area.

CONCLUSION

Although pregnancies with multiples may be considered high risk, it is reassuring to note that the vast majority result in normal infants. Proper rest, nutrition, and prenatal care will bring about the best chance of a healthy mother and healthy babies. Being informed of the risks will help you deal with the unknown and make you an informed health care consumer.

Highlights from NOMOTC's 1992 Multiple Pregnancy Survey

- 50% of parents had other children before the birth of multiples
- 61% did not plan on having other children after the birth of their multiples
- 40% of mothers were aged 26 to 30
- 35% of fathers were 31 to 35
- 39% of mothers suspected a multiple pregnancy in their first trimester
- 36% were told of the multiple pregnancy by their doctor
- 71% of mothers were on bed rest during weeks 25 to 36 of pregnancy
- 54% of pregnancies reported lasted 36 weeks or more
- 86% of the multiples were born healthy

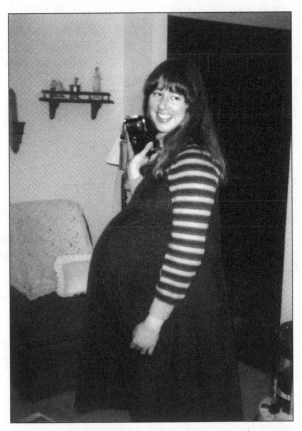

Gaining 70 pounds is not uncommon with twins.
They were born the day after this picture was taken.

2

"HOW Many Babies?"

SUPERTWINS

Shortly after my triplet daughters were born, I was lying in bed in my hospital room. The door was open, and I could hear one lady say to another as they walked by, "Let's take a look in the Special Care Nursery windows. I hear they have a set of triplets in there, and I've never seen triplets before!" I thought to myself: Come to think of it, these are the first triplets I've seen — and I have to take them home!

Jill Heink, Lexington, Kentucky

Shock, disbelief, and panic are probably the three most common reactions an expectant mother and father admit to having after learning they've got higher order multiples on the way. The babies' birth also brings more adjustments, as parents must cope with the demands of being outnumbered by their babies. This is the world of higher order multiples or supertwins.

BY THE NUMBERS

Higher order multiples can come in several varieties. Triplets is the term for three babies carried at one time, while quadruplets are four babies carried at one time. Quintuplets is the term for five babies, and in recent years the United States has seen the birth of sextuplets, six babies born at one time, and septuplets, seven babies.

Supertwin (i.e., higher order multiple) births are on the rise in the United States, the rate having doubled since the 1970s. This increase is believed to be mostly a result of fertility-assisted medical procedures as well as the aging of the parent population. As the anecdote above suggests, however, triplets, quads, or more are still very rare. The total of all higher order multiple births is only a fraction of all multiple births — a mere four percent. Out of all births, the rate of supertwin births is one in 576 or about two tenths of one percent.

Triplets, quads, and more can occur in several different combinations. In the most rare instances, a single fertilized egg will split three or four times, producing babies that are genetically the same. We call the results of this three- or four-way split "identical" triplets or quads. Only two sets of identical quintuplets are known to have survived.

Triplets, quads, and quints can also result when more than one fertilized egg is present, and one of them splits into two, yielding a combination of identical children and fraternal children. Data from the Triplet Connection and Mothers of Supertwins reveals that close to 60 percent of the families registered with these organizations have a combination of identical and fraternal children. Higher order multiples may, however, be all fraternal.

THE MEDICAL TEAM

A supertwin pregnancy is a high-risk pregnancy. The three, four, or more babies make an extraordinary demand on your body for space and nutrition. The majority of higher order multiples are born early, and there is a higher chance for complications at birth. On the other hand, medical and clinical research continue to bring improvements in both prenatal and neonatal care for mother and babies. A higher order pregnancy is a real team effort, from the mother and father right down to the lab technicians.

CHOOSING YOUR DOCTOR

There is a growing body of research and knowledge about managing supertwin pregnancies, but because triplet, quad, quint, etc., pregnancies are still relatively rare, not all of this information is uniformly distributed. If you are expecting higher order multiples, you need to find a good medical team for this pregnancy. Ideally you can find an obstetrician who has experience with delivering multiples or at least has experience with many high-risk cases. This is not always possible, especially in a small town or rural area. Information is more accessible today than ever before, so expectant supertwin parents need to work with their physicians to find the latest information about managing a higher order multiple pregnancy.

If these are your first children, now is also the time to choose a pediatrician. Other parents are good sources of information about local pediatricians, and you should try to follow up recommendations with a phone interview or even a personal interview. Some things to ask about might include education and training, office hours and availability, sick child and well child visits, and fee schedules. There is nothing wrong with asking for a discount for multiples!

CHOOSING A HOSPITAL

Another important aspect is the hospital in which the babies will be delivered and, thus, the type of neonatal care available. The level of care in a Neonatal Intensive Care Unit (NICU) plays an important role in the care of the newborn babies. NICUs are classified by levels, with Level I providing basic care. The rest range up to Level IV, which offers the most advanced care for premature and sick babies. Triplets, quads, or more on average are smaller and deliver earlier than singletons or twins. Complications can arise suddenly for any one of the babies. You should seriously consider delivering at a hospital that has at least Level III care, even if it means relocating some distance for a number of weeks. The higher the level of NICU care available, the better the chances for each baby.

You should make a visit to the NICU before your babies are born. This is a good time to learn about some of the equipment and techniques that the medical team uses to care for the newborns who need this treatment. The first visit can be a shock. The babies may seem too tiny and hooked up with a hundred wires to various machines. By speaking with the nurses and physicians ahead of time, however, you get a feel for the work done in the NICU and the dedication of the medical team to the lives of their young patients.

While visiting the hospital you should also check out the maternity floor and nursery and talk to the staff about what to expect during labor, delivery, and recuperation. Practically all higher order multiples are delivered by Caesarean section, so the preliminary hospital visit is a good time to talk about recovering from surgery, stimulating breast milk production after delivery, etc. At this time, you may also want to ask what sort of lab work is done to check on the babies' zygosity and blood types.

Some hospitals now have prenatal classes available for parents expecting multiples. If no such class is available, you may still consider attending the regular prenatal class. You may also want to take a

CPR class, or at least the infant/child portion, early on in the pregnancy. After the babies are born they may need to come home on apnea monitors, in which case you would be required to learn CPR before the babies can be discharged. CPR is a very valuable skill to learn, whether the babies are on monitors or not.

ULTRASOUNDS

You can expect to have many ultrasounds throughout the pregnancy to check on the growth and development of your babies. So far there is no evidence that ultrasounds cause any problems for babies or for mother, although the procedure becomes more uncomfortable as time goes on. Some OB practices have their own equipment, although sometimes you need to go to a hospital or other separate facility. Depending on insurance coverage and requirements, you may want to have the doctor write a letter explaining the need for each ultrasound to the insurance company.

SELECTIVE REDUCTION

A number of families expecting higher order multiples (usually quads or more) are sometimes presented with the option of selective reduction to eliminate one or more of the fetuses being carried, such as reducing a quad pregnancy to a twin pregnancy. The purpose is to improve conditions for the remaining babies, giving them a better opportunity for a healthy outcome. The reduction procedure, done under ultrasound guidance, consists of injecting a chemical into the fetal sac to stop the development. The fetus is then gradually absorbed by the body. This decision must be made within the first trimester of the pregnancy, so parents may feel pressured to make the decision as quickly as possible.

This is a serious decision for the family. While a reduction may relieve some of the stress of a higher order pregnancy, there is also the slight possibility that the procedure may disturb the entire pregnancy enough to cause loss of the remaining babies. Before making this decision, the parents and medical team need to look at a number of factors, such as the mother's prior history of miscarriage, her general health, complications that may have already arisen during the pregnancy, and so on. Parents also need to examine their personal feelings about going through the procedure and the possibility of regretting the loss of the reduction later on. It is very important, then, that parents review all their options. Ideally, they would have the chance to communicate with other families that have faced the same decision. Expectant parents might network through a local parents-of-multiples club, an Internet group, or a national support group for multiples (see Resources, Appendix A). Parents may wish to consult with a counselor, clergy member, or medical ethicist for still other viewpoints in this area.

NUTRITION AND WEIGHT GAIN

Nutrition is a very important component to delivering healthy babies. It is the fuel that provides the raw materials for their growth and development. A growing number of studies show that, on the average, the more weight you gain during pregnancy the higher the birth weights of your infants. A woman expecting triplets, quads, or more should aim at gaining between 45 and 70 pounds, depending on what her pre-pregnancy weight was. This is indeed a lot of weight, but data collected from more than two thousand supertwin pregnancies indicate that women who have gained this much weight usually lose it by their sixth-week postpartum checkup.

GAINING WEIGHT

Gaining the 40-plus pounds needed to develop healthy triplets, quads, quints, and more actually may be very difficult for you. You may suffer from nausea, especially in the first three months, and even after morning sickness subsides you may have a hard time eating as you grow larger. You may feel full all the time and have no real desire to eat.

The recommended weight gain is based on an average taken from a large amount of data. You might fall outside this range — possibly because of your metabolism or some other reason — and yet still deliver healthy babies, even if you did not gain as much as half the recommended pounds. Regular ultrasounds will give an indication of how well the babies are growing, which is the most important consideration. It's very important, then, that you focus on eating the proper food rather than gaining a specific number of pounds. You should talk to your doctor early on, perhaps even consult a prenatal nutritionist or registered dietician, about how much protein, calcium, and specific minerals you should consume.

There are recommended nutrition guidelines that have been

successfully used by many women with supertwin pregnancies, such as the Brewer Diet for Normal and High Risk Pregnancy and the California Department of Health Services Daily Food Guide. Some of the basic principles of these diets were outlined in the "Nutrition" section of Chapter 1.

MANAGING THE HIGHER ORDER PREGNANCY: LOW TECH AND HIGH TECH

LOW TECH

Each pregnancy is unique. A high level of technology has contributed a great deal to improving the outcomes of supertwin pregnancies, but you still have a lot of control in your high-risk pregnancy.

You need to "listen" to your body; you need to ease your activities when you feel yourself tiring; you need to note changes in how you are feeling and discuss them with your doctor. Both you and your partner need to educate yourselves about the pregnancy and be alert for any complications. Simply being informed and aware contributes greatly to a healthy outcome for you and your babies.

WATCHING FOR PROBLEMS

You must be constantly alert for signs of preterm labor. These are covered in Chapter 5, but include signs such as: regular contractions; vaginal discharge of water, mucus, or blood; dull backache; constant pressure on the pelvis or thighs; and an overall feeling that something is wrong. Any of these symptoms may also be a part of a normal pregnancy. Be aware of your body and watch for changes day-to-day.

Carrying extra babies means extra work for your body in just about every aspect of daily life. The extra weight of the multiple fetuses pushes down and out on the uterus and all the other organs as well. This can lead to preterm labor, probably the most common problem in a supertwin pregnancy.

PREVENTING PRETERM LABOR

A "low tech" method for preventing early labor is simply getting off your feet with bed rest. This means lying down in bed or in a reclining chair for a good portion of the day. Some women can rest for short periods in the morning and afternoon and do fine, but others will need to limit their activity to lying down all day every day. This may mean quitting work as early as 16 weeks into the pregnancy or working out care for other children and the household with many months to go before delivery. Also, doctors generally recommend that you go on "pelvic rest," meaning limited sexual activity, to avoid starting up preterm labor. These restrictions obviously affect both parents, financially and emotionally, and need to be discussed and worked out. Bed rest is a real challenge for everyone, and preparation can help make the most of these months of restricted activity. You need to stay mostly on your left side and avoid lying on your back to prevent restriction of the flow of blood to the uterus.

A woman carrying higher order multiples can expect to visit her doctor's office more often than for a singleton pregnancy, even if things are progressing smoothly. Generally, you can leave your home to go to the doctor's office. Obtaining a "Handicapped" parking sticker from your county clerk's office is helpful during a pregnancy with supertwins (as well as after the babies arrive).

GETTING SUPPORT

You and your partner should also look for emotional support as needed during the pregnancy. Support groups such as the local clubs for families of multiples, the National Organization of Mothers of Twins Clubs, Inc., and national support groups for families of triplets, quads, and more can provide valuable "I've been there, this too shall pass" fellowship as well as information and statistics. If help is needed, then the family must find it by calling family and friends and seeking out volunteer or paid help from churches, service groups, or local help agencies. It's important to take as much stress out of the pregnancy as possible, which is another way to help give the babies a healthy start.

HIGH TECH

Through medical and clinical research, physicians continue to develop methods and interventions to help families have the best outcome for their multiple birth children.

MONITORS, MEDICATIONS, AND TESTS

In a higher order multiple birth pregnancy, the uterus is stretched so tightly as the babies grow that the expectant mother may not feel the onset of early contractions. An electronic home monitoring device can be used to record any contractions. The monitor is obtained from a company that offers the equipment and support staff. As another intervention, a physician may prescribe a tocolytic medication to stop or prevent preterm contractions. Chapter 5 will offer more information.

The medical team may also begin some studies of how the babies are doing. These can include Non-Stress Tests, Contraction Stress Tests, or a Biophysical Profile. They are performed somewhere around the thirtieth week of gestation or sooner, if one or more babies seems to lag in development or if the mother develops preeclampsia. These tests are used to detect complications. These various tests are discussed fully in the "Prenatal Assessment" section of Chapter 1.

COMPLICATIONS

Due to the strain on your body and crowded conditions that the babies face, other complications can arise throughout the pregnancy. Higher birth order pregnancies are especially susceptible to developing preeclampsia, also called toxemia. HELLP syndrome (Hemolysis, Elevated Liver enzymes, and Low Platelets) is a special variation of preeclampsia. Recent reviews of medical data are showing that HELLP is probably the most frequent form of preeclampsia seen in women carrying supertwins, especially older women. Some physicians recommend that a patient expecting quads or more, or a patient showing signs of poor progress in a triplet pregnancy, should have a uric acid blood test drawn every week, along with further blood studies to keep tabs on kidney and liver functions.

Preeclampsia occurs in roughly a third of triplet pregnancies and as high as 90 percent of quad and higher pregnancies. Bed rest is the first approach to managing preeclampsia, but delivery is really the only cure. In a supertwin pregnancy, the preeclampsia often occurs before the babies are at term, so delivering them runs the risk of prematurity complications. It is thus very important to avoid developing preeclampsia if at all possible. Again, it is very important that the family and medical team work together.

Another complication which is more frequent in supertwin pregnancies is premature rupture of membranes, known as PROM. In this condition, the membranes of the amniotic sac surrounding the fetus and holding in the amniotic fluid break before the thirty seventh week of pregnancy. It is estimated that PROM occurs in about 15 percent of triplet pregnancies. The rupture generally starts premature labor as well. At this point the decision has to be made about delivering one or all of the babies. If the pregnancy has progressed far enough, generally between 32 and 34 weeks, the medical team most often goes ahead with delivery. At less than 32 weeks, the decision has to be weighed more carefully.

In very rare instances, monozygotic multiples with a monochorionic placenta are affected with a condition known as Twin-to-Twin Transfusion Syndrome (TTTS), as discussed in Chapter 1.

OTHER COMPLICATIONS AND DISCOMFORTS

All of the discomforts of pregnancy mentioned in Chapter 1 hold true for the expectant mother of supertwins, but because of the more crowded conditions from the growth of three or more babies they may occur much earlier or be more severe. All sorts of unusual symptoms can occur in a higher multiple pregnancy. You need to be attuned to changes and patterns (time of day, what was eaten, and so on) and pass this along to the medical team. In all these instances you need to consult with your physician about the best way to handle these discomforts.

One final concern you need to be aware of is that carrying the babies too long can also cause a problem. The placenta in a supertwin pregnancy is far more stressed than in a singleton pregnancy. As a result, it often starts to pull apart as time goes on. The medical team needs to keep a close watch on the condition of the placenta to make sure that it is still intact, especially as you approach or pass 35 weeks gestation.

LABOR AND DELIVERY

Almost all triplet, quad, and higher pregnancies are delivered via Caesarean section to cut down the risk of fetal distress during delivery. Once the decision is made to deliver, you will have very little labor time left. Since there is such a realistic possibility that labor will start early, you and your partner need to discuss with the medical team early on what to expect in the delivery room, who will be present, the type of incision (vertical or horizontal) and the reasons for it, what sort of anesthesia will be used under what circumstances, and so on.

DELIVERING THE BABIES

You may be surprised at the number of people who are in the delivery room for the birth of triplets, quads, or more. Along with the surgical crew — usually the obstetrician, surgical nurses, and anesthesiologist — there will also be a team of nurses (at least one for each baby and possibly more), a neonatologist, a pediatrician, and possibly some interested residents or other physicians. It can be quite a crowd, but all are dedicated to having the best possible outcome for the babies.

The team works quickly to deliver the babies. You probably will spend some time in the recovery room and generally keep the IV and catheter in for some hours after delivery. A C-section is major surgery, and each woman will have her own process of recuperation. The abdomen may be very sore as the anesthesia wears off, and there may still be symptoms from any complications that set in during pregnancy. You should let the staff know how much pain you are in. It is a good idea to try to get up and move around as soon as possible to help the circulation and the digestive tract. You usually can see your babies in the nursery (or have them brought to you) as soon as you feel up to it.

DEALING WITH THE DELIVERY

The emotional aspects of the delivery are also important. For some families the delivery will be a real triumph and a tremendous relief, with babies and mother doing well and medical care proceeding as planned. For other families the delivery may have come weeks early, with resultant complications for one, two, or possibly all of the babies. A long hospital stay with many procedures may be ahead. This latter situation can throw family life into a shocked turmoil with many medical decisions to make, possibly at a moment's notice. For a mother in need of physical recovery, it can be very depressing as well as painful.

For other children in the family it can be a very confusing time, as the parents need to devote time and energy to the newborns.

It's important to pay attention to everyone's feelings and get support. This may be a time that the family needs counseling, whether from the hospital social worker, another professional, a support group, or family and friends, to help recognize these feelings and deal with them as best they can. The days or weeks after a premature birth are an emotional roller coaster, and the better prepared the parents are, the better they can handle the ride.

IN THE NICU

Each supertwin birth is a unique experience. While tremendous progress has been made toward more and more healthy outcomes, the risks of preterm birth and complications are still there. Even if the pregnancy has progressed well, the medical care has been excellent, and the parents have given their best efforts, problems may still occur. The babies may be very sick in the NICU. See "Premature Babies/NICU" in Chapter 6.

COMING HOME

The nature of the first months of caring for multiples will depend upon the start the children got at birth. If the babies are very premature they will need to spend time in the NICU. When they come home they may be accompanied by special equipment, such as apnea monitors or oxygen tanks. Some insurance companies will cover the cost of in-home nursing, which is something to check out well before the babies are born. Even if the cost is not fully covered, you might consider some form of help for the first weeks, whether paid or volunteer.

As a mother of triplets, one of the hardest things to deal with is that you have two arms and three babies. Touch becomes a way to convey tenderness when you are unable to hold all in your arms.
  Sandy Sherlock, Chico MOMs, Calif.

Babies come home from the hospital as they are ready. You may find yourself in the situation where one or two babies are still in the hospital while one or two are home. This is always a very stressful situation, especially if the hospital is some distance from the home. Another limiting factor is that you will almost always have had a C-section. You generally need to take it easy for several weeks after the surgery and may not be able to drive for that time. You will need to prioritize your time based on your circumstances and try to divide up time between the children at home and the children at the hospital as circumstances allow. Do not feel overwhelmed by guilt feelings about which children have your attention. Families need to think about a contingency plan well before the babies arrive and call upon their support systems for child care, transportation, and so on. If during the pregnancy anyone has said to you, "Let me know if there's anything I can do," this is the time to say yes!

MAKING ADJUSTMENTS, PLANNING AHEAD

The changes that take place in a multiple pregnancy can turn a family's life upside down. You may have a physically difficult pregnancy. Even without complications, a higher multiple pregnancy is just plain uncomfortable. You may feel as if you have lost control of your body and your destiny. For the father, the supertwin pregnancy means assuming complete responsibility for all aspects of family life — caring for other children, caring for the mother, running the house, preparing meals — usually while working full time outside the home. The family may lose a substantial part of its income when the woman goes on bed rest. Medical bills may start to mount if the pregnancy involves a hospital stay. There is also a fear of the changes in store and anxiety as to how the family will cope once the babies are born and in need of care. As unpredictable as life may seem, it's important that you start making adjustments and planning ahead for the arrival of the newborn triplets, quads, or more.

HELPING SIBLINGS COPE

For other children in the family a multiple pregnancy is a big adjustment. If you need to go on strict bed rest you need to carefully work out a daily routine for the children, including their meals, snacks, and activities. It's also very important to let the children know what is going on, being realistic but reassuring if things are not going as well as hoped. Children need to feel that they have some control in the situation; school-age children and even preschoolers can be given some choices about their routine (meals, playtime, etc.) and be assigned extra, appropriate responsibilities around the house as part of the family effort. Toddlers may need scheduled attention time from you to help them cope with a change in their routine. Outside help comes in especially handy to help care for other young children.

GETTING HELP

You need to look around at your outside "human resources." Are family and friends willing and able to help with child care, meal preparations, housekeeping, and so on? If you have a wonderful support system of eager volunteers, it's not too outlandish to fix a schedule board to make sure that assistance is spread around evenly throughout the busy days ahead. Meals can be prepared and frozen ahead of time as well.

If you are on your own, you need to check into resources the community offers in the way of both volunteer and paid help. Check with your insurance agency to see if in-home nursing care is covered and under what circumstances. The local phone book should have a list of community service agencies, both publicly and privately funded, that might also be a source of help. The time to find out about extra help is before the babies come.

You should make an effort to talk to other parents of multiples and find out how they have managed. You should also join any local support group for families with multiples. These clubs generally have a wealth of information about coping with multiple births and also have club sales where families can find used equipment, clothing, and toys at bargain prices. Most clubs also have monthly meetings with speakers and workshops about topics relevant to families with twins, triplets, or more. Clubs also host family events such as parties and picnics which are fun for everyone. The National Organization of Mothers of Twins Clubs, Inc., has resources for parents of supertwins and information on local groups.

OBTAINING HELP FROM THE GOVERNMENT

There are government programs that you need to know about before your babies are born. One of these is the Women, Infants, and Children (WIC) nutritional program administered by each state through the local Health Department. Through WIC, qualifying families can receive nutritional counseling and vouchers for supplemental food. The Supplemental Security Income (SSI) program is administered by Social Security to help provide some financial assistance to people with certain disabilities, including premature infants under 1,200 grams (two pounds, 10 ounces). Low birthweight premature infants between 1,200 grams and 2,000 grams (four pounds, six ounces) may also qualify, depending on their medical conditions and family resources. The family can only receive benefits after filing with the Social Security office; benefits are not retroactive. If the children might possibly qualify for this assistance, it is very important that you (or someone acting in your behalf) call the Social Security Administration immediately to start the paperwork. More details can be found in Chapter 4.

BASIC EQUIPMENT

Before the babies arrive you will want to have some basic equipment on hand. If you are going to buy new equipment you should ask the store about a discount for buying multiple items, such as cribs, swings, high chairs, and so on. Parents of multiples yard sales are good sources of baby equipment. You need to check into the latest safety standards before buying or borrowing any equipment, new or used. Again, see Chapter 4.

PURCHASING A STROLLER

Most families invest in a good triplet/quad stroller so they can go out and about with the babies by themselves. The larger strollers are generally special-order items from a retail baby or toy store or available through one of the national supertwin organizations. A parents-of-multiples club meeting is a great place to ask about

> **W**e would let the babies have a few toys that were not "share" toys. They did not have to share with each other or with visitors if they did not wish to do so. This gave them a little more security about their best playthings, and it was satisfying to see them share when they were not forced to do so.
> *Chris Fulmer, South Dade POMC, Homestead, Fla.*

different styles and possibly find a used stroller. You need to decide what style will suit your needs. Many families also have a variety of strollers for different situations. For instance, a family with triplets, quads, or more might also want to have a double stroller and a single stroller, or two double strollers, for running errands with just one or two of the children.

BUYING A CAR

Another important consideration is the family vehicle. With three or more in car seats, most families find they need a fairly large vehicle to take everyone at once! The minivan and full-size van are very popular among families with triplets, quads, or more because of the extra room and the easy accessibility to the back seats (and the car seats). Some of the larger sports utility vehicles can also be very roomy for large families. Parents have to shop around for the style and price they like. The best sources of information about the utility of different makes and models are other families of multiples. Other places to look include the *Consumer Reports* magazine and car buying guides. This is an important purchase, so you would do well to get research underway before the babies arrive. Parents-of-multiples clubs are good places to get recommendations for vehicles. You might attend a club party or picnic; the parking lot outside these events will be filled with vans, minivans, and other large vehicles! Other parents will be glad to show what sort of features their vehicles offer.

OTHER ITEMS

Finally, many companies offer special gift packages to parents of triplets or more, including diapers, sundries, baby food, formula, etc. Some of these are listed in "Resources," Appendix A. Usually the manufacturer requires a letter with photocopies of the babies' birth certificates. If time allows, you can prepare a form letter ahead of time and address all the envelopes before the babies are born. You should file with your state's Bureau of Vital Statistics immediately for birth certificates (usually the hospital gives this form to parents as standard procedure; if not, you should ask for it) and make copies for the letters. You will also want to file for your children's Social Security numbers right away.

BREAST-FEEDING

You also need to consider how you will feed your babies. Nutritionally, breast milk is the best food for babies. Breast milk contains all the right levels of nutrients that the babies need. Breast milk also contains natural antibodies, manufactured in the mother's body, to help babies resist infections in the first four months of life. In addition, breast-feeding offers a wonderful closeness, a skin-to-skin contact, between mother and baby. A final practical consideration is that breast-feeding is much less expensive than the cost of infant formula.

The logistics of breast-feeding three, four, or more babies may seem "un-doable," but this is not the case. As with most other aspects of pregnancy, delivery, and early care, each case will be unique.

As far as being able to supply enough milk for all the babies, breast-feeding is a remarkable supply and demand operation. Most women will be able to make as much milk as their babies need as long as they are getting enough rest, eating a healthy diet, and drinking lots of fluids. While you can produce the hundred ounces or more that the babies will need, perhaps your greatest challenge is to manage the flow of milk. The volume of milk produced does indeed cause the breasts to swell. As a nursing mother, you will need a good supply of supportive nursing bras; you may have to try several brands and sizes before finding what works best for you. A woman breast-feeding triplets or more needs to be careful to make sure she does not become engorged (i.e., leave too much milk in the breast because of illness, not feeding the babies on a schedule, etc.). This could lead to mastitis (breast infection). Another challenge is controlling let-down, the reaction that causes milk to flow. Sometimes the let-down can occur at unexpected times on hearing a baby cry. At such moments the mother nursing triplets, quads, or more may find that she is suddenly "gushing!" It is a good idea to lay in a supply of nursing pads to keep inside the bra, especially when going out.

GETTING STARTED

You should let the nursing staff know right away that you want to start nursing and, if possible, ask that the babies be brought to your room. If you are going to feed the babies in the NICU, you should ask for a comfortable place for feedings and ask for help with getting the babies started; sometimes it helps to have an extra person available to help position the babies at the breast to aid latching on. Also, the babies should be weighed on the nursery scales before and after each feeding to see how much milk they took in. If one child needs more milk, he/she can receive more with a bottle.

Since many triplets, quads, and quints are preemies, the babies can take a while before they are able to latch on and nurse. In these instances you can use an electric breast pump to express the milk from your breasts, which can then be bottle-fed or administered through a tube leading to the babies' stomachs. While using a pump is not exactly a rewarding experience, it does get the job done for most women who want to provide breast milk for their babies. Most hospitals have a room for pumping as well as a lactation consultant who can help with getting started. Pumping is very difficult for some women. They find it painful and/or they just cannot seem to get enough milk out. This is not surprising considering that a woman who has just delivered triplets, quads, or more has just come out of a difficult pregnancy and is probably recuperating from a C-section. Also, producing milk has an emotional as well as physical component, so a mother's frustration can just compound problems. At this point she could try reducing her time on the pump and see how much milk she can produce at different intervals on a more relaxed schedule. If possible she should also try nursing a baby at the breast, which is generally far more stimulating than a pump.

Breast-feeding depends on a combination of physical and emotional factors. Even though they may struggle in the early days (especially in their first experiences with breast-feeding), many, many women have gone on to nurse their triplets or more, some for well over a year. Motivation, patience, and support are needed to get through difficulties. You need to rest, relax, and eat right to breast-feed.

DEALING WITH FRUSTRATIONS

Sometimes a woman who is highly motivated to breast-feed will find that things are just not working out: she's not making enough milk, she feels physically bad when she pumps, she develops an infection, she is having trouble with getting her babies to latch on, and many other possible problems. She may find herself frustrated, sad, exhausted, in pain, feeling guilty for wanting to quit, or all of the above. You should not feel you have "failed" if you cannot provide enough (or any) milk for your babies or if nursing is not turning out to be the experience you thought it would be. Certainly any milk you can provide for your babies will help, especially if they are premature. Possibly you can adjust (mentally as well as physically) how much milk you can provide. The best advice is to take the process one day at a time and make decisions about continued breast-feeding based on what is best for the family as a whole. Babies need a happy mother and father, so that is the final criterion for how much and how long to breast-feed.

CONTINUING NURSING

While most books and medical personnel advise allowing the babies to feed on demand, most mothers nursing higher multiples will find it saner to schedule the babies as much as possible; otherwise a mother may find herself nursing practically around the clock.

Each baby is different and will nurse with a different level of efficiency. It will take time to establish a routine. Generally, babies get to come home from the hospital when they weigh more than four pounds. At this point you will want to get the babies nursing at three- or four-hour intervals, with each baby taking roughly 30 minutes to nurse. A mother nursing triplets or quads could nurse two at a time and feed the children in about an hour. It is suggested that all babies eat at the same time, even if it becomes necessary to wake them up to do it. Otherwise you could be nursing at any and all times. Babies do not always want to nurse just because of hunger, however, so you may find that one or more babies wants to nurse in between time. You may want to try pacifiers or water bottles to satisfy this need.

Nursing two babies at once requires a little practice to find the best position for everyone. Using pillows helps to hold the babies in position, and special nursing pillows are made to make this easier. If you are nursing triplets, one baby will feed alone, so it's a good idea to rotate the babies through this position. It's also a good idea to keep a chart tracking which child has nursed at which breast.

BOTTLE FEEDING

Many different types of formulas are available — for instance all soy, with extra iron, and so on — to meet different needs. Families using infant formula need to discuss the different brands with their health care providers before the babies are born. You may find that some early problems, such as the baby developing too much gas or reflux (spitting up), can be eased with a different type of formula.

Most mothers who breast-feed also do some bottle feeding, either using infant formula as a supplement or expressing breast milk for bottle feedings (many women who return to work are able to continue breast-feeding in this way). You may

When alone during feedings, I would sit on the couch and have one baby next to me along the side of my right leg and the other lying along my left leg. The bottles would then be propped by my legs. For higher multiples, the third (or fourth) child can lie next to these babies on the couch, and then your hands are free to hold the bottles of the babies who aren't next to your legs. When burping, I would take all bottles away and hold these between my knees, burp all separately, lay each down, and begin again with the bottles.
Jennifer Wilwart, BAMOMs, Tampa, Fla.

need to do some experimenting with some of the different types of nipples available. Some babies switch easily from the mother's nipple to a bottle nipple, but some babies only want to use one kind.

Most health care providers no longer recommend sterilizing bottles for use if the bottles are being washed in a dishwasher, but you should talk to your own physician about this. If using formula, you may want to consider using room-temperature water and powdered formula to prepare bottles. Tap water and well water varies from place to place, so you will need to decide if you want to use bottled water; again, this is something to discuss with your health care provider to make sure the babies will get all the nutrients they need, such as fluoride. Since hot water contains a greater percentage of dissolved minerals, you should not use hot tap water for preparation of bottles. Warming the bottles in water is generally considered the best approach. There is also some question about using microwave ovens for warming up bottles, especially since some ovens tend to spot-heat, leaving one hot area while all the rest seems cool. Most babies are fine with room-temperature bottles. You should also discuss with your health care provider whether you should warm up the bottles and the best way to do it.

Bottle feeding allows others to help. Also, after the babies have enough head control, you can prop bottles during a feeding. There are even special pillows available to keep the bottles in place. There are some brands of bottles that have a straw attachment for a "no-hands" feeding. Propping is not recommended for every feeding; babies need the eye-to-eye contact and snuggling that are also important parts of feeding. However, for late-night feedings or for times when only one parent is home, propping can help get the job done. Parents should never leave the babies when they are drinking from propped bottles. You should try to sing or to talk to the babies while they are feeding. Somewhere around eight or nine months (or the adjusted age for preemies) the babies will be able to hold their own bottles. After 12 months you can start thinking about weaning to a cup.

DAILY ROUTINE

Organization and a workable schedule are the keys to surviving supertwin babyhood. You must work on establishing an eat-play-sleep interval for your multiples or chances are good that you will be exhausted in a matter of days. As with many other aspects of baby care, this is easier said than done, and babies are not always interested in staying on schedule. You will need to be a little bit flexible while still working it out. As a general rule, you should try to ease your babies into three-hour intervals of diapering, feeding, playing, and back to sleep. Once you get a working schedule you need to stick to it. Friends and relatives who have had singleton children may comment about how "uptight" you are about your children's schedule, but parents of multiples need to hold to their system, for the babies' sakes and their own!

Being the mother of triplets, I found the best thing for myself and my children was scheduling. I kept my kids on the schedule from the hospital - but I compressed it so that I could have all three fed and changed in one hour and fifteen minutes. I only allotted 15 to 20 minutes for each to eat. If they take longer than that, they are using up more calories than they are getting.
Lori Hanold, Bay Area MOMs, Odessa, Fla.

Charting is a very useful way to track how each baby is doing and is especially helpful when several people are helping care for the babies. All that is needed is a pad of paper with each baby's name written in a column. Whoever feeds or changes a diaper should mark down the time, how much the baby ate, if there was spit-up, etc. This will help parents see what eating/sleeping/diapering patterns each baby is establishing.

Plan very uninteresting night-time feedings for the babies — no bright lights, no singing, no playing. Just change diapers, feed, and back to bed. You will need to discuss with your health care provider at what weight you can expect your babies to sleep through the night.

All babies have their cranky days and nights, and some babies are just fussier than others. Some babies have colic; they cry continuously. Sometimes this can be traced to excess gas and can be remedied by changing formulas or by more frequent burping. You should check with your health care provider for all possible approaches. Firm swaddling, car rides, rocking and swinging, or just steady, monotonous sounds ("white noise," such as a fan or running water) can calm the fussy baby. Sometimes there is no apparent reason for the colic, however, and parents will be advised that the babies will just need to grow out of it. If one or more of the babies is hard to comfort, you will have a rough time getting the rest — both physical and mental — that you will so desperately need. Here is where it is so important to have some extra help during the first few months so that you can get some rest or a "quiet" break when the chance arises. You need to keep an eye on the long-term and tell yourself that your multiples won't be babies forever; that this, too, shall pass. A good sense of humor also goes a long way toward getting through a frustrating day.

OUT AND ABOUT

Mobility is a real challenge with higher multiple births. With triplets or more, you are already outnumbered; you have the quandary of who will hold the third (and possibly fourth, fifth, etc.) baby. A good triplet or quad stroller is a good investment toward mobility, as is a vehicle large enough for several car seats, a stroller in the back, a big diaper bag, and two or more adults. Even with a stroller and a vehicle, however, you will soon see that it can be difficult for one parent to take out all the children at once on doctor visits, to run errands, etc. The best advice is to try to line up at least two adults for going out. If only one parent will be able to take the babies to appointments or to get other business done during the day, this can still be done with careful planning.

> If you have very limited time in the morning, or have to leave early and know it will be hectic, dress the children the night before in comfortable clothes such as sweats. In the morning you will only have to change diapers. It saves a good half-hour of dressing triplets. More time for me, and we deserve it!
> *Daria Duglenski, Waterbury Area MOTC, Waterbury, Conn.*

The final system depends on each family's circumstances — whether the vehicle is parked in the garage, in the driveway, on the street (or if the family is using public transportation). You need to park the vehicle with much thought to loading and unloading; the more room for a stroller next to the vehicle, the better. You should check with your local office of motor vehicle registration about possibly getting a handicapped parking permit.

You must be prepared for breakdown contingencies when out with the children, and you may want to consider a cellular phone or some sort of emergency radio for the road. A family should always have drinking water, extra blankets or outerwear, emergency flares for nighttime, and so on, in the vehicle. In the event of a breakdown or accident, you will have to decide based on the particular situation whether to move children out of the vehicle. Generally, they're safer inside in car seats, but this is not always the case. In the vast majority of hours driving, of course, everything is fine and without incident.

> **W**hen the triplets were very small and I was going to the doctor by myself, I would put kids in the same car seat/carrier to carry into the office — so I didn't have to use the stroller. This was much easier and saved a lot of time.
> *Lori Hanold, Bay Area MOMs, Odessa, Fla.*

Once the destination is reached and the car is parked, you then have to consider getting out. Your goal should be this: never leave the children in the car by themselves, ever. This can be a real trial for parents if only one parent is home to go pick up a prescription or some other emergency. Some parents do leave children in car seats locked in the car, while the adult runs into an office or shop to pick up something. In some towns this may seem safe enough and safer than unloading all the children from car seats and into a stroller, particularly when the weather is bad. You will need to decide what seems the safest thing to do. You should also keep in mind, however, that people passing by the car will definitely be alarmed to see children left unattended and may call the police. The best thing to do is recruit another adult to ride along and stay with the children. If there is an older sibling, you will need to consider how well he or she could handle an emergency (or how likely to roll down the window at the request of a friendly-looking stranger). It is best never, ever to take a chance. Try to find businesses offering drive-through service, delivery service, or pay-at-the-pump service.

You also need to get into the habit of counting heads immediately after unloading the children. It's quite possible for one person or helper to assume the other parent or adult went out to bring in the last child, while the other adult assumes vice versa. Leaving a child in a car for even a relatively short time can have disastrous consequences on a very hot or very cold day. You must absolutely account for all children right away.

FACING THE PUBLIC

Something that you may not have expected is the attention that multiple babies bring, especially in an eye-catching stroller. You should brace yourself for both good and bad experiences with the public. Some people will think nothing of coming right up to the stroller and asking all sorts of questions or making all sorts of remarks. Here are some examples:

- Are they twins? (This is probably the most-asked question, no matter how many babies are in the stroller!)
- Boy, do you have your hands full!
- Did you take fertility pills?
- Which one is the oldest?
- Which one is the best?
- Are they identical? (This is asked even if they're obviously dressed as boys and girls.)
- You don't want any more, do you?
- What's wrong with that one?
- I'm glad it's you and not me, honey!

Most of the information about multiples that the public sees is presented as entertainment on talk shows or news programs, so it's not all that surprising that most people have many wrong ideas about multiples. Many people assume that couples take fertility pills and get an instant family. Each family will have to decide how to react to some of these remarks and whether to ignore people who come up uninvited. Parents can get a real ego boost from the kind remarks of some people. They can also get their singleton children into the lime-light by letting a brother or sister introduce the babies. They should be prepared for some truly rude comments, however.

MULTIPLE DEVELOPMENT

Since they are born, on average, some weeks earlier than sin-gletons, many higher order multiples will show developmental delays. You will need to adjust milestones — such as rolling over, crawling, and walking — to the babies' "adjusted age," which is based on the original due date of the babies. At the age of twelve months, two months prematurity is still a significant percentage of the baby's life. But studies show that multiples catch up to singletons by school age. If there are ongoing complications from birth, parents need to look into early intervention programs.

MULTIPLE JOY

It is clear that caring for multiple birth children presents a real challenge for parents. It should be pointed out that parenting

These triplets provide three times as much to smile about.

triplets, quads, quints, or more is also a tremendously rewarding experience. You shouldn't look at life with multiples as being hectic so much as being dynamic and exciting. The emphasis on organization, schedules, recruited help, and so on are meant to help you get on with the real business at hand: enjoying each of your children as individuals and enjoying their unique bond as multiples.

Highlights from NOMOTC's 1998 Higher Order Multiples Survey

- Parents of triplets and quadruplets who experienced complications during the pregnancy - 80%
- Mothers who had been put on bed rest prior to delivery - 90%
- Mothers delivering all of their babies by Caesarean section - 90%
- Multiples who were born between 32 and 35 weeks - 54%
- Multiples who were born between 36 and 38 weeks - 15%
- Babies going home less than a week after their birth - 25%; those home within two weeks - 50%; those home within one month - 75%
- Mothers reporting that it was extremely stressful to be home while one or more babies remained in the hospital - 30%
- Mothers joining a local parents-of-multiples club for support - 82% (the majority felt that it offered the most support during pregnancy and right after birth

Eight-month-old fraternal twins

3

"How Could This Happen?"
(AND OTHER QUESTIONS)

Are they identical?
How do you maneuver the stroller through the aisles?
Were you on fertility drugs?
Do you have your hands full all of the time?
Are they double trouble?
Do twins run in your family?
Are you sure they are twins? They don't look alike...

For some parents of multiples, questions like these seem to echo endlessly. Actually, it has been that way for ages. Twins and other multiples have been the source of fascination and folklore for centuries, from the mythological Romulus and Remus to the biblical Jacob and Esau. Depending on the culture, twins were either revered or feared. Some were thought to bring on bad luck or poor crops, and the twins or the mother were sometimes killed. In some African tribes twins were honored and treated like royalty. The question of fatherhood was a mystery, as some believed that twins must have been fathered by two men.

The average person has many misconceptions regarding twins. One of the most common is that twins are people who look identical. The general public has little interest in boy/girl twins and those twins who look completely different from each other. Some will even argue with the mother (who carried the two in her womb) that these un-alike multiples could not be twins!

TYPES OF TWINS

There are two basic types of twins: *monozygotic*, commonly referred to as *identical* twins, and *dizygotic*, referred to as *fraternal* twins. There are also other rare and unusual types of twins, such as polar body twins. The specific cause of twinning is still a mystery.

IDENTICAL TWINS

Identical, or monozygotic, twins develop from one fertilized egg (mono=one, zygote=egg). This egg divides into two individuals who will share all their genes in common. No one knows what causes the egg to divide in half. These twins are genetic clones of each other. They will therefore always be the same sex and have identical features, eye and hair color. Their handprints and footprints are similar, but the fingerprints are different. This type is what most people think of when they think of twins.

FRATERNAL TWINS

Fraternal, or dizygotic, twins develop from two eggs (di=two, zygote=egg) that are fertilized separately by two different sperm. This usually happens when the mother produces more than one egg at ovulation. These two fertilized eggs develop separately and have their own unique genes. They are no more alike than single brothers and sisters genetically. Dizygotic, or fraternal, twins may be the same sex or opposite and may appear similar or look completely different. They may have different hair and eye colors and be different sizes. Some may not even appear to be related!

MORE THAN TWO...

Other multiple types are possible, such as triplets which consist of three babies; quadruplets (or quads) which are four babies; quintuplets (or quints) which are five babies; sextuplets which are six babies; and septuplets which are seven babies. These are all referred to as higher order multiples or supertwins. Higher order multiples can be any combination of the two basic twin types.

TYPES OF TRIPLETS

Triplets can result from a single fertilized egg that splits three ways to produce three identical individuals (the equivalent of identical twins). They would look the same and all be the same sex. They would be identical triplets, but this is very rare. Most often the mother produces three separate eggs at ovulation, which are then fertilized and become three un-alike individuals. This would be the equivalent of fraternal twins.

Another combination of triplets could result from the mother producing two eggs that are fertilized, and then one of those eggs proceeds to divide in two to produce two identical individuals. This would result in triplets in which two are identical and the third is a fraternal to the others. You could have two identical girls and a boy, or two identical boys and a girl, or all the same sex, with two being identical.

QUADRUPLETS

There can be different types of quadruplets just as there are different types of triplets. There can be any combination of fraternals and identicals within the four. According to data from the Triplet Connection and Mothers of Supertwins (M.O.S.T.), close to 60 percent of the families registered with these organizations have a combination of identical and fraternal children. Many of the other higher order multiples result from multiple ovulations and thus are fraternal.

UNUSUAL TYPES OF TWINS

In addition to all the different combinations of identical and fraternal multiples, there are some other, rarer types of twins.

MIRROR-IMAGE TWINS

Mirror-image twins occur only in identical twins. Here is how it happens: in approximately 23 percent of identical twins the egg splits later than usual, most often day seven or beyond. The original right half of the egg becomes one individual, and the original left half becomes the other. These twins will often have "mirror images" of their

My identical twins are mirror-image twins. Their hair whorls are in opposite directions, one favors her left hand and the other the right. They cut their first tooth on the same day, but in one it was the right lower incisor, and in the other it was the left lower incisor!
Rebecca Moskwinski,
Michiana POMC, Granger, Ind.

features, such as hair whorls that run clockwise in one and counter clockwise in the other, a birthmark on the right shoulder of one and the left shoulder of the other, etc. There is no specific test for determining if twins are mirror-image. The determination is made by observation only, and the twins must be monozygotic, or identical.

This may be a partial explanation for the fact that a little over one third of identical twins are left handed, double the rate in the general population. In extreme cases all of the internal organs are reversed in one of the twins, with the heart on the right, the liver on the left and the appendix on the left.

POLAR BODY TWINS (HALF-IDENTICAL)

Polar body twinning is very unusual and very rare. The process is quite complicated. The polar body appears when the egg has been developing, even before fertilization. It is a small cell that does not function and will usually degenerate and die. It is thought that in some cases, when the egg is old, the splitting off of the polar body takes place in an abnormal way. It then becomes larger, receives more nourishment, and does not die as it usually does. Instead, it acts as a second egg. The polar body and the egg share identical genes from the mother, but they may then be fertilized by two separate sperm from the father. This will result in twins who share half their genes in common (from the mother) and the other half different (from the two sperm). They share some features of identical twins and some features of fraternal twins and thus are so-called *half-identical twins*.

MIXED CHROMOSOMES OR CHIMERISM

Another form of twinning that has been identified is called chimerism. This is thought to occur if two separate sperm fertilize two separate eggs which then fuse, producing one individual with different sets of chromosomes. Some have been identified that have more than one distinct red blood cell type or individuals who are both XX and XY (the sex chromosomes — XX being female and XY being male.) This phenomenon might also be associated with fused placentas causing intermixing of the circulations. It is very rare, and fewer than twenty-five cases have been identified. It is more common in other mammals, such as calves.

SUPERFECUNDATION

Twins can have different fathers. One well-known case was described in 1810 in the United States. A woman had both a white and a black lover, and she became pregnant and gave birth to twins, one white and the other mulatto. Each twin had a different father. This is called *superfecundation*. It happens when the mother ovulates more than one egg and has more than one partner during her fertile period. One egg is fertilized with sperm from one partner, and the other egg from sperm of the second partner. These types of twins are always fraternal or dizygotic.

SUPERFETATION

Superfetation occurs when a women ovulates more than one egg but the eggs are released at different times, sometimes up to 24 days apart, and they are fertilized when they are released. The resulting twin pregnancy has different conception dates, so the babies may be quite different in size. The births may be separated by days or weeks. It is quite an unusual event. In some cases, the births of twins may be weeks or months apart due to deliberate medical intervention. This is called *interval birth*.

INCIDENCE OF MULTIPLES

Your chance of having twins varies by the type of twin and the country of residence. (See accompanying chart).

The twin rate has been increasing. Recent statistics from the National Center for Health Statistics in the United States in 1999 showed that there were 114,307 babies born as twins (or 57,154 sets), 6,742 as triplets, 512 as quadruplets, and 67 as quintuplets and other higher order multiples. The twinning rate is 28.9 per 1,000. This translates into a probability of having twins as one in 35 and of having higher order multiples as one in 541. This shows a 3 percent increase in the twin rate from 1998 to 1999. Since 1980 the number of twins

RATE OF MULTIPLE BIRTHS BY COUNTRY

Australia	1/72
Belgium	1/55
Canada	1/85
Finland	1/64
Japan	1/120
United Kingdom	1/70
United States	1/35
Sweden	1/70
Switzerland	1/80

has risen 67% and the twin birth rate by 53%. The major causes of the increase are older-aged women having babies and also fertility drugs, which account for about 80% of the increase.

INCIDENCE OF TWINS BY TWIN-TYPE

The rate of identical twins is constant at approximately four per thousand. It is remarkable that the incidence of identical twins remains the same no matter where a person lives, and it has remained the same throughout history. The rate of fraternal twins, on the other hand, can change depending on where a person lives, the mother's age, etc. Fraternals account for the differences in the twin rate, the fraternal rate being approximately 22.8 per thousand in the world.

Any given mother would have a better chance of having fraternal twins, as there are two thirds more fraternal or dizygotic twins than identical or monozygotic twins. However, your own chance of having twins depends on your personal history, age, race, and many other factors.

INCIDENCE OF TRIPLETS AND HIGHER

The birth statistics also showed that the rate of triplet and higher births in the United States doubled since 1990, quadrupled since 1980, and quintupled since 1971. In the early 1970s, only about one of 3,500 births was a higher order multiple. By 1980 it was one of every 2,700 births and by 1999 this rate had lowered to one of 541 births. Triplets account for 92 percent of these higher order births. The rate of *naturally* occurring triplets (no fertility drugs used) is close to one in 8,000; quadruplets one in 700,000; and quintuplets one in 65,610,000 births. The major factor underlying the increase in triplet and higher births appears to be the use of ovulation-enhancing drugs and assisted reproductive techniques such as in vitro fertilization. Only one third of the increase reflects the increased shift in maternal age.

FACTORS AFFECTING THE TWIN RATE

Only fraternal twins tend to run in families. Identical twins happen by "chance" and can happen to anyone, regardless of whether there are twins in the family or not.

Many people believe that twins "skip a generation." Twinning is passed on as a genetic trait and appears in the women only. If you are a female and your mother had fraternal twins, you would have an increased chance of having fraternal twins yourself. Your brothers would not have an increased chance of having fraternal twins themselves, but they may pass the genetic trait on to their daughters who would then have an increased chance of having twins. This makes it appear that twins skip a generation.

For women, twins running in your husband's family appears to have no effect on your chances of conceiving twins. However, this is still being studied. Many physical and environmental factors having nothing to do with heredity can trigger a twin pregnancy. You could still have twins, but they likely would not be caused by any trait in your husband's family.

It is well-known that fertility treatments can cause multiple births. This affects only the rate of fraternal or dizygotic twins. These methods use many different types of drugs and treatments. Most of them rely on stimulating ovulation with hormones or, more recently, inserting fertilized eggs into the mother. Fertility treatments are not thought to cause identical or monozygotic twins.

There are also many other factors that increase the rate of fraternal births. They include social habits, maternal age, number of pregnancies, geographic location, seasons, and nutrition.

The incidence of fraternal twins varies by race. Africans have a higher rate, about 16 per thousand, and Asians have the lowest rate, about three per thousand. The rate in Caucasians is about eight per thousand. In the United States the Hispanic twinning rate (20.1 per 1,000) is substantially lower than the rate of non-Hispanic whites (31.5 per 1,000) and that of non-Hispanic blacks (32.1 per 1,000). A well-known tribe in Africa called the Yorubas has the highest twinning rate in the world, one in 22. This increase is due to fraternal twinning, as their rate of identicals is the same as the rest of the world. Their diet consists of large amounts of a particular species of yam (Dioscorea rotundata). This yam contains a high level of a substance similar to the hormone estrogen, which is thought to bring on multiple ovulation.

The older one's age, the higher one's chance of having frater-

FACTORS AFFECTING THE RATE OF FRATERNAL TWINNING

- Heredity
- Social Habits
- Maternal Age
- Number of Pregnancies
- Fertility Treatments
- Seasons
- Geographic Location
- Nutrition

nal twins. The twinning rate is doubled for ages 35 to 40 and then decreases again, probably due to a decrease in fertility as one ages. The rate increases again for the age group 45 to 49 years. Older women are having multiples at an increasingly high rate. Since 1990, the twin birth rate has risen 80% among women 40-44 years of age (from 24.7 to 44.5 per 1,000) and almost 600 percent among women aged 44-49 compared to only a six percent rise for women under age 20. There were more twins born to women ages 45 to 49 in 1997 than during the entire decade of the 1980s. This, however, accounts for only five tenths of one percent of all twins born, reflecting the relatively fewer births in older women. In other words, you are less likely to give birth over the age of 45. But if you do, there is a 33 percent chance that it will be a multiple birth.

Being well nourished increases the chance of twinning, but the rates drop off with malnutrition. Certain social habits, such as eating certain yams grown in Africa, can increase your chances of twinning. The more pregnancies you have had, the greater are your chances of having fraternal twins. By your fourth or fifth pregnancy, your chance of having twins is four times higher than for your first pregnancy.

Geographically, rates of fraternal twins are greater in northern areas than in those farther south. Also, different races and countries have varied rates of twinning. In the United States, Massachusetts and Connecticut reported the highest proportion of twins, 25 percent higher than the U.S. rate, while Nebraska and New Jersey had twice the national level of triplet and higher births.

The most fraternal twins are conceived in July, the fewest in January. This is thought to be due to the effect of the length of daylight on the secretion of Follicle Stimulating Hormone.

CAUSES OF FRATERNAL TWINNING

It is felt that fraternal twins are conceived due to higher levels of Follicle Stimulating Hormone (FSH) in the mother. This hormone stimulates the growth and ripening of eggs. Mothers of fraternal twins tend to have increased height and weight, earlier start of the menstrual cycle, and shorter menstrual cycles, all of which are probably hormone-related.

Once you have had fraternal twins, your chance of having another set of twins is three to four times that of the general population.

CAUSES OF IDENTICAL TWINNING

It is not really known how identical twinning occurs, but there are some theories. One theory is that it may be related to aging of the egg after ovulation: an "over-ripe" egg. Another theory states that since the rate of identical twins is higher in mothers who are either very young or very old, identical twins may be due to the hormonal imbalances seen at these ages. Supporting this, mothers of identical twins have been shown to have an earlier menopause, which is also due to hormones.

Having two sets of identical twins would be a rare occurrence. The odds of having more than one set of identical twins are at least one in 70,000.

COMPLICATIONS IN IDENTICAL TWINNING

It is possible to have more complications with identical twinning because of the unusual splitting that takes place in the egg that produces identical twins, but most of these complications are rare. Types of problems include Siamese or conjoined twins, in which the twins are connected in various parts of their bodies. This happens only in identicals. This condition is rare and happens in one out of 33,000 births, with most of conjoined twins (about 70 percent) being female. Also, Twin-to-Twin Transfusion Syndrome (TTTS), another cause of problems in twin pregnancies, can occur only in identicals. (See Chapter 1).

DETERMINATION OF TWIN TYPE (ZYGOSITY)

Finding out for sure if a twin is fraternal or identical is called zygosity determination. It is often important to know what type of twins you have. It can help in understanding their development, explaining some of their social behaviors, and, of course, satisfying curiosity. It can also be important if medical illnesses occur, for such reasons as determining the heredity of the illness or whether organ transplantation is needed.

There are several methods that determine twin type, or zygosity. They vary in accuracy and expense. Many times, insurance companies do not cover the cost of this determination. The methods include:

(1) SIMILARITY METHOD

This is perhaps the most obvious method and the one used by the common person. If they look alike, they are identical or monozygotic; if they look different, they are fraternal or dizygotic. Experienced observers can be quite accurate in labeling the twin type using things such as hair; eyes; skin color; shapes of nose, lips, and eyes; fingerprint analysis; and tissue grafts between twins. These experienced observers, usually researchers, can claim a 94-96 percent chance of correctly identifying the twin type, compared to blood tests.

(2) PLACENTA METHOD

Analyzing the placenta(s) has been the common way that obstetricians have determined twin type in the past, and placental analysis is still performed today. Unfortunately, this method can be quite inaccurate and depends on the expertise of the doctor. In the past it was assumed that one placenta meant that the twins were monozygotic, or identical, and that two placentas meant that they were dizygotic, or fraternal. This has proved to be untrue. Parents can often be misled when given the twin type based only on examination of the fetal tissues by an inexperienced clinician.

More important than the placenta itself are the fetal membranes, which can be helpful in determining twin type. They are the thin membranes filled with fluid that surround the fetus and are attached to the placenta. The amnion is the inner membrane, and the chorion is the outer membrane. A shared amnion always means monozygotic twins, but is very rare. Two amnions and one chorion also means monozygotic twins. If there are two amnions and two chorions the twin type can be either mono- or dizygotic.

Fraternal or dizygotic twins will always have two placentas, as the two eggs implant separately into the uterus. However, if the eggs implant close together the placentas can become fused and take on the appearance of one placenta. Twins can then be mislabeled monozygotic.

However, identical twins do not always have one placenta. Monozygotic twins come from an egg that splits into two. The timing of the split will determine the number of placentas. If the split happens after the egg has already implanted into the uterus, there will be one placenta. If the split happens earlier, before implantation, then the two eggs can implant separately into the uterus and form two separate placentas. The twins will still be identical.

(3) BLOOD TESTING

Using blood tests can give an accurate determination of twin type. There are many other blood groups besides the usual ABO blood type. There are also serum proteins and enzymes. The more blood groups studied, the more accurate the identification will be. Using eight blood groups, there is a 97 percent chance of correctly identifying identical twins. With the use of more blood groups, the accuracy can climb to nearly 99 percent. HLA typing is a similar measure of many blood proteins and can be 100 percent accurate. This is the type of testing that is done for matching donors for organ transplants. It must be performed in a specialized laboratory. Blood typing tends to be much less expensive than HLA typing.

(4) DNA TESTING

This is called DNA fingerprinting. This method of twin typing is virtually 100 percent accurate and is performed only at specialized laboratories. DNA contains the genetic building blocks of an organism. In DNA fingerprinting, the DNA is separated into smaller segments and compared. The chance of two individuals having the same DNA sequence at the same time would be extremely rare unless they were monozygotic twins. The test can be performed from blood specimens or from scrapings of cells from the inner cheek, called a buccal smear. This method, while being one of the most accurate, is also the most expensive.

FERTILITY TREATMENTS

As noted previously, fertility drugs are one of the causes of the increase in multiples in recent years. Ever since the successful 1978 birth of Baby Louise, the first "test tube" baby, medical treatment of infertility has grown by leaps and bounds. Fertility treatments increase the possibility of a multiple birth. Many women have their dreams of motherhood fulfilled with the aid of fertility treatments. Others suffer countless disappointments.

Successful infertility treatment often requires painful procedures, numerous medications, and, of course, money. These treatments can also bring with them unexpected emotional costs. Newer treatments have more successes, but they also produce the possibility of difficult moral dilemmas when higher order multiple pregnancies result. Parents-to-be may be asked to choose among selective termination of some of the fetuses to save the others, termination of the entire longed-for pregnancy, or carrying a difficult pregnancy of four or more fetuses with the possibility of losing them all or risking severe malformations. These are not easy choices.

All fertility treatments carry an increased risk of multiples, some more than others. Fertility treatments include medicines to enhance ovulation and assisted reproductive techniques, such as in vitro fertilization. According to the National Center for Health Statistics, approximately 43 percent of live births resulting from assisted reproductive techniques were multiples. There was a range of success from 43 percent down to 19 percent depending on age, with the lower percentages corresponding to the older women (40 and above).

FERTILITY MEDICATIONS

The most common fertility treatment used is medication that helps stimulate ovulation. Clomiphene citrate (Clomid) and hMG (human menopausal gonadotropin) have been used for many years to stimulate ovulation. Multiple pregnancy rates range from 25-30 percent, with 75 percent of those being twins.

In recent years the fertility medication hMG has been used to stimulate ovulation in women who are already ovulating normally. It has been used in conjunction with in vitro fertilization treatments and the GIFT program (See below). This is called superovulation therapy or controlled ovarian hyperstimulation. Sometimes gonadotropin-releasing hormone (GnRH, such as luprolide acetate) is added to permit a greater degree of ovarian stimulation. With these therapies, multiple ovulation is the goal to increase the chance of pregnancy. The monthly probability of pregnancy averages 10-20 percent per cycle.

Unfortunately, the risk of multiple pregnancy with superovulation is hard to foretell. It can't be predicted based on the mother's characteristics, the quantity of hMG, the estrogen hormone levels, the number of stimulated follicles, or the number of sperm introduced. Adding gonadotropin-releasing hormone (GnRH) treatments allows for natural feedback processes and reduces the chance of multiple birth. There is a reported 7-10 percent incidence of multiples, usually twins, when using this.

IN VITRO FERTILIZATION

There are three types of this treatment being used today:

(1) IVF-ET

In Vitro Fertilization and Embryo Transfer has the longest history. It is standard practice to stimulate the development of multiple eggs in the ovary with medication, then harvest and fertilize these eggs, and finally transfer apparently normal embryos into the uterus. The transfer of many embryos leads to multiple gestations. The incidence of multiple births with this method is approximately 32 percent.

(2) GIFT

In Gamete Intrafallopian Tubal Transfer, the egg is fertilized in the fallopian tube. The incidence of multiples is similar to IVF-ET. However, with this method there can be the additional risk of naturally ovulated eggs being fertilized at the same time. This can lead to a pregnancy with a larger number of fetuses than the number of eggs transferred.

(3) TET or ZIFT

Tubal Embryo Transfer or Zygote Intrafallopian Transfer is a technique in which the egg is fertilized outside the body and the embryos are transferred into the fallopian tube rather than the uterus. The number of multiple births is strongly associated with the number of embryos transferred. The risk of multiples ranges from zero following transfer of one or two embryos, to 21 percent with the transfer of three and 57 percent when four embryos are transferred.

Recently European doctors have used between two and three embryos as the optimal numbers to transfer during these procedures. This will produce adequate results with an acceptable risk of multiple pregnancy.

There is a better chance of conceiving with the transfer of more embryos, but this increases the chance of a multiple birth. This is an ethical dilemma: to balance the desired goal of pregnancy and the risk of a multiple pregnancy and all its inherent complications. This has received more attention in European countries and Australia than in the United States, and guidelines have been developed in those countries. Newer techniques of freezing embryos (cryopreservation) and growing embryos longer before transfer have improved the success of single-embryo transfers. Use of donor eggs is also a possibility for women who cannot ovulate on their own. All of these techniques have been developed much faster than the development of ethical guidelines.

Although the multiple births associated with fertility treatments are mainly fraternal due to the multiple eggs used, there is also an increased incidence of identical or monozygotic twins observed compared with the expected rate. While the expected rate of identical twins in any pregnancy would be four tenths of one percent, it has been found that the rate in fertility treatments is actually one and three tenths percent.

This is an area of ongoing research. It may be related to "damage" to the outer coating of the egg — the zona pellucida — from which it "hatches." Attempts to "help" the egg to "hatch" to increase the pregnancy rate of in vitro fertilization (IVF) may increase the incidence of identicals.

THE VANISHING TWIN

An interesting phenomenon has been noticed now that ultrasound exams are available for most pregnancies, facilitating detection of pregnancy at earlier and earlier stages. There have been many cases in which early-pregnancy ultrasound exams showed twins, only to have a subsequent ultrasound show only one fetus, with no sign of the other having been present. Sometimes the mother had experienced mild vaginal bleeding or cramps, and at other times she had no symptoms. This is the *vanishing twin* phenomenon.

The vanishing twin has been studied by Charles E. Boklage, M.D., and others, and it has been found to be more common than first realized. In one study, 325 twin pregnancies were identified very early by ultrasound exam and followed through the entire pregnancy. The study reported that 61 (18.8 percent) ended as twin births, 125 (38.5 percent) ended as singleton births, and 139 (42.8 percent) ended as a complete loss of the pregnancy.

Generally, the vanishing twin fetus is absorbed back into the uterus or degenerates as pregnancy advances. The likelihood of survival for the other co-twin is good.

There may be more twins than we realize. Boklage has concluded that the "true" twinning rate is closer to one in eight at conception. He feels that for every live-born twin pair, there are at least six singletons who have lost a twin without anyone ever knowing it. Some feel that the survival of just a few more of these twin conceptions could increase the twinning rate remarkably. This could be another explanation of why the rate of twins has recently increased.

Anyone may have had an undetected twin in the womb. It is conjectured that since twins are more likely to be left-handed than the normal population, left-handed singletons may be surviving co-twins of a vanishing identical!

CONCLUSION

Multiple births are fascinating to study and sometimes difficult to understand. Being informed can help with the barrage of questions you are bound to receive from acquaintances and sometimes total strangers. It can also be important to the health or development of your multiples as well as in planning future pregnancies.

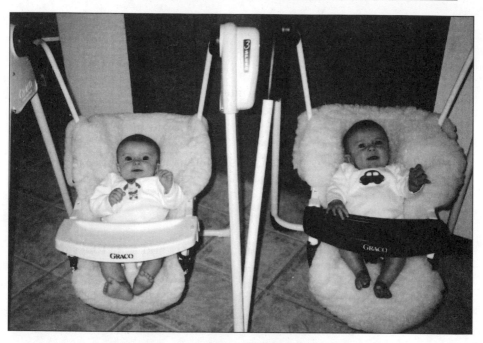

Multiple sets of swings and a double Snuggli® pictured below, can be very handy.

4

"How Do We Get Ready?"
PREPARATIONS

The best piece of advice I can give about being a mother of twins is that you honestly do not have to buy two of everything. When they are young, both of them will not use a swing, walker, etc., at exactly the same time. Even when they are older they will fight over a piece of trash more often than a toy, so toys do not necessarily have to be multiplied.

Michelle Mickler, Rantoul, Ill.

When you are expecting multiples, the thought of buying two or more of everything can be daunting. Most families of multiples will confirm that many items can be shared or borrowed. Before the babies arrive, you will want to have some basic equipment on hand. If you are going to buy new equipment, you should ask the store about a discount for buying multiple items such as cribs, swings, high chairs, and so on. Parents-of-multiples clubs' yard sales are good sources of baby equipment. Check into the latest safety standards before buying or borrowing any equipment, new or used.

BASIC LAYETTE LIST

Many parents worry about the amount of clothing and diapers they will need to outfit their multiples. Visions of dollar signs oppress their minds. Below is a basic minimum layette list for twins. Keep in mind, however, that you may need more or fewer items depending on your finances, the frequency that you do laundry, the climate you live in, and personal preferences. Also, twins tend to bring out the generosity of many relatives, so you may find yourself inundated with matching outfits. You would do well to stick to the basics and leave to friends and relatives the purchase of "cutesy" outfits that are worn infrequently. You may find that multiples tend to fit in newborn-sized clothing for a longer period of time, since at birth they tend to be smaller than singletons.

CLOTHING	Amount Needed	✔
T-shirts or "onesies"	8	
Terry cloth sleepers	8	
Blanket sleepers	4	
Sweater or snuggle sack	2	
Bibs (cloth)	12	
Bibs (plastic)	2	
Socks/booties	8	
OPTIONAL:		
Gowns	6	
Outfits	6	
Hats or bonnets	4	

DIAPER NEEDS		
Cloth diapers (if not using disposables)	8 dozen	
Cloth diapers for burp pads	2 dozen	
Diaper pail (may want one for every floor of the house)	1-2	
Diaper covers (cloth diapers)	8-12	
Disposable diapers	150-180/wk	
Baby wipes	2+	
Diaper bag	1-2	

BEDDING		
Crib sheets	8	
Mattress pads	4	
Blankets	4	
Receiving blankets	8	
Quilts	2	
OPTIONAL:		
crib bumpers and pads	2	

FEEDING

If Breast-feeding:

Breast pump (manual or electric)	1
Breast pads (cloth or disposable)	30
Nursing pillow	1

If Bottle feeding:

Bottles, nipples, covers	20
Bottle brush	1

OPTIONAL:

Bottle warmer	2
Special bottles and holders for hands-free feedings (e.g., Podee® Bottles)	

EQUIPMENT

Twin stroller	1
Crib (many have one crib for the first 5-6 months)	2
Baby bathtub	1
Car seats	2

OPTIONAL:

Foam bath aid (for tub)	1
Changing table	1
Dressers	2
Nursery monitor	1
Swings (some consider this essential)	2
Soft baby carriers	2
Baby carrier backpack	1
Rocking chair	1
Portable crib	1
Rocking or bouncy seats	2
Playpen	1

MISCELLANEOUS

Baby nail clippers	1
Thermometer	1-2
Acetaminophen drops	1
Wash cloths	8
Hooded bath towels (optional)	4
Pacifiers	4
Cool mist humidifier	1

EQUIPMENT FOR THE NURSERY

The final arrangement for the nursery will depend on what sort of space is available. Once the babies are home, they can be put any place which is secure, handy, and off the floor. Newborn multiples are generally smaller than singletons, and they can easily fit in one bed for a few weeks or even months. The babies may also derive comfort from being placed in close proximity to each other during the early weeks after birth. Eventually each baby will need his or her own bed, which can really fill up the nursery. When choosing a crib, especially a used one, you need to look at the distance between crib slats and the locking mechanism on the lift side. Also, you need to check out the finish or paint on the crib, making sure it is completely safe for babies who like to gum and gnaw on their cribs. You need to be sure the bedding, such as crib bumpers, will not pose any suffocation dangers for the babies. Generally, babies do not need pillows in the first year.

> **D**efinitely one of the best purchases made in our household was that of a rocking chair. When both babies were still crying even though they were fed and changed, I would just grab them in my arms and settle in for a nice rock in my rocker. When they're little, just scooping them up in your arms with them facing you works well. For older babies, holding them facing out gives them a chance to watch any activity in the room while they settle down or drift off to sleep.
> *Patti Carroll, Eugene, Ore.*

The nursery setup also depends on space and how you prefer to change diapers, store clothes, etc. Many families like a changing table or dresser with a surface dedicated to changing diapers because it helps to save their backs when changing double the amount of diapers. Others simply prefer to change the diapers on a bed or floor. Grace Zick of Nassau County MOTC, Baldwin, N.Y., suggests placing the changing table with the supplies in the main living area or where you spend the most time, not necessarily the twins' bedroom. You may want to consider such extras as a mini-refrigerator to hold prepared bottles for nighttime feedings and possibly, in a bathroom, a slow cooker holding warm water for taking the chill off bottles.

Baby swings are very useful for soothing fussy babies, and numerous parents of higher order multiples feel these are "musts " for handling two or more babies. Some models of swings even come with battery-operated motors (rather than crank mechanisms) to keep babies rocking gently and quietly. Always make sure you are in the same room when the babies are in a swing. Another useful item for fussy babies is a "bouncy" seat. These can keep your babies contained and entertained while you are busy in the kitchen, etc.

A highchair is not really needed until the babies can sit up by themselves. Most parents use an infant seat in the first six months for keeping the babies in one place and for early solid feedings. Plan on getting a highchair for later feedings. (See picture, page 78.) Plastic trays that unlatch with only one hand can be very convenient when juggling more than one baby. Make sure there is a safety strap on the chair and that you use it every time. Susan Bennett, Napa Valley MOTC, Napa, Calif., loves her highchairs on wheels. She uses them even at bath time to carry one baby and pull the other to the tub. Having the children in highchairs, especially when they become more mobile, can keep dinner time from becoming a "free-for-all." While you will still have to deal with the messes, highchairs do keep the children separated and in one place.

Storage becomes an interesting challenge as the babies add more clothes to their wardrobe. Hanging storage baskets can be used for socks, shoes, etc. Laundry baskets, storage cubbies, and so on are also useful. Some parents may want to check out stores that specialize in storage units to maximize their closet space. Grace Zick suggests "captain's" storage beds with the drawers underneath to save valuable floor space in small rooms. She also suggests placing coat hooks at the children's level on the wall or inside a closet door. It encourages responsibility and saves busy parents extra steps. She also customizes her children's closets inexpensively with wire shelving and double clothing rods, one over the other.

The most important thing to keep in mind in furnishing the children's room or rooms is to anticipate what the children will be able to do a few months ahead of time. As the babies move into toddlerhood, you must be on the lookout for possible dangers in the nursery. It's not at all unusual for multiples to work together to pull out dresser drawers or, even more serious, pull over dressers, shelves, anything. A playpen may come in handy for keeping the children in a safe place for a few minutes, but multiples can help each other out. One child might possibly get out by using his/her siblings as stairs! Many children are climbers from an early age and easily pull themselves up on top of changing-tables and dressers. You should never underestimate what several toddlers or preschoolers can accomplish. If the toddlers are growing into risk-taking climbers, make sure all furniture is securely fastened to the wall or removed. A baby monitor comes in handy to keep tabs on what the children are doing well into their preschool years.

CAMERAS

While not generally thought of as "equipment," a camera is important. From the birth through the first day of school, pictures will help you remember important events. Your children will be excited to see the picture story of their birth and infancy. Try to have a camera that is easy to use and available at all times. Patti Beemer of Colorado Springs MOM, Colo., suggests always having a camera ready and in a handy place for easy access. "Whenever something happens, take a deep breath and reach for your camera. Many times what may seem like crises — children making a mess, being silly, etc. — will later be the most special memories."

If your twins look very similar and you want to be able to figure out who is who in photos, Monica Cluff of Valley Twins Club, Buellton, Calif., suggests placing baby alphabet blocks (like "E" for Edward, "W" for William) corresponding to how your babies are placed in the photos. Another suggestion is to put the same baby on the left (or right) in each photo. This works especially well if one of the children's names starts with an "L" or an "R" but will work regardless, as long as you are consistent. Another trick is to have a small chalkboard or white board that you can include in those early pictures that has the babies' age written on it, such as "6 weeks." This will avoid wondering how to label the pictures when you finally have time six months or a year later!

It is nice to have separate baby books for each multiple, as these will be important keepsakes for them when they get older. Be sure to take some pictures of each multiple alone. This will ensure that all the children will have at least some of their own pictures. Some parents like to take pictures once a week for the first eight weeks and then once a month for the first year. It is fun to follow the babies' growth over time in this way. Another way pictures can be useful is suggested by Grace Zick: "Since it quickly becomes impossible to save all your children's special works of art, take photos of them and create an album of memories. You might also try this with a designated videotape."

DIAPERING

Diapering soon becomes a routine fact of life. The debate about whether cloth diapers or disposable diapers are better for the environment goes on, so each family will need to decide for themselves which is the most earth-friendly approach in their locale.

Cloth diapers are obviously a lot more work, and if you do not own a washer and dryer, it may just be too difficult to handle all the dirty diapers the babies generate. Also, if both parents work outside the home you will almost certainly need to use disposable diapers with a sitter or day care center. Cloth diapers need an outside cover. Some special products are now available for holding on cloth diapers that use velcro and do not require safety pins. These can be convenient and save a lot of pin sticks. A diaper service may solve the problem of washing hundreds of diapers and can be cost-effective compared to disposables, which are expensive. Anita Hinrichs of Albuquerque MOTC, N.M., loves her diaper service: "You don't have to rinse or wash. They pick up the dirty diapers and leave enough clean diapers. You never have to worry about laundering them or running to the store for diapers." You could try a combination of cloth and disposables to save money. Cloth diapers are handy to have for use as burp cloths, also, whether or not you decide on cloth diapers for diapering.

Some companies offer parents of triplets or more a complimentary package of diapers per child. Families can usually call the consumer toll-free number for these manufacturers and request money saving coupons. Families should also check with their local parents-of-

> **W**e kept a roll of masking tape on the twins' changing table while they were in disposables. It was great for securing those tabs that accidentally got baby lotion, oil, or worse on them. It also helped later when they could pull the tabs themselves to remove their own diapers. A long piece around the front of the diaper prevented such shenanigans!
> *Nancy L. Winn, North Dallas MOTC, Plano, Tex.*

> **L**ose the diaper bag! Buy a backpack to store needed items. You will need both hands to handle the children. Put your wallet in the backpack and quit carrying a purse. Buy a fanny pack in lieu of a purse.
> *Chris Gaietto-Lemmon,Northeast & Westchester MOTC, Cincinnati, O.*

multiples club to see if there are any diaper outlets in the area that sell factory seconds at a discount price.

Newborns may need up to 80 diapers each per week, especially if using cloth diapers. With the newer disposable diapers that trap wetness, you may need fewer than that. These amounts will decrease as the babies grow and eat less often during the day.

Baby wipes can be a major expense with more than one baby. However, the convenience is hard to do without. Sherry Bingham of Edmond MOMs, Okla., shares her recipe for home-made baby wipes: "Buy a plastic tub, size #9. The best paper towels to use are large good-quality brands. Cut the roll of paper towels in half and remove the center core. Place two and one half cups of warm water in the tub, along with two tablespoons of baby shampoo (or baby bath) and one to two tablespoons of baby oil. Put the paper towel roll in and flip. Pull the towels from the center after all the water is absorbed. These are about one fifth the cost of regular wet wipes, and they are much easier on the bottom of a baby with diaper rash because they contain no alcohol. Someone gave me the tub with instructions printed on the lid for a shower present, and I haven't used any others since." Shannon Black of Kalamazoo, Mich., still uses the thicker store-bought wipes but tears each one in half vertically to save money. She likes the smaller piece better than a large one but still has a large one available if needed. She also uses them to help remove spots on clothes as soon as she notices them to keep stains from setting.

> **A**lways keep a big diaper bag in your trunk that is a back-up to your regular diaper bag. Use it to keep electric plug-ups, aspirin, extra diapers, bibs — stuff you would not normally keep in a regular bag.
> *Monica Cluff, Valley Twins Club, Buellton, Calif.*

CLOTHING

When the babies are small they will not require much in the way of clothing. If your babies were born in a warm climate or in summertime, just the diaper and some T-shirts and gowns will suffice in the early weeks. Receiving blankets

> **E**asy solution for nasty stains: 1 scoop Biz Bleach®, 1 scoop Clorox Color Bleach®, 1 gallon water. Soak clothes in mixture for a few hours and then wash as usual. Works on old stains, too.
> *Jennifer Alvis, Albuquerque MOTC, N.M.*

can be useful for swaddling fussy babies and can double as burp cloths. Booties are not necessary and never seem to stay on. When you are busy, you will not want to spend your time searching for lost booties or matching up numerous pairs! One-piece shirts that snap at the crotch can be very convenient for dressing. As a general rule, twins require about one and a half times the amount of clothes that are needed for one baby.

Choosing two or more different colors can be helpful in identification of the babies when they are young. Even fraternal twins can look remarkably alike when they are infants. Many mothers choose a color family for each multiple and use it consistently throughout the infant years, such as blues and greens for one and pinks and reds for the other. This can help everyone to identify the multiples at a glance and avoids much confusion.

Dressing multiples alike or not is a decision you must make for yourself. Many people have definite opinions on this matter. Most parents do dress their multiples alike at certain times, such as for pictures and special events. Small infants will not be affected one way or the other, but toddlers and preschoolers may have definite ideas about how they should be dressed. As long as the issue isn't forced, occasionally dressing your multiples alike should not permanently affect their individuality.

> Save yourself time and money by getting more mileage out of the pile of "onesies" your babies rapidly outgrow. Even when onesies fit perfectly, they can be difficult to snap when the babies are active and trying to flip over. Not having the time or cash to buy dozens of new T-shirts, I pulled out the pinking shears and cut the bottoms off the onesies. The new shirts fit fine and the pinking shears kept the bottoms of the shirts from fraying, saving me and my wallet a trip to the store.
> *Carolyn Susi, Greater Portland MOTC, Gorham, Me.*

CAR SEATS

First, each child will need his or her own car seat or safety seat. Babies must always ride in a car seat, never in someone's lap. Since this is a vital safety item you should spend some time shopping around, comparing designs and checking out recommendations from other parents. Some hospitals provide infant car seats to all newborns when leaving the hospital. There are convertible car seats designed to fit a baby from newborn through about two years of age. These seats face the rear for infants up to about 12 months and then they face forward after 12 months. Straps on the car seat are adjusted as the baby grows. Other car seats feature a detachable infant seat for babies up to about 20 pounds; after this, you must get a toddler-sized car seat. Detachable car seats are very popular with many parents. They like being able to keep the babies in a sturdy framework while moving them in and out of the vehicle (especially convenient when babies are sleeping). Infants should ride in the back seat facing the rear of the vehicle until they are one year of age and 20 pounds.

The safety seat should recline at 45 degrees to prevent small infants' heads from falling forward. Putting a rolled towel under the front edge of the seat can help in positioning. The harness straps must fit snugly on the body. Small rolled blankets tucked on each side of the baby's shoulders and head can help. Do not put any blankets under the seat, however. Make sure snowsuits have an opening between the legs for proper fit into the seat.

Keeping older children in safety seats can sometimes be a problem, especially when they become more mobile and independent between the ages of nine and 23 months. Set a positive example yourself by buckling up on every trip. Make it an inflexible rule that the car will not move until everyone is buckled up. Have an older child be in charge of "counting the clicks " — there must be a click for everyone in the car. If older children climb out of their seats, pull the car over when it is safe and remind them that you will not move again until they are in their seats. Be patient and consistent about this as it is often a phase. Giving in only once not only sets a precedent that your child will keep testing, but it also is unsafe.

If you are considering a used safety seat to purchase through a garage or parents-of-multiples club sale, be sure to check whether the seat has been recalled. SAFERIDERS, located in Texas, offers a toll free number to check on recalls and also has seat instruction manuals that can be sent upon request (see Resources, Appendix A). Check that the

seat is not more than five years old. If it is, the quality could be questionable. Watch for cracks or broken buckles that don't stay locked. Check for exposed foam padding and cracks between the seat and shield.

Regardless of design, be sure you know how to install and adjust the car seat properly. The best designed car seat will do absolutely no good if it is not installed properly in the vehicle. Recent reports have shown that deployed front-seat airbags (which are designed to cushion adults in a crash) have seriously injured babies and young children in some instances. It is recommended that no child under 12 years of age ride in the front seat of the vehicle if it is equipped with a passenger-side air bag. Parents should keep current on the latest safety information regarding placement of car seats.

STROLLERS

Most parents of multiples will agree that some type of twin stroller is a must for getting out and about. A variety of types is available, and the selection can vary from inexpensive umbrella strollers that are clipped together to top-of-the-line deluxe strollers that have to be specially ordered. Each family must decide which features are most important and fit their budget. Some parents-of-multiples clubs may offer used strollers for sale. Twin strollers are becoming commonly available at infant stores, while triplet and higher strollers usually are only available through specialty catalogs and higher order organizations (See Resources, Appendix A).

There are several types of strollers to consider. For young infants, convertible carriage/strollers can be convenient, but usually cannot be used easily for older toddlers. The side-by-side stroller usually consists of a variation of an umbrella stroller, some clipped together by convertible clips and others permanently anchored together. These can be quite wide and sometimes are difficult to maneuver through doorways or down store aisles, but they tend to be light and portable and have plenty of leg area for the babies. Tandem strollers have face-to-face seating and are long, but no wider than a normal stroller. They can sometimes be difficult to maneuver, and the twins must share leg-room. Newer tandem strollers have the seats positioned one behind the other. These tend to be shorter and easier to push and can be commonly found in most infant departments. Triplet and higher strollers are quite expensive. Many families use combinations of twin and regular strollers for higher order multiples.

Most strollers are designed for babies four months and older. Infants usually can be placed in the umbrella-type stroller. The other

> **Y**our twin stroller is your ticket to freedom! If you plan to go anywhere alone, you really need a stroller. I even use mine to take my toddlers to the doctor's office. Having one baby strapped in (i.e., not destroying the office) while the other one is being examined is extremely helpful. They are also helpful during short visits to homes and businesses. With the babies strapped safely in the stroller and given a toy or some juice, you can do whatever you came to do and conduct your business, especially in offices that are not child-proof.
>   *Sherry Bingham, Edmond MOMs, Okla.*

[76]   TWINS TO QUINTS

styles have seats that recline and can be padded around the edges with blankets to accommodate small infants. Some mothers use a regular stroller and a soft infant carrier or sling when the babies are young. Be sure to choose a durable stroller; parents of multiples tend to use their strollers longer, and they must accommodate the weight of two or more children. Larger wheels make for a more comfortable ride and ease in pushing. It is better to spend a little more on the stroller to gain safety, comfort, and durability.

> I have found that it is difficult to get twin strollers in and out of the car and through some doorways. I have begun to keep a small stroller in the trunk and a backpack carrier (a front carrier when they were smaller) and use this method of transporting the little guys in and out. It also works well at the doctor's office, as I can keep one in the stroller as I prepare the other one.
> *Teresa Edgington, Northeast MOTC & EHMOTC, Cincinnati, O.*

Another consideration is a baby backpack. Barbara Noyes of MOTC of Rockland County, Blauvelt, N.Y., used a backpack for both her sets of twins. She found that it doesn't limit moving about as much as a stroller, and it is great for stairs. She has used one at parties because the babies can be up at the adult level while leaving her hands free. She and her husband were also able to carry the babies in backpacks when they went hiking. Barbara also points out that carrying a baby on your back burns more calories than pushing a stroller. Susan Elder of Capital District MOTC, Wynantskill, N.Y., also has found a back carrier to be a great help. "I use it when a baby needs to be held and I need both hands for other things," she says. "It's especially helpful at dinner time and when the babies are sick or teething. When I first started using the back carrier, my back got tired after just a few minutes, but as with any exercise I've gotten stronger and can wear a baby for much longer. I've even vacuumed while wearing a baby on my back. The best part about it is — they love it!"

SAFETY ISSUES

Parents should put safety first in all their preparations in the nursery and the home. As noted previously, make sure to check older equipment that you might buy at garage or yard sales for safety. There is no cost savings if you are putting your children in danger. Always use safety straps on seats and strollers. Never leave your child unattended in a high place such as a table top or changing table. Active babies can squirm and kick enough to move an infant seat over the edge of a table. You don't want your babies' first experience in rolling over to be off the top of a bed.

The National S.A.F.E. Home Foundation, Inc., recommends smoke alarms for every bedroom in a home, especially a child's bedroom. Children who play with matches often do so in their bedrooms, so a smoke detector is important. Twenty-five thousand children age four and under are injured in residential fires each year. More information on the S.A.F.E. Home Foundation's programs to prevent residential fires appears in Resources, Appendix A.

NAMES

Choosing names for a single baby can be a difficult task, but choosing numerous combinations of names for a multiple birth can be quite taxing. Here again, this is a decision that is very personal for each family. It's wise to remember that the multiples will have these names for life. Rhyming names may be cute when the multiples are infants, but they may lose some of their luster when the multiples become adults. Also, the rhyming names can be difficult to distin-

Highchairs keep babies contained and make mealtimes easier and safer.

guish from each other and may be confusing when calling and talking with the children as they mature. Constantly having to correct yourself ("No, I wanted Holly, not Molly!") can get frustrating and may encourage others to lump the multiples together, such as always just calling them "twins." Whatever you name your multiples, be sure you as a parent *always* use their proper names and not "twins" or "triplets." Try to insist that others do the same.

FINANCES

Having multiples can put a drain on any family's finances. It is important to keep your perspective and realize that two or more will not necessarily double or triple your costs. Tiny babies require only basic clothing and can sleep in the same cribs initially. Trying to anticipate your costs and planning ahead for major purchases can help. Following a budget is also helpful. Parents need to be honest and not emotional with each other when discussing finances. Maintaining a team effort and being aware of what you are spending money on will help you keep to your budget. Cutting back on convenience items, such as eating out, can really be a cost savings.

One major expense that parents should be aware of is health insurance. Make sure that you know about any rules or paperwork that will need to be completed to get the multiples on your policy as soon as possible. If each parent has a policy, check out both to find the one that will give the most coverage at the lowest cost. Consider the cost of "well-baby" visits and immunizations and any out-of-pocket expenses. You should also consider upgrading your life insurance policies.

There are government programs that parents need to know about before their babies are born. The Women, Infants and Children (WIC) nutritional program is administered by each state through the local Health Department. Through WIC, qualifying families can receive nutritional counseling and vouchers for supplemental food to help pregnant women, nursing mothers, and young children get the nutrition they need. Each state sets its own eligibility requirements, based on income and number of family members, including the babies a woman is still carrying. Many families expecting triplets, quads, or more may find that they do qualify, so it's worth a call to the Health Department.

The Supplemental Security Income (SSI) program is administered by Social Security to help provide some financial assistance to people with certain disabilities. Under current guidelines, premature infants under 1,200 grams (two pounds, 10 ounces) would automatically qualify for some monetary assistance for up to a month after the child comes home to live with the parents, regardless of the parent's income and resources. Low birthweight premature infants between 1,200 grams and 2,000 grams (four pounds, six ounces) may also qualify, depending on their medical condition and family resources. The family can only receive benefits after they've filed with the Social Security office; benefits are not retroactive. If the children might possibly qualify for this assistance, it is very important that the family (or someone acting on their behalf) call the Social Security Administration immediately to start the paperwork. Some families have been told that they did not qualify when in fact they did. You need to be persistent about filing with the agency, keeping track of the dates and getting the names of the representatives with whom you spoke. There is also an appeals process if the request is turned down. Approval usually takes three to six months. Once approved, you receive a first lump sum payment, based on the application file date. This is why it is so important to file as soon as possible after the babies are born if there is any possibility that any of them would qualify for this program.

PARENTS-OF-MULTIPLES CLUBS

A good way to prepare for your upcoming multiples is by attending a local parents-of-multiples club meeting. You will find kindred spirits there who can help you with tried and true problem-solving techniques. Many clubs will allow a pregnant mother to attend meetings for no charge until she has delivered. Numerous clubs have sales of used equipment and clothing that can help you to furnish your nursery inexpensively. Clubs can give you crucial one-on-one support and help you weather the most stressful times. Life-long friendships have been formed from such contacts.

The National Organization of Mothers of Twins Clubs, Inc. (NOMOTC), is the largest organization of parents of twins and higher order multiples, with a membership of more than 23,000 nationwide. The purpose of the organization is to promote education about multiple birth and to support research as it pertains to multiples. NOMOTC is managed by a network of volunteers who

Babies can share one crib when small.

represent local chapters. NOMOTC is a non-profit organization and is funded by dues, donations, and grants. With nearly 500 clubs composing the organization, members can find support that may not be available locally. The Support Services programs include bereavement support, special needs support, single parent support, and higher order multiples support. Listings of referral agencies, cope centers, research studies, and educational materials are available upon request.

NOMOTC publishes a bi-monthly news magazine, called *MOTC's Notebook*, which contains articles of interest to parents of multiples, research information, club ideas, expert and age-specific columns, and much more. Other publications are available. Two video programs, one focusing on prenatal and postnatal care, *Your Multiples and You, Conception to Six Months*, and another focusing on parenting during the toddler and preschool years, *Your Multiples and You, Toddlers and Preschoolers*, can be purchased.

Contact NOMOTC by mail at the Executive Office, P.O. Box 438, Thompson Station, TN 37179-0438; by phone at 1-877-540-2200; by e-mail at NOMOTC@aol.com; or visit its award-winning website at www.nomotc.org.

CONCLUSION

While you may not have been prepared for the announcement that you were having more than one baby at a time, you can prepare yourself for the homecoming. Shopping wisely, following advice of other parents of multiples, and making contact early with a local parents-of-multiples group can help you in your exciting preparations for the future.

5

"It's Finally Going to Be Over?"
LABOR AND DELIVERY

After carrying my twins to the original due date, I had no idea how labor would frighten me. Labor began at two a.m. as a dull ache. After I woke up my husband, we began timing the contractions. Discovering the contractions were only eight minutes apart, I showered and went to the hospital. When my physician arrived at seven-thirty he performed an amniotomy, breaking my water. Only three hours later, after a vaginal exam, I was being rolled into the delivery room. When the doctor told me to push I jokingly asked, "How?" The entire delivery room broke into laughter, breaking the tension. After three pushes baby A appeared. One push later baby B was delivered feet first. The room broke out into cheers. As the babies were whisked to the nursery, my husband softly touched my cheek. "You did a good job, Kelly. It's over!"

Kelly Willenberg, Columbia, Tenn.

The last few months of a multiple pregnancy can be filled with many worries. Will the babies be born prematurely? Will there be a vaginal delivery or a Caesarean section? How long will labor last?

THE ONSET OF LABOR

During the final weeks of pregnancy, you may find yourself becoming easily fatigued and frightened about the upcoming delivery. Common complaints during this time include being unable to rest comfortably, needing frequent position changes, and desiring to urinate more often. You may experience a sudden burst of energy and find yourself cleaning closets or the oven for no apparent reason. This is known as the "nesting syndrome." This happens to some women one to two days before the onset of labor and is sometimes the first sign of the impending labor.

The majority of uncomplicated twin pregnancies will be delivered vaginally, so you will have to go through the process of labor to deliver your multiples. Fortunately, you only have to go through the labor process once to open the cervix so that all the babies can be born. Some women are scheduled for Caesarean sections because of abnormal positions of the babies, medical complications in the mom or babies, higher-order pregnancies, etc.

SIGNS OF LABOR

There are three major signs of labor: passing the mucus plug, rupture of the membranes or "bag of water," and regular uterine contractions.

The mucus plug, sometimes called "bloody show," may appear with or without any other signs of labor. It can be clear in color or blood-tinged. Usually the amount is only two to three tablespoons. If you see this sign, you don't need to rush to the hospital. You should wait for other signs of labor.

Passing of the mucus plug should not be confused with the water breaking, or "rupture of membranes." When the latter occurs, a small or large gush of the pale, straw-colored fluid will be seen. It cannot be controlled like the loss of urine can. It can start out as a slow leaking, or it may occur as a popping sound, followed by a drenching gush of fluid.

If you think your membranes have ruptured, go to the hospital even if you are not having contractions. In about one fourth of pregnant women, the rupture of membranes happens before regular contractions begin. Remember, once it does occur the protective barrier between the outside world and the babies is broken, and bacteria could enter. The rupture of membranes is considered an emergency if it occurs before the thirty-seventh week because it can signal the onset of premature labor.

The most common sign of labor is the start of labor pain, or uterine contractions. The contractions should be regular. Start timing them from the beginning of one contraction to the beginning of the next. When they are every five minutes for at least one hour, you will usually be told to go to the hospital. However, some doctors prefer that you come in sooner, so always follow his or her advice.

FALSE LABOR

The difference between true labor and false labor can sometimes be difficult to determine. The table below lists some of the differences. False labor can happen in a multiple pregnancy more than one time and shouldn't be regarded as a "failure." Sometimes it can require hospitalization for bed rest and monitoring of the mother's and babies' conditions.

| True Labor vs. False Labor | |
TRUE LABOR	FALSE LABOR
Contractions keep progressing	Contractions stop after rest
Contractions become regular	Contractions remain irregular
Contractions increase in duration	Contractions are short
Contractions increase in intensity	Contractions are not intense
Walking increases the intensity of the contractions	Walking has no effect on contractions
Contractions are felt in the upper part of the uterus	Contractions are felt in the lower part of the uterus

PRETERM LABOR

One third of all multiple pregnancies deliver before the thirty-third week, so every mother of multiples should be familiar with the signs of premature or preterm labor. This occurs more often in higher order multiple pregnancies. You must be constantly alert for signs of premature labor.

A normal pregnancy lasts approximately 40 weeks. Preterm labor is defined as labor that occurs before completion of the thirty seventh week of pregnancy. Thirty percent of preterm labor is associated with premature rupture of the membranes. Preterm labor can be traumatic.

SIGNS OF PRETERM LABOR

Some signs of preterm labor include: regular contractions, more than four per hour; a vaginal discharge of water, mucus, or blood; a dull backache; a constant pressure on the pelvis or thighs; and an overall feeling that something is wrong. Sometimes the uterus may be so overstretched that the mother may not be aware that she is having contractions.

Sometimes electronic home monitoring devices are used to help record any contractions, although this does not help prevent preterm labor. The monitor is obtained from a company that offers the equipment and support staff. Generally a nurse from the company supplying the monitor trains you in its use and sets up a monitoring schedule. At home you strap the monitor to your abdomen for about an hour, during which you lie still and relax. You then connect the monitor to a telephone and send the data to the monitoring personnel, usually a nurse, at the other end of the line. The nurse analyzes the data and advises you if you are in premature labor. Along with the monitoring, many expectant families find that this daily contact with a trained professional is reassuring.

One detector of preterm labor is the fetal fibronectin test. Fetal fibronectin is a marker found in vaginal secretions. The test is usually done only in high risk pregnancies or in women who already have some symptoms of preterm labor. It is also limited to women who have intact membranes and very minimal cervical dilation and are between 24 and 34 weeks gestation. Newer tests can give results in an hour or less. This test virtually predicts which women will go on to have a preterm delivery. If the test is negative, there is only a one-in-333 chance of delivery within a week of the test result. This can be a valuable aid to the health care team in deciding which women can safely be watched with bed rest and which will need more aggressive treatments, such as labor-stopping drugs.

Some infections can be associated with preterm labor. These include severe respiratory infections, urinary tract infections, and vaginal infections. The latter can include sexually transmitted diseases as well as bacterial vaginosis and vaginal strep infections. Treatment of the underlying infection with antibiotics can prolong the pregnancy and help prevent preterm labor.

One procedure, called a cerclage, is done for women who have specific cervical problems causing frequent miscarriages, usually without associated labor. It is generally performed at about 13 weeks and can help prevent a premature delivery. It is not an option once preterm labor has begun, however.

TREATMENT OF PRETERM LABOR

Several treatments are available for preterm labor. Use of them depends on the condition of the mother and babies. Treatments can range from bed rest to medication and even surgery. Bed rest can be a very trying time for an expectant mother (See Chapter 1). Sometimes, despite the best treatment, labor cannot be stopped.

Medicines used to stop labor are called "tocolytic" medications. These relax the smooth muscles of the body, including the uterus. Some common types of tocolytic drugs are ritrodrine, terbutaline, nifedipine and indomethacin, which are sold under various brand names. These come in pill form or can be given through an IV. Stronger medicine is magnesium sulfate, which can only be given in the hospital.

Tocolytics have very noticeable side effects. Some can raise your heart rate from 10 to 30 beats per minute and cause you to feel weak, shaky, and jittery. The medications also relax blood vessels, making some women experience headaches and feel very warm. It is very important for you to keep your medical team up-to-date about any side effects and discomforts. If you are too uncomfortable on medication, the dosage should be changed or stopped.

Mag sulfate causes complete muscle relaxation. Common side effects include pronounced weariness and sluggishness, a burning sensation around the IV, headaches, nausea, vomiting, and fluid retention with swelling. It is very uncomfortable, but it generally does the job of stopping premature labor.

If a mother has an extended stay with continued preterm labor, the doctors may inject a steroid called betamethasone to help promote more rapid lung development in the babies and decrease other problems associated with a preterm birth. It is usually given over a period of two days. It is the only medication that has been shown to improve fetal survival when given to women in preterm labor. Sometimes other medicines, such as thyrotropin-releasing hormone (TRH), are given to further stimulate development. The medical team will often begin some tests of fetal well-being, such as a Non-Stress Test, Contraction Stress Test, or a Biophysical Profile. These are discussed in Chapter 1.

CONCERNS ABOUT TOCOLYTICS

There are concerns about the safety of tocolytics. All women should know that tocolytics were not developed specifically for pregnancy, but rather for such other conditions as asthma. The drugs are taken only after 20 weeks gestation, when much of the babies' early development is safely underway. Women should be aware that there are no definitive studies proving that tocolytics improve fetal outcome.

Another controversial treatment is the terbutaline pump, a device that can be used at home to administer the intravenous medications. The pump is put together as a small box strapped to the body, usually the leg. Inside the box is a vial of medicine attached to a needle which sends the drug into the bloodstream. Questions have been raised about the safety of this device. The FDA has issued a warning to health care professionals about the use of the terbutaline pump. However, a number of women feel the benefits of these medicines in preventing very premature births outweigh the risks to themselves and their babies. Each family must carefully consider the pros and cons of such treatments and decide only after being fully informed.

STAGES OF LABOR IN A VAGINAL DELIVERY

FIRST STAGE OF LABOR - CONTRACTIONS

Labor generally has four stages. The first stage is called the active phase. This is when you start having regular contractions. This stage does not end until the opening of the uterus, called the cervix, is fully dilated. It can take anywhere from 12 to 24 hours for a first-time mother to become fully dilated, although there is a lot of variation. Because the process can take a long time, you will usually be asked to stay at home during the early stages of labor. Make sure to ask the health care provider for instructions. With some multiple pregnancies, you might be asked to come to the hospital when there are any signs of labor at any time. Once you are in active labor, you should not eat

I had a great experience with my labor and delivery, except for all the false alarms I had in the late stages. When my water finally broke I was rushed to the hospital. I was given an epidural within an hour and was in the delivery room within another 20 minutes. My girls were 15 minutes apart, and I was in the best mood and can remember every minute of it. I was five and a half weeks early, and my girls were four pounds three ounces and four pounds eight ounces. We all came home the following day! Please know: it CAN be a pleasant experience!
   Patti Clauss, Duvall, Wash.

any solid foods, although clear liquids in small amounts are acceptable.

Coming to the hospital is usually exciting and scary. You can expect to have your cervix checked by a health care provider to determine how much you have dilated. You may be disappointed to find that you are only two or three centimeters and have a long day ahead. Some routine procedures may be expected, depending on the health care provider. A fetal monitor strap for each baby may be put on your abdomen. Blood is usually drawn and an intravenous (IV) line may be placed on your arm.

The stretching, or dilation, of the cervix takes place at its own pace and will be very individual and unpredictable. Sometimes going from one centimeter to the full dilation of 10 occurs very quickly. Other women may remain at two to three centimeters for hours, then progress more quickly through the later stages. Still others have a logical but slow progression. A common occurrence is a feeling of discomfort, anxiety, and irritability at approximately eight centimeters, often called the "transition stage." Remember: the cervix needs to dilate only once for the births of all the babies.

Sometimes when contractions aren't intense enough and labor is progressing too slowly, the health care provider may order a medication called pitocin to help speed up the active phase of labor. With pitocin, instead of a gradual onset of labor you can progress quickly from no contractions to strong painful ones. This can be difficult if you are unprepared for it. Pitocin is also used to induce labor and to help prevent excessive bleeding immediately following delivery.

SECOND STAGE - PUSHING

The second stage of labor, the pushing stage, is usually hard work and may take an hour or more, especially in the first pregnancy. This is very individual. You may feel a heaviness or rectal pressure caused by the head of one of the babies. The nurses and medical staff will assist you in pushing and bearing down. This stage ends with the birth of your babies!

Sometimes the health care provider will make an incision at the lower wall of the vagina nearest the rectum, called an episiotomy, to prevent an uncontrolled tear of the vagina or rectal area. You may receive a local anesthetic for this procedure if you are not already numb in the area from a previous anesthetic. Sometimes the health care provider will assist the delivery of the head with forceps or a vacuum extractor if you are not able to push the babies out.

BIRTHS

The birth of the first baby is exciting, and there is always a frenzy of activity in the labor suite. You must remember to save strength to push the second baby out. The time between the births of the first and second babies can vary from as little as three minutes to up to an hour or more. Usually there will be a pause before the second baby is in position and you feel the urge to push again. The baby's heart rate will be closely monitored, as the second baby is at a higher risk for complications. Sometimes the second baby must be re-positioned for delivery by the health care provider. Any distress in the second baby may force a quicker delivery using forceps, or even a Caesarean section.

You may be feeling exhausted from a long labor and delivery and may need encouragement to give more effort in pushing out the second baby. After the second baby is delivered, you will usually have a chance to bond with both babies. However, if the babies are preterm or having any difficulties, they may need to be placed immediately into incubators.

THIRD STAGE - PLACENTAS

After the births, the third stage of labor will then take place. This involves the delivery of one or more placentas, sometimes called the afterbirth. You will continue to have contractions until the placenta or placentas are delivered. There is no need to push in this stage. The average length of time of this stage is five to thirty minutes.

FOURTH STAGE - AFTER DELIVERY

The fourth stage of labor is the hour immediately following the delivery of the placenta. During this time, the health care team will be watching closely for the amount of vaginal bleeding. The health care provider may be repairing any tears or the episiotomy, if one was performed. To prevent bleeding, the nurse or health care provider will be checking that the uterus remains well contracted by placing a hand on the top of the uterus and massaging the area if necessary. Sometimes pitocin will be given through an intravenous line for one or two hours following delivery to decrease blood loss by helping the uterus contract.

Following delivery and completion of the fourth stage of labor you may be both exhausted and exhilarated. Although labor and birth is viewed as the main event, in reality it is the first step in one of life's great adventures.

CAESAREAN SECTION IN MULTIPLE BIRTH

Many health care providers feel that all multiple births require Caesarean section due to the possibility of complications. A C-section is the removal of the babies through the abdominal wall by means of an incision into the abdomen and uterus. A C-section might be necessary in the event of a breech (bottom or feet first) presentation, significant uterine bleeding, or if one multiple is significantly larger in size than the others. Emergencies in the health of the mother or babies, such as preeclampsia and prematurity, also might require a C-section. A woman with a higher order multiple birth will nearly always be delivered by C-section. There are many cases of women who have experienced a vaginal delivery of the first baby and then due to complications had to proceed to a C-section for delivery of the second baby.

Some women are disappointed or feel that they have "failed" if a planned vaginal delivery results in a C-section. Keep in mind that the goal of everyone should be healthy babies and a healthy mother, no matter how that is accomplished. Except in the case of a dire emergency, you can be awake during a C-section and still experience the joy and wonder of the birth. Fathers can usually be present at a C-section as well. Due to the frequency of a C-section in a multiple birth, you would be wise to familiarize yourself with the procedures to help prevent excessive anxiety.

Try to remember that a C-section is surgery, and the recovery will be more prolonged and uncomfortable than with a vaginal delivery. You can expect up to six weeks of recovery, just as you would with any abdominal surgery. There is a higher incidence of complica-

Make contingency plans for delivery. My husband and I had decided that we did not want to take pictures during delivery, that eyewitness memories were sufficient for us. But the epidural was inadequate for the C-section that I wound up requiring, and they ushered him out and put me under too fast for us to have time to think to request that someone take pictures.
Lisa Teeple, Parents of Twins and Triplets Org., Whites Creek, Tenn.

tions, such as blood clots and bleeding. There will be soreness at the incision site and more difficulty in picking up the infants. Breast-feeding positions may have to be adjusted due to abdominal soreness, but breast-feeding should be otherwise unaffected. You should make sure that you have made arrangements at home for recovery time after a C-section. These should include household help and aid in heavy lifting for a few weeks.

NATURAL CHILDBIRTH

Natural childbirth is a prepared childbirth experience in which you and your partner attend a prenatal education program and learn exercises and breathing patterns which can be used during labor and childbirth. Variations of Childbirth Preparation Classes are available and are usually taught in local hospitals. Some hospitals offer special classes just for women expecting multiples. Try to find an instructor who is familiar with multiple births and plan to attend classes early. You may have planned to have a natural childbirth only to find that things don't go the way you planned. If you enter delivery with an open mind and accept that medication may be needed for pain, nausea, or the initiation of a C-section due to a crisis or exhaustion, you will feel better about the outcome, no matter what.

For labor and delivery, consider having professional labor support. We had two doulas (women trained to provide nonmedical childbirth assistance and support), and it was the best decision. Our twin girls were born after a short unmedicated labor. Our two-year-old was present also, and when it came time to deliver, one of the doulas stayed with her. My husband appreciated the extra support, the doctor didn't seem to mind, and I was able to stay as relaxed and focused as possible. We went over our birthing plan, and when the staff would suggest something like internal monitoring or an IV that might impede my walking around, my doula, Ann, would calmly advocate for me in a non-threatening way. I think of doulas as a bridge between the mom and medical staff. They also helped with nursing and taking pictures.
Kathy Hazelton, Naugatuck, Conn.

ANESTHESIA IN LABOR AND DELIVERY

Different types of pain control can be offered to you in labor. All have different advantages and side effects. The choice of anesthesia used depends on the situation and whether there is an emergency or not. For pain control most health care providers opt for labor epidurals, and for C-sections most choose a regional technique. General anesthesia is usually reserved for emergency situations.

NARCOTICS

One option might be the administration of intravenous (IV) or intramuscular (IM) narcotics. Some examples of the drugs utilized are: morphine, meperidine (demerol®), butorphanol (stadol®), and fentanyl (sublimaze®). IV and IM narcotics have some disadvantages, and these should be considered when choosing pain management. Side effects include drowsiness, slowed breathing (or respiratory depression), nausea, vomiting, constipation, and depression of the babies.

EPIDURALS

The labor epidural consists of placing a needle between the bones of the back in an area called the epidural space. After a very small tube, called a catheter, is threaded in, a diluted local anesthetic is injected. The injection numbs the lower body so you do not feel pain during contractions. This type of anesthetic allows you to be awake and actively participate in the labor and delivery without significant pain. Side effects of this type of anesthesia include itching, lowered blood pressure, nausea and/or vomiting, dizziness, urinary retention, temporary loss of movement in the limbs, and weakness. Mothers who have labor epidurals have a higher chance of C-section because of not being able to push when it comes time to do so in the labor process.

ANESTHESIA FOR C-SECTIONS

Two types of anesthesia are used for Caesarean sections: general and regional. General anesthesia is usually done in an emergency situation in which the mother's and/or the babies' lives are in jeopardy. A breathing tube is inserted into the airway to prevent getting stomach contents into the lungs in the event of vomiting. This is the most frequent side effect of this type of anesthesia, and it can be fatal. This is one reason you should refrain from eating solid foods when in labor. Also, the drugs used in a general can sometimes cause problems with the babies' ability to breathe.

Two types of regional anesthesia techniques can be performed: a spinal block and an epidural block. In the spinal, a small dose of a local anesthetic is injected into the spinal canal, causing a block of sensation and movement. This type of anesthesia is quicker and easier to administer than an epidural. However, the block can more easily cause numbness higher up in the body, and there is a chance that you can develop a spinal headache after surgery. An epidural block is the same as a labor epidural but uses a stronger dose of medicine. Since a catheter is in place, more anesthetic can be administered if necessary for a longer surgery. It provides numbness from the nipple line down, and you will be awake and unable to move your legs. Sometimes it is hard to feel your own breathing because of the numbness in the chest. You may feel pulling and pressure during the delivery, but no pain.

The possible side effects of a regional block include an inadequate block, the block occurring "too high" and leading to the use of general anesthesia. There is also a risk of lowered blood pressure, nausea and vomiting, or spinal headache.

CARE OF THE NEWBORN

APGAR SCORES

Designed in 1952 by Dr. Virginia Apgar, this system evaluates the physical condition of the infant at birth and five minutes later. The five areas the health care provider checks are heart rate, breathing rate, muscle tone, reflex irritability, and color. Two points are awarded for each area that is normal, with a maximum of 10 points. A score of seven to 10 indicates the infants are in good condition, although they might require suctioning to clean out the mouth and nose. A score of three to six indicates an infant in moderate distress. This score can sometimes indicate that there is too much anesthesia in the mother and that it has affected the baby. A score of zero to two indicates a baby in severe distress. These infants will require intubation, a tube in the windpipe, to keep the baby breathing at a rate of 50 times a minute. These babies may require other emergency treatments.

IN THE DELIVERY ROOM

A brief physical check of each infant will be done in the delivery room. Areas covered include examination of the umbilical

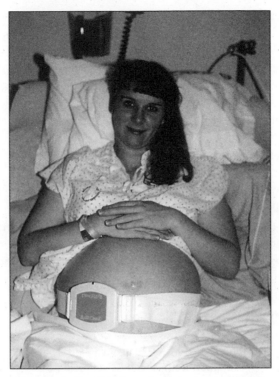

Minutes before birth and everyone is healthy.

cord for the number of blood vessels, examination for any bleeding areas, examination of the placenta (to indicate how normally it was developed for nourishing the baby), and examination of the number and placement of the placentas and membranes (to aid in determining the type of multiple). The sex of the infants is determined, weight and height are recorded, and any congenital abnormalities will be scrutinized. A shot of Vitamin K may be given, as well as the instillation of silver nitrate or other antibiotic drops into the eyes. These are all normal occurrences after delivery of newborn multiples.

AFTER THE DELIVERY

Recovery from a multiple delivery may be the same as from a singleton delivery. However, if you were at bed rest during the pregnancy you may notice that your muscles are quite weak and you have little stamina until you build up your activity levels again. In all women the uterus can become overstretched from the pregnancy and lead to some increased bleeding after delivery. After-pains, which are uterine contractions that help to stop bleeding, can be quite painful, especially in later pregnancies. Loss of muscle tone in the over-stretched abdominal muscles can make it difficult to walk around initially, and the overstretched folds of skin can be distressing. Those who developed hemorrhoids will find that they do not go away immediately after delivery. Be sure to give yourself time to recover and arrange for some help during those first few weeks.

CONCLUSION

Having multiples will be a significant occurrence in your life. Although childbirth is a natural process, it can influence your health. The main goal of your health care provider should be your health and the health and well-being of your babies. Your labor and delivery will be unique to you and will be remembered throughout your life.

Highlights from NOMOTC's 1990 Medical Survey
Support from Health Care Providers

- Mothers who knew they were expecting multiples by the end of the second trimester - 80%
- Doctors considering the multiple pregnancy to be high risk - 66%
- Mothers having previous pregnancies who felt the multiple pregnancy was more difficult - 63%
- Mothers who felt they received adequate answers to their questions from their health care providers - 87%
- Multiple births occurring one to eight weeks before due date - 69%
- Multiple births in which at least one multiple was placed in the NICU - 60%
- Mothers who felt their health care provider helped them deal with the emotions associated with prematurity of the babies - 58%
- Mothers delivering by Caesarean section - 56%
- Those who felt they were adequately informed of their multiples' zygosity - 60%
- Mothers experiencing some type of postpartum depression - 47%
- Mothers suffering the loss of one or more multiples during pregnancy, delivery, or shortly after birth - 2%

6

"Oh, Aren't They Cute," Part I
INFANCY

I remember dragging myself out of bed to the dual crying of my infant fraternal twin boys. It is time for their next feeding, and it seems as if I just fed them. Making my way to the kitchen for their bottles, I hear my husband stumble through the dark into their bedroom. As I warm their bottles in the otherwise quiet house, I can hear him talking to the boys to calm them. I join him in the bedroom, and we each take a baby in our arms and together carry them into the living room to feed them. It's 3:00 a.m., and the first time we have had a moment to talk!

Pam Edelman, Osceola, Ind.

After the excitement of delivery, you soon face the reality of caring for two or more small infants. Shorter hospital stays may even find you on your way home before you have fully recovered from the fatigue and stress of labor and delivery. You also may not have had time to adjust to the new role as a mother of multiples. These anxious feelings are common in every first-time mother and sometimes even in experienced mothers.

EARLY WEEKS

The time after delivery is generally busy and sometimes euphoric. The new babies and the attention from families and friends may distract you from the considerable changes your body is undergoing. Emotions may rise and fall as hormone levels normalize and you begin adjusting to lack of sleep from caring for the babies.

LOSING THE TUMMY

Remember that it took many months to stretch your abdominal area out. Try to begin a gentle exercise program as soon as you regain strength and feel less tender. After a Caesarean section, it may be longer before you can exercise. You may have begun Kegel exercises to help strengthen the pelvic floor before delivery (See Chapter 1). These can be continued immediately after delivery.

GETTING HELP AT HOME

During the first two to four weeks at home, or longer, it is very helpful to have some household help available. This could be a relative, a friend, or even hired help if it is an option. With new family-leave policies, more husbands are taking time off to assist their wives in the first weeks at home. Try to get help lined up well ahead of the babies' birth, if possible. This stage of motherhood goes by quickly only in retrospect. The best advice we can give is to concentrate on infant care and delegate all other household tasks to someone else. First-time mothers should try to sleep whenever the babies sleep, not use that time to clean house, etc. This is more impractical if there are other children in the household. Try, if possible, to enlist the other children's help in such tasks as fetching diapers and helping to change the babies.

> When I had my twins I was overwhelmed with all the work involved. How I got a grip was scheduling. They were awakened together and fed together, put in for naps together, and so on. Be persistent and stay on your scheduled routine. They will eventually adapt.
> *Karen Knox, MOTC of Rockland County, N.Y.*

SCHEDULING THE BABIES

Every new mother discovers, sometimes to her surprise, how demanding caring for a newborn can be. When babies are multiplied by two or more, you can find yourself never getting out of a bathrobe all day! It takes time for babies to adjust to life outside the womb, and many will not settle into any kind of schedule or routine for several weeks. Many mothers find it convenient to keep a chart of feedings, diaper-

> Keep a legal pad handy to jot down feeding times and amounts, medicine doses, bowel movements (if necessary), etc. We divided the legal pad into two columns, one for each baby!
> *Susan Helsley, Winchester, Va.*

ings, medications, and bowel movements. The National Organization of Mothers of Twins Clubs, Inc., has convenient charts for multiples which help keep track of these important facts.

Everyone will be happier if you initially try to adjust to the babies' schedule, rather than trying to make the babies adjust to yours. Some babies have days and nights confused. It is helpful to gently and gradually nudge the schedule toward more daytime waking and to try to sleep with them in the daytime initially. Bringing them into the living area where there is light and noise during the day and keeping their room dark and quiet at night will help infants to adjust.

> I have learned that if you're organized and keep a strict schedule, everything runs smoothly, even on the most trying days. Always have formula ready for the entire day. Have bath time at the same time every day. I find that the bath at the end of the day winds them down for the night. And pray every morning for patience.
> *Carol Thomas, Oviedo, Fla.*

STRESS, FATIGUE, AND POSTPARTUM DEPRESSION

Constant night feedings, babies crying, and sleep deprivation can make a new mother feel very stressed. You may find that you are more irritable than normal. The sudden shift in hormone levels following delivery, combined with stress and fatigue, can make you cry easily and feel out of sorts. This is very common and is usually a temporary situation lasting less than two weeks.

If you are still feeling blue all the time and it has been over a month, you may have a more serious medical condition called postpartum depression. Mothers who have this condition may find that they feel "down" all the time and may lose interest in caring for their infants, even much-longed-for babies. Sleep is either impossible or they do not want to get out of bed. There is a feeling of hopelessness that just will not go away. Appetite is affected. Prolonged crying bouts are common. These feelings go on for weeks and sometimes months. Some mothers may harbor thoughts of harming themselves or their babies. You should recognize that if your symptoms of sadness and despair last longer than two weeks, or if they are particularly severe for any amount of time, you should consult your health care provider.

Postpartum depression is a medical condition caused by

chemical imbalances in the brain. It can be treated by medication. A mother should not feel inadequate or embarrassed to admit she needs help. Sometimes the spouse or a family member needs to recognize what is going on and get the mother the help she needs.

PREMATURE BABIES/NICU

The NICU (neonatal intensive care unit) is a highly technical world of care for premature babies. It can be very frightening for parents to see their babies in this setting, hooked up to wires and electrodes and looking so tiny and vulnerable. The staff will do all they can to help you understand what is taking place and keep you informed of your babies' progress.

The care of your premature babies will be a multi-disciplinary approach involving physicians, nurse practitioners, nurses, and ancillary personnel from such other departments as physical therapy, lab, and x-ray. You are not expected to understand all the information that is given to you at one time. Do not be afraid to tell physicians or nurses that you do not understand something and ask them to relate the information in simpler terms. Because they deal with technology every day, they sometimes forget that most of us have little or no medical knowledge.

> For an easy way to give medication, take an extra nipple and a nipple ring. Put the medicine in the nipple right before you are ready to feed your baby. Give the baby the nipple with the medicine first, then squirt a little formula in the nipple to rinse any remaining medicine out of the nipple. Then offer the baby the bottle. Before the baby even realizes it, he/she's had the medicine!
> *Nancy K. Berube, Cape Fear MOTC, N.C.*

Depending on their gestational age and development, your babies may be placed on a ventilator at birth to assist with their breathing. An analysis of their blood to check oxygen and carbon dioxide levels will be done at regular intervals to aid in weaning the babies from the ventilator. If your babies are extremely premature, they may be given surfactant, a substance that helps premature lungs function more maturely.

Keep a notepad and paper by the telephone so that you can jot down pertinent information and any questions you think of between telephone calls and/or visits to the NICU. The physicians or nurse practitioners should give you an update every day on the condition of your children. Don't get caught up in the world of numbers that involve your babies. There are so many tests with so many different results that can fluctuate from hour to hour and day to day. Concentrate on your babies and the general trend of their progress. Don't watch the monitors on your visits. Watch your babies. Let the nurses watch the monitors. They will let you know if something needs to be done.

THE NICU ROUTINE

NICUs have their own routine, and you will soon adapt to it. Try to visit your babies at the same time each day. As you establish this routine and the babies grow, their behavior will change and their activity will increase when you visit. Do not be afraid to touch your babies. The nurses will let you know the best way for you to touch and stroke your children. It will not hurt them to feel your touch, and it will help you so much.

By all means, TALK to your babies on each visit. Since water is a great conductor of sound, the babies have heard your voice in the womb and will recognize it. A small tape recorder can be placed inside your babies' isolettes so that the nurses can play tapes that you have recorded. This is an excellent way to involve older siblings in the babies' lives. Tapes of stories being read by you or other members of the family, lullabies, or simple conversations are all good, especially if the babies are hospitalized in another town and your visits are less frequent.

Your babies may be fed at first by a feeding tube inserted into their stomachs through their mouths. This is not painful. You may provide breast milk for the babies to feed on. The nurses will instruct you on the proper collection techniques, storage at home, and transportation of the milk from home to the hospital. As the babies grow and the demand for milk increases, the nurse will show you how to calculate the amount you need to provide each day.

Most nurseries will allow you to bring receiving blankets and clothes from home for your babies to wear when they reach the feeding and growing stage. At first they may only be allowed to wear booties. Keeping the clothes clean and in good supply at the bedside allows you to participate in the babies' care.

If the condition of your babies is stable and they are feeding and growing, you may be allowed to do "kangaroo care." This procedure allows you to hold your baby in direct skin-to-skin contact. Ask if your hospital allows this. The nurses will direct you in the kind of clothes to wear when you visit and how long the babies can be out of the isolette. Dads can participate in "kangarooing" also.

After your babies reach a certain size and are free of ventilator tubing or other procedural lines, they can be placed in the same isolette or small crib to interact together as they did in the womb. The physician must be consulted and give his/her permission, and it may take a little persuading on your part, but it can be done. European hospitals have been doing this for quite some time with good results.

DEVELOPMENTAL CARE

Many NICUs have implemented a plan called developmental care. You may find covers over the isolettes and infants "nested" in blanket rolls. The blanket rolls that "nest" the babies provide boundaries much like the walls of the uterus do, thus simulating the uterine environment and fostering growth. Care is given in clusters of time so that the babies are given periods for rest and growth. The babies may only be weighed once or twice a week at first depending on how premature they are, how fragile their skin is, and how well they can keep their body temperature at a normal level. The covers over the isolettes simulate the dark womb environment, which also fosters growth. Most hospitals will allow you to bring your own cover if you wish. A crib comforter that has one dark side is a good choice.

BONDING WITH YOUR PREEMIES

Expectant mothers look forward to the moment when the babies are born and they can hold them for the very first time. When premature infants need specialized care in a hospital's neonatal intensive care unit, there may be some concern on your part that you will miss the opportunity to immediately bond with your children. While health issues are the most important, the NICU staff will involve you as soon as possible in your babies' lives. During the first critical days, you may only be able to gently stroke your babies. Be sure to speak to them, as your voice will convey the love, security, and warmth which only a parent can give. As the babies become stronger, you will begin to massage their legs, arms, and backs. Eventually they will be strong enough to be held for increasing periods of time. At first this will be frightening because of their fragile appearance, but your confidence will increase with each visit.

Leaving the hospital without your babies will be very difficult. Be sure to discuss a daily schedule for phone calls and visits with the NICU staff. Set up a calendar to mark the babies' progress. A daily morning phone call will provide you with an update on the babies' weight, medications, and progress through the night. Plan daily visits to the unit to bathe, feed, and rock your babies as they grow stronger. Pumping breast milk for them will provide a personal connection, as will the knowledge that you are contributing to their growth.

Use the time before the babies arrive at home to regain your own health and strength. Be sure to get plenty of sleep, since premature infants have demanding feeding schedules and you will not have this luxury again for many months. Purchase several of the smallest infant sleepers to dress your babies in when they come home. Preemies tire easily, and fussy clothing which is difficult to put on will exhaust them very quickly. If you need to pump breast milk or bottle feed the babies when they come home, purchase preemie nipples to use for the first two or three months.

If possible, talk to other parents of premature infants. Your hospital may sponsor an NICU support group, and your local parents-of-multiples club will probably have members who have had the same experience.

FEEDING YOUR MULTIPLES

Mothers approach the issue of how to feed their babies in different ways. You may have felt comfortable about breast-feeding one baby, but feeding two raises different questions. Since you will be spending a lot of time feeding your babies, it's important that you feed in a way that gives you as much satisfaction as possible.

BREAST-FEEDING

Breast-feeding is the best method for feeding babies. Regardless of whether your babies are premature or full term, successful breast-feeding is possible and highly rewarding. As a mother of multiple birth children, you will often face challenges which may seem overwhelming, but with the proper help and knowledge you will be able to enjoy the experience of nursing your children. Low birth weight and poor weight gain in the early weeks are issues that can be faced by parents of multiples. Other problems occurring in the first weeks after the babies' birth may include sleepiness, small mouths, poor sucking reflexes, extended stays in the NICU, nipple confusion, etc., which could cause the most committed mother to withdraw from the idea of nursing multiples. Whether or not your multiples were born prematurely, it's important to educate yourself about premature nursing issues, so that you will be able to approach breast-feeding with confidence and the assurance that most obstacles can be overcome. In short, given most circumstances, breast-feeding can be a wonderful experience for you and for your babies.

BENEFITS OF BREAST-FEEDING

There is much scientific evidence of the benefits of breast-feeding, as listed on the chart. Your babies will be more resistant to infection and have fewer allergy problems. Breast milk is easier to digest, so there is little chance of constipation and a lowered risk of diarrhea.

BENEFITS OF BREAST-FEEDING

Breast milk
- Contains antibodies
- Is nutritionally the best
- Is easy to digest
- Is not constipating
- Produces lower incidence of diarrhea

Breast-fed babies
- Have fewer allergies
- Have fewer upper respiratory infections
- Have enhanced intellectual, visual, and oral development
- Have lower incidence of chronic childhood diseases
- Have lower risk of SIDS

There are benefits for the mother, too. Mothers who breast-feed benefit from lower costs and more convenience. There will be less time making up bottles and formula. There is also a lower risk of ovarian cancer and pre-menopausal breast cancer in women who have breast-fed.

BENEFITS OF BREAST-FEEDING TO THE MOTHER
- Decreased costs
- More convenience
- Decreased risk of ovarian cancer
- Decreased risk of pre-menopausal breast cancer

You can breast-feed twins regardless of their size or the size of your breasts. Breast-feeding works on a supply and demand basis. The body will make as much milk as the babies need. The more you

CHECK LIST FOR BREAST-FEEDING
- Support from family, friends, church, and club
- Hired help (full or part time)
- Lactation specialist or lactation nurse (hospital or private)
- Hospital pre- and postnatal classes
- Twin-sized nursing pillow (borrow or buy)
- Double breast pump (rent or buy)
- Visit hospital NICU facilities (before delivery)

nurse, the more milk you will make. Supplementing with formula will cause the body to make less milk. If you feel your babies are not getting enough milk, you need to nurse more frequently, NOT give a bottle.

The babies will need at least eight to 12 feedings per 24-hour period. You can tell if the babies are getting enough milk if they are gaining weight properly, have six to eight wet cloth diapers (or five to six wet disposable diapers) per day, and three to four bowel movements per day. Supplementing your infants with any other kind of fluid is not necessary.

To produce milk for the babies it is important to eat properly, drink plenty of fluids, and get a lot of rest. It is advisable to drink water at each nursing session. Be sure not to take any type of medication without consulting your health care provider.

NURSING PRODUCTS

A twin-sized nursing pillow or a large firm body pillow has helped save many mothers' backs and supports the babies upward, toward the breasts. Back pain alone can affect the milk production, let-down, and flow. The pillow should be on your list of things to bring to the hospital when the babies are delivered. This can help to ensure that your first experience at nursing is at its best and can help you to attempt tandem nursing by supporting both babies' tiny heads at the breast.

A footrest is helpful to raise the knees in such a way as to take stress off the back and raise and support the babies' heads toward the breasts. This can be especially beneficial for someone who has back problems.

A well-fitting nursing bra is a must, as well as nursing pads to catch leaking milk. Invest in or rent a good quality breast pump, especially if you plan to return to work while still nursing.

DEALING WITH LEAKING MILK AND SORENESS

Carrying enough milk in the breasts to supply twins or more can cause some unique challenges. Breasts will often leak at night during sleep, especially if a feeding is delayed or missed. Using menstrual pads in the bra at night can help soak up milk from leaky breasts that normal nursing pads cannot handle. This will help prevent awakening in the morning in a pool of warm milky sheets. A cloth diaper is useful to catch leaking milk from the opposite breast during let-down. Gently but firmly apply pressure with your free hand or forearm, if needed, against the cloth and your breast. In time the breasts will adjust to the amount of milk you are carrying and will not leak as much, if at all. If you are wearing your nursing bra, just tuck the cloth between your nipple and the cup on the bra. The amount of milk you lose will be adjusted to by your breast for the next feeding. Between daytime feedings use breast pads in the nursing bra for leakage.

Breast soreness usually occurs only at the beginning, when nursing is getting established. Disposable diapers dunked in very warm water and then applied to each breast can help in these early days when the milk comes in and the breast is uncomfortable. Proper positioning of the babies can help alleviate sore nipples. The nipples will toughen up as you continue to nurse.

A FATHER'S ROLE IN NURSING

You are very important in helping support your wife during this time. Just having confidence in her ability to feed the babies can help boost her own confidence and help her milk supply. You can also assist her in combating fatigue. In the early weeks, many parents have found that having someone bring the babies to the mother in her bed (usually the dad) is helpful during night time feedings. This can allow the mother the best opportunity to recover from delivery and regain her strength. She can nurse one at a time, lying on her side and resting. As the first baby is nursed, the helper can begin to prepare the second baby for feeding. When the first baby is finished, the helper will trade babies with the mother. As the second baby is nursed, the first can be burped, changed, and settled back down to bed. All the while the mother has been able to stay in bed and rest (even sleep) during breast-feeding.

Mothers can pump their breasts, which allows others to give supplemental feedings once breast-feeding is established.

NURSING POSITIONS

There are many nursing positions, and you are encouraged to use the ones that work best for you and the temperament of your babies. The most common is the football hold, with

> Get one of the pillows specifically designed for nursing twins and use it. It makes holding the babies easier, and if one baby doesn't nurse as long as the other, you can more easily entertain the baby who is finished.
> *Joy Duncan Rooks, Wetumpka, Ala.*

one baby under each arm. This usually requires the use of a support pillow. Another popular position is called "spoons," and this does not require the use of a pillow. See pictures on page 126 for hints.

NURSING EXCLUSIVELY

If your choice is to nurse exclusively, then you should try to stay away from supplementing with formula from day one. Mothers often feel insecure about nursing multiples and let comments from family and doctors lead them to choices they did not want to make. Know that you can do this. Many mothers are successfully nursing twins, triplets, and more. As long as you and the babies have been medically assessed and found healthy, you have a great experience ahead of you.

If you have low birth weight babies and are exclusively breast-feeding, avoid supplementing with any juice or water. These supplements will only supply empty calories that will not help the babies gain weight and only serve to jeopardize nursing. Babies need the higher fat intake from mother's milk.

During warm weather, mothers often worry that babies need water or juice to avoid dehydration. Be assured that your milk is sufficient to maintain the hydration of your babies. You can add a "snack" breast-feeding in addition to a regular feeding if your child needs fluids before the next scheduled feeding. If you give a bottle of water, only a few ounces are needed.

TANDEM NURSING

Feeding two babies at the same time is called tandem nursing. One of the benefits is that two babies are satisfied at the same time so there is less crying. Another is that it stimulates the breasts more for better milk production and let-down. Not everyone is comfortable with tandem style nursing, but you might experiment with it at least in the early weeks to help bring in and establish the milk supply. This style of nursing does take some help and practice at first. But it can be worth it in situations where you are in a hurry or two babies are very hungry at the same time. It could prevent frazzled nerves!

If you choose to try to tandem nurse, you should also remember the benefit of one-on-one nursing as well. When you have time, nurse only one and take advantage of this bonding time. It can be very rewarding and will usually not throw off the babies' schedules. Try to take advantage of both types of nursing and use each to suit the time available and the babies' needs.

NURSING EXCLUSIVELY ONE-ON-ONE

There are many reasons why tandem nursing may not work out. When you are dealing with one or more sick or handicapped babies, nursing one at a time is the only choice. The temperament of one or more babies can also be a factor. Some babies are not willing to nurse together, or one may need more help staying latched on. The need may be short-term, and you may try tandem feedings again later when everyone is healthier or calmer. For whatever reason you choose to nurse one-on-one, be assured that there are benefits to this choice. It may be argued that it is more time consuming, but the trade-off of valuable one-on-one time with each baby is a big plus. This benefit alone has been the reason many moms choose to nurse their babies this way. Keep in mind that you will need to use some organizational tips to keep this type of nursing as stress-free as possible.

Feed one full breast to a baby per feeding, breaking midway to burp. Keep a cloth diaper handy to

> I found that it was too confusing to keep track of which baby nursed on which breast last. It was just one more thing I had to remember. Since I had identical twins who were close in size, I just nursed one on the left exclusively and the other always on the right and never got lopsided. I was careful to alternate from a regular hold to a football hold to rotate their heads, though.
> *Rebecca Moskwinksi,*
> *Michiana POMC, Granger, Ind.*

catch the milk from the other free breast, which can leak during let-down for the first baby. Rotate your babies, making sure the same baby does not nurse at the same breast each feeding. A chart can help you keep track of this. Often the babies vary in strength, endurance, and style of suckling, even in identicals. Rotation helps the babies be visually stimulated from both sides throughout the day, and it is useful to have your breasts stimulated by both babies.

If one baby is sick or unable to finish nursing a full breast for a few feedings in a row, try pumping or hand expressing the remaining milk to keep the supply up. Another technique is to offer the other baby that breast to see if he will finish it off, but only after he has already had his own full breast.

In scheduling who feeds first, most mothers use the "survival mode": they feed whoever wakes or cries first. However, this could condition the louder, more aggressive baby to always get fed first and not give it an opportunity to learn patience. Demand feeding is also helpful in relieving stressful situations when both babies may be overly hungry at the same time. Look for signs of alertness combined with rooting or sucking behavior and nurse that baby first. This will allow you to nurse one in peace before the other gets too much out of control. If at home, use a baby swing, pacifier, or infant seat to help distract the waiting baby. If the other is alert and aware that you are nursing the sibling, bring that one near you in a rocking infant seat at your feet. When needed, gently rock the seat with your foot and talk to the infant occupying it. If you deal with them before they are out of control and crying, you will all enjoy the feeding better and have less stress.

NURSING WITH SUPPLEMENTS

If your choice is to nurse with supplemental feedings, either of breast milk or of formula, you need to become familiar with pumping and bottles. If you do not need to pump your milk for other reasons, it is suggested that you do not start pumping to supplement until your milk is in and going strong. Your milk does get richer more quickly if you nurse your babies frequently and exclusively the first few weeks.

Once you feel the babies are thriving and you have the technique mastered, you could start experimenting with pumping and/or adding formula supplements. Try only taking away one specific breast-feeding a day at first. Give yourself at least a week of this schedule. It will also help you to see if the babies are tolerating the formula or developing any allergies or sensitivities.

RETURNING TO WORK

Once they are tolerating a supplement schedule, you can wean them from more feedings if desired, usually by one feeding time a week. This will be helpful if you return to work, so the babies can drink bottles filled with either formula or breast milk while with the sitter. You can choose to pump at work or not, depending on whether you will supplement with formula or breast milk.

You can nurse your babies for as long as you like on a minimum schedule of once in the early morning before work, again when you pick them up from the sitter, and once more in the evening. You can add a snack feeding at night if you desire, for bonding purposes if nothing else. Just remember that it does not have to be all or nothing. Once breast-feeding is established, your breasts will efficiently adjust to the supply and demand and your individual schedule. Though it may feel as if your milk is gone, it is not. If your babies are suckling they are getting milk, even if it is just enough for a snack and bonding time.

NURSING CHALLENGES

Nursing multiples can be a challenge no matter what the circumstances. Some mothers face particularly difficult issues beyond the normal challenges of nursing more than one baby. When babies come prematurely or suffer from health problems, these mothers are facing incredible odds in choosing to breast-feed their babies. Mothers have breast-fed in the face of: prolonged stays in the NICU, triplets and more, low birth weight babies, severe prematurity, cleft palate, Down Syndrome, tongue tie, and reflux syndrome, just to name a few. These mothers have been successful using lactation consultants, supplemental pumping, and the systems such as SNS (see below). Nursing and pumping can make all the difference to preemies. Even if your goal is not full-time or long-term nursing, you could still consider short-term nursing and pumping of colostrum and breast milk, which can really help preemies get a kick-start on their difficult path.

The SNS system is a product designed to feed previously pumped milk or formula to the babies via a tubal system that lies across the breast and extends down to the nipples. The babies suck on the nipple and the tube at the same time. This helps to stimulate milk production and flow via the suckling while the baby receives nutrients from the tube, avoiding frustration and hunger. The goal is to eventually wean off the system to full breast milk. It can help alleviate nipple confusion. If you use this system, it is best to have the help of a lactation nurse or lactation consultant for the first few tries. This system has been used successfully with mothers and babies who were born as much as 11 weeks prematurely and had NICU stays of several months. In such cases, mother and babies graduate to natural breast-feeding in time.

SPECIAL CONCERNS

I have inverted nipples. Can I still nurse?

Yes! Women who have inverted nipples and/or babies with poor latching abilities can benefit from a nursing cup. These special cups are designed to go over the nipple between the bra and the breast. It will help pull the nipple out to be more defined, allowing the babies to latch on more effectively.

What can I do if my doctor is not allowing actual breast-feeding for my preemies yet?

If the doctors have not allowed breast-feeding for your babies in the NICU, your pumped milk can still be a great treasure of nutrients for them. An electric double pump is the best for bringing in your rich milk quickly. Try to buy or rent one from the hospital or have the staff refer you to a medical supply service. If you tell them you have twins in the NICU, they may allow you to rent temporarily rather than commit to a long-term rental agreement. You should pump for the babies as if they were at home and on a schedule. Find out the schedule the nurses have the babies on in the hospital and try to keep to that schedule yourself. This will help with the transition when the babies come home.

One of my babies was released from the hospital while the other one has to stay in the NICU a bit longer. How can I manage to breast-feed both of them?

If you have only one baby in the hospital and one at home, you can have the at-home baby nurse at one breast while you pump from the other at the same time, preferably with an electric breast pump. This will help stimulate your let-down and help you pump more efficiently for the baby still in the hospital. This is best done sitting up with the baby in the football hold with pillow support while the pump is in the other hand.

My babies are underweight and are experiencing slow weight gain. Should I supplement them?

Low birth weight and slow weight gain are difficult issues. Be confident that you can supply rich milk to your babies and they will thrive. Often babies will have difficulty in the early weeks whether you nurse them or feed formula. Switching to formula will only add to the problem of bringing in your milk to its richest potential and may introduce possible nipple confusion to the babies. If a doctor or nurse suggests that the babies need to be on formula and that your milk may not be good, get a second opinion – involving testing of your milk, if need be. Be sure personal opinions are not the basis of their suggestions. As long as you and the babies are healthy, proceed with nursing them as planned.

My babies have to be weighed weekly. Is there a method of helping them to gain faster without supplementing formula?

When you are breast-feeding and the babies are gaining slowly, it is not uncommon for weekly weight checks to be ordered by the hospital or your pediatrician. Do not let this undermine your confidence. It should help assure you that things are going well. If the doctors express continued concern in spite of your efforts and weight checks, there are things that you can do to help the situation without resorting to formula supplements. It is suggested that you hire a lactation consultant if you do not already have one. Consult her for advice and heed it.

If you do not have access to a consultant, then try the following. Since the back milk, or the milk that comes later during nursing, is richer than the front milk, then it would be in the best interest of the babies to get as much back milk as possible. Breast-feed the babies as usual, but pump following each scheduled nursing to get a few more ounces if possible. At the end of the next feeding, feed this pumped back milk to the babies to top them off, so to speak. Continue this cycle of nursing, topping off and pumping until you see them put on weight more regularly. Once they show signs of better weight gain, taper off toward a more natural nursing schedule without supplements. Sometimes all the babies need is a week of this type of feeding cycle to get them growing faster.

What can I do to stimulate my babies to nurse when they just want to sleep all the time?

Due to prematurity and/or low birth weight, some babies can be sleepier than your average newborn. Depending on how premature the babies are, they may not even have the ability to know they need to wake up and eat. It is not unusual for babies to be released from the hospital with instructions to wake them every three to four hours to feed. You can stimulate them to awaken by arousing them from their sleep gently and unwrapping them from their warm blankets. Changing their diapers can help, as can giving them a warm sponge bath. If they fall asleep halfway through a feeding, pull them from the breast immediately and burp them. Also stimulate them with a diaper change or unwrapping.

I let my babies fall asleep while nursing all the time. Is this something I should change?

It is wise not to encourage babies to fall asleep at the breast while nursing. In the early weeks, this cannot always be avoided, especially with preemies. Try to continue to encourage them to be alert at the breast, and remove them promptly when they doze before finishing a feeding. If they have finished your breast and are comfort-sucking, it is okay to allow this as long as they aren't falling completely asleep at your breast. Removing them just before they actually fall completely asleep and laying them down in their bed to finish the process is a good habit for mom and children. This leads babies to develop healthy sleeping habits for the future. If you have a difficult time keeping your babies awake to finish the breast, be patient and be consistent in encouraging them. In time they will grow out of this sleepy stage.

GETTING HELP WITH NURSING

La Leche League International (LLLI) is one source of support, products, and educational information on all aspects of nursing children. If you call them in the early stages of pregnancy, they will send multiple-related support information to help you. Call 847-519-7730 for more information and see Resources, Appendix A.

> It took me exactly six weeks until my breasts became tough enough so that my feet didn't fly up into the air every time they latched on!! None of the books really tells you that. It will hurt for a while, but you'll get through it and it will be wonderful. As soon as I came home from the hospital I was in for a surprise. The milk that I thought had already come in, CAME IN! Wow, was I surprised. I didn't know that one's breasts could do such magic! Anyway, you'll feel some pain, and you'll feel lumps, but this is normal. I thought I had a breast infection for awhile because of the lumps. Soon I realized that as soon as you get a lump you can nurse that breast until you feel relief, and the lumps will go away with frequent nursing. Don't get discouraged — just hang on. It's guaranteed to get better.
> *Kathie Ricci, Berkshire County Mothers of Twins, Lee, Mass.*

A lactation nurse (LN) or lactation consultant (LC) is a valuable investment to consider when facing the choice of breast-feeding multiples. Considering the cost to your babies and the actual cost in terms of dollars, the investment is well worth it. The International Board of Lactation Consultant Examiners at 703-560-7330 or the International Lactation Consultants Association at 919-787-5181 can help mothers with more information and referrals. These agencies are capable of giving assistance over the phone. You should not hesitate to call if you are having difficulty finding resources near you. Be sure to tell them up-front that the babies are multiples and if prematurity is involved, so that they can refer you to someone who specializes in those issues.

Parents should try researching what type of lactation support is offered at the hospital where the delivery will take place. Most have an LN or LC available during the hospital stay. Calling ahead of the due date to introduce yourself and discuss concerns and needs can lay the groundwork for support that will be crucial during those early days and weeks. You may need to ask the Social Services department of the hospital for help in getting this assistance set up for you. The LC can come into the NICU ward to assist you in pumping or in actual nursing attempts. You will need to have this cleared with the head nurse or neonatal physician on duty.

Many hospitals offer breast-feeding classes before and after delivery as well as on-site help for mothers in the hospital. A mother of twins can be in a unique situation regarding lactation classes. Often the classes offered during pregnancy are not possible because the mother is high risk or at bed rest. Later, there is the problem of getting both babies to the classes when the mother is still trying to recover from the delivery. Recruiting someone to help get the babies to the class can reduce some of the stress. Review this need for special attention with the class instructor ahead of time. The instructor may be willing to work with you one-on-one after the class for little or no cost. Sometimes problems can be solved by these professionals in a few minutes. Many times you just need to know that you are in fact doing the right things and only need to give the process a little more time. Either way, no one has ever regretted seeking out the help of an LN or LC.

A local parents-of-multiples club can be a great source of help and direction. Many clubs are introducing a support system for mothers who want to breast-feed their multiples. There is a list of mothers available who successfully nursed their multiples. You can always find someone at a meeting who can really understand what you are experiencing. Sometimes you just need to know that you are not alone.

BOTTLE FEEDING

Some women are unable to breast-feed due to illness, personal preference, or because their multiples are adopted. Women with higher order multiples may need to use a bottle for some or all of the feedings. Modern bottle feeding can be healthy for babies. Formulas provide all the nutrients babies will need in the first few months. Ask your health care provider for the type of formula that is best for your babies.

TYPES OF FORMULAS

Different types of formulas are made for different circumstances. Most babies don't need special formulas. Formulas are usually fortified with iron and come in pre-mixed, concentrated, and powdered forms. Whichever you choose, make sure to follow the instructions for preparation *exactly*. Infants have become very ill when fed formula that was too diluted or too concentrated.

> Rent a water dispenser with hot and cold water in it. If we needed a quick bottle, all we had to do was run half hot and half cold, add the formula, mix, and we were ready to feed! It came out the perfect temperature for our boys!
> Melissa K. Smith, Double Delight MOTC, Windsor, Ill.

PREPARING FORMULA

Make sure to have an adequate number of bottles to prepare formula in advance. This will save time and frustration when the multiples are crying from hunger. Fifteen to 20 bottles may be needed for twins. Some mothers find that color-coding the bottles helps them keep track of what each infant has consumed. There are numerous styles of bottles and nipples, and most will work out just fine. Some babies prefer certain types of nipples to others, so you may need to experiment in the early stages. Too much switching of nipple styles, however, can confuse the babies. Pick a bottle and nipple style that you think is best.

Always keep prepared formula cold in the refrigerator. Formula may be warmed in a bottle warmer or simply in a pan of warm water. It is not necessary to heat the formula. Babies will thrive on formula at room temperature as well as warmed formula. Be very careful about heating formula in a microwave oven, as it may not warm evenly. Babies have been scalded by formula warmed in a microwave when it has become overheated and has boiled over when shaken. Dishwashers are usually adequate to sterilize the bottles and nipples. Ask your health care provider what type of sterilization process will be needed, if any. Sterilization is usually only necessary in the early months.

FEEDING MORE THAN ONE BABY AT ONCE

Don't be afraid to use bottle props! Although the traditional baby books tell you never to prop a bottle, with twins it allows you to feed your babies when they are hungry whether you have your hands free or not. The babies avoid getting frantic waiting for their turns, and you can still look at your babies and entertain them while they eat. Happy feeding!
Debra Grossbaum, West Suburban Chapter MOTC, Dover, Mass.

Try to spend some time cuddling your infants when feeding them. This is where the father and other family members can be of assistance. Sometimes when you are by yourself, it is impossible to hold the babies while feeding them. Propping a bottle on a pillow occasionally can be done without harm to the babies as long as there is plenty of opportunity for cuddling and holding the babies at another time.

SOLID FOODS

Your health care provider will give specific instructions on when to start solids with the babies. Generally, babies do not need solid foods until they are four to five months old. They will get all the nutrition they need from breast milk or formula until that time. Early feeding of solid food can often cause food allergies. In addition, a baby's immature intestine does not yet have the capacity to digest solid foods. Most of the solids will pass through undigested until the baby is older. Contrary to popular belief, early solids will not make the babies sleep through the night any sooner.

> **B**lend food, then put it in ice cube trays. When it is frozen, put it in plastic bags with labels for babies. This is much cheaper than store-bought food.
> *Heidi Levison, Coastside MOTC, Brisbane, Calif.*

Solids are usually begun with rice cereal mixed with formula or breast milk. You can add strained vegetables next. Try to introduce only one new food at a time to check for reactions. Most babies love fruits because of their sweetness, so try to get them accustomed to the taste of other blander foods first so they will not reject them.

Try to remember that the babies are getting most of their nutrition from the breast milk or formula. Don't be concerned with how many solids they take in. Avoid feeding solids through a bottle with a larger opening. Babies do not need to be force-fed in this manner. Getting them accustomed to the textures of the food and to a spoon is your goal - not getting more calories into them.

Many mothers find it more economical to prepare strained infant foods themselves, using a food grinder or a food processor. Steam and puree the fruits and vegetables and freeze them in ice cube trays for future meals. This way, you can control the amount of salt and sugar and serve the foods free from added chemicals.

METHODS OF FEEDING SOLIDS

Early on, feeding the babies in an infant seat will be more convenient and more comfortable for the babies. Later, when they can sit up, a good highchair will make life easier. Try to get one that can be unlatched with one hand, if possible. Plastic chairs are lighter and easier to move around. There should be waist and leg straps to prevent the children from sliding down and out of the chair. Use them every time. When the babies are older, their tendency to wander during a meal can be prevented by the use of a highchair and will be much less distracting for everyone. Be careful about seating arrangements, though. Placing babies next to each other could cause a lot of disruption in the meal if each multiple reaches for the other's food.

Unless one baby is ill or on a special diet, most mothers find that using one bowl and one spoon to feed all the babies is easier. While one baby is mouthing and swallowing the food (usually a slow process), you can give the next one a spoonful.

As your babies become accustomed to eating solid foods, they will want to take over their own feeding. Let them feed themselves as soon as possible, as this will be a big time saver. The best bet is not to care about the mess they make during this important time of learning and development. When the babies are able to sit up by themselves and are swallowing easily, they can begin small finger foods, usually after seven or eight months. Small, easily handled, and easily chewed foods are best. Watch out for foods that can cause a child to choke. These include nuts, whole hot dogs, hard candy, grapes, and peanut butter.

CRYING

Until babies develop verbal skills, the only way they can communicate is by crying. However, as you and your babies get to know each other you learn how to sort out those cries and what they mean. With multiples, it can seem as if there is constant crying because when one baby stops, another may start. This can be very stressful. If the crying persists for a very long period of time, you should call your pediatrician. Prolonged crying may indicate colic or a medical condition, and your health care provider should be informed of this situation.

Colic refers to a pattern of crying in a newborn baby. It usually occurs at a specific time of day, often in the late afternoon or evening. It becomes a pattern of behavior. Often the babies will expel some gas, and this seems to relieve some of the crying. Most of the time, however, it seems to occur for no apparent reason. Most often, colic affects infants during the first two to three months after birth, except for the first two weeks. There is no known medical cause of colic, and it does not mean that your babies are not healthy.

CALMING A CRYING BABY

There are many successful ways to calm a crying baby, and it will take patience as well as trial and error to find the method that works best for you and your infants. Try giving the babies a warm bath, gently massaging their arms, legs, and feet. Water often has a calming effect and also may make the babies sleep. Swaddling or tightly wrapping an infant in a light blanket has long been a method to calm fussy babies. Monotonous noises such as dishwashers and clothes dryers can be calming, so many parents put the infant seat near these appliances when they are running. Some parents use tapes of ocean sounds to soothe their babies. Many parents find the combination of the engine noise and the movement of a car ride will be the only thing that will calm the babies. Often, babies will fall asleep in their car seats while you have the opportunity to get out of the house for awhile. Taking a walk with the stroller can have the same effect. Baby swings and rocker seats are tried-and-true methods of calming fussy babies. Carrying the babies in a sling while you walk around is also a method that is centuries old. Holding the babies across your arm on their stomachs can often help, especially if they seem to be gassy.

If the persistent crying is making you very stressed, place the babies safely in their cribs and go to another room until you are sufficiently calm to try again. The crying will not be harmful to the babies, and they will often stop after 15 to 20 minutes. Remember never to shake a crying infant, as this can be damaging or fatal. Be aware that lack of sleep and constant crying can push any mother to her limits. Enlist the aid of friends or families to give you an interval away from the babies, or hire a teenager or mother's helper if you can. Try to keep it all in perspective. Most babies outgrow this stage by three months. A sense of humor is invaluable during these stressful times.

SLEEPING

Along with prolonged crying, the other problem most parents of multiples ask about is getting their babies to sleep. Shannon Michael of Bothell, Wash., puts it well: "We keep wanting our babies and young children to follow our established ADULT sleeping patterns. But how long did it take us to learn our current sleeping habits? Sixteen to 20 years! When I accepted this fact, all the various nuances of my children's sleeping patterns became significantly less stressful because as someone once said, 'This too shall pass.' And it does. After all, my almost five-year-old twin daughters no longer wake me up at night to nurse, something that at 18 months I thought they'd never quit doing. Now it's the 'I had a bad dream so I want to sleep with you' phase. And when they're teens, they'll be keeping me awake at night because I won't be able to sleep until I know they're safely home in their beds!"

AMOUNT OF SLEEP

Every baby is different in its need for sleep. Some babies will sleep at regular intervals for hours at a time, while others are more content with frequent short naps. Much of it depends on your baby's temperament, nervous system, and size. Fraternal twins may have completely different needs for sleep. In the early newborn stages, the baby's small stomach will make him hungry at frequent intervals, and he will awaken to eat more often. Preemies will need to eat even more often, so they will frequently sleep less. This is normal and will improve as the preemie grows.

The time babies start sleeping through the night can depend largely on whether they need a night feeding or not. The larger baby, usually over 10 pounds, will be able to sleep up to six hours or more at a time without a feeding and thus will sleep through the night sooner.

Surprisingly, most multiples do not seem bothered by a sibling's crying, even when in the same crib. Usually this becomes more of a problem when the multiples are older. Many parents find that very young multiples sleep best when placed together, as they derive comfort from each other's presence. Parents will often find them wrapped around each other or sucking on each other's hands.

GETTING BABIES TO SLEEP

Methods of getting your babies to sleep can vary according to the temperament of each baby. The best thing you can do is to have a routine schedule and stick to it. This has been the most repeated tip from mothers of multiples all over the country. Many mothers use the night time bath as a soothing method. Using the same routine, such as the bath and a story, also signals to the babies that they need to settle down.

Many babies respond well to monotonous movements, such as rocking. As already noted, others respond to noises, such as the sound of a car engine or a dishwasher. Tina Kapinos of Buffalo Grove, Ill., uses a tape of ocean sounds to lull her twins to sleep. Chandra Emerson of Bluegrass MOT&M, Cynthiana, Ky., says a vibrating bouncy seat is the best way to soothe her babies. An infant swing can have the same effect. Rocking them to sleep will work, but you may find that you will tire of this. Getting your babies used to soothing themselves will go a long way to helping everyone to get to sleep. Sometimes they will cry a little, but they will then settle down to sleep. Alice Burke of Waterbury MOTC, New Britain, Conn., feels this has made her twin boys great sleepers who now go to bed with little complaint.

Tight swaddling is a method that has worked through the years. Marie Woodruff of Ocean County MOTC, Tom's River, N.J., states that she would wrap her babies in a T-shirt or pajama top she had just worn and nestle them into bed or their bouncy seat. The warmth and her scent seemed to soothe them. She would also use a sweater to help prop them on their sides, and this seemed to make them fall asleep much faster.

Nancy Hottel-Burkhart of the Kingdom of Morocco shares a method used by Turkish women to put two babies to sleep. She states you should sit in the middle of a queen- or king-sized bed or on the floor with your back supported well up to your shoulder blades. Have your legs completely extended in front of you and together. Place a pillow on your lower legs, from the spot between your arch and your toes and up to your knees, centered well on your legs and not falling to the left or right. Put one baby on the pillow, and line your legs on the outside with pillows or blankets if necessary. By lifting each leg up and down slightly in alternation, you can rock the baby to sleep. Then your arms are free for the other one. How much you rock, how close together your legs must stay, and just where to put the baby depends on its age. Nancy started at birth with one child on her calves, and at almost two years old she was still using this arrangement with a baby's head propped up on her feet. Take turns which baby goes on your legs and which in your arms. This will work until they get too big to fit your legs or jealousy takes over in preference for your arms.

You will have to find by trial and error the method that your babies respond to best.

BATHING

The sight and smell of a freshly bathed baby is wonderful. Yet the task of bathing two or more small newborns can be tiring. Newborns don't require a bath every day, so bathing only one a day and alternating the days may be easier. Too much bathing can dry out a young infant's skin and lead to rashes and flakiness. Tub baths should not be started until the umbilical cord stump has come off, usually within two weeks. Until that time, sponging the babies clean is all that is required. Following that, a baby can even be bathed in the sink for the first few months. Once you switch to the bathtub, a bathing sponge or infant tub can make the job easier. Whatever equipment is used, it is easy to get distracted by one baby while the other is in the bath. Parents need to be especially careful about not taking their eyes off the baby in the bath. An infant can drown in one inch of water in just a couple of minutes. Therefore, you should never leave a baby unattended in the bathtub even for a minute. Bath time can be a good opportunity for siblings to get involved in the care of the babies.

> After a circumcision, instead of putting vaseline right on the sore area, coat the diaper instead. For baths, use a turkey baster instead of a cup when rinsing off your child. It works to direct the water, and the kids also seem to like having the water squirted between their toes.
> *Kris Urbowicz, Abilene, Tex.*

UMBILICAL CORD CARE

Keep the umbilical area clean and dry, and wash around it with rubbing alcohol. If the area ever becomes red or develops a foul odor and drainage, have the baby checked for a possible infection. The shape of the belly button (going "in" or "out") will develop on its own and will not be influenced by anything that you do, such as using straps or coins over the area. Hernias in this area will often go away on their own by age one or two.

GETTING OUT IN PUBLIC

Getting out and about with the babies will be a challenge, but it can be a welcome change from the household routine. Keep a bag packed with the essentials for taking the multiples out of the house. Useful items might include diapers, wipes, clothing changes, snacks, and a few toys. Try to repack the bag immediately when returning home so it will always be ready for the next outing.

Be sure to schedule some outings for yourself without the babies. Having two babysitters when the children are infants can be more reassuring, but more expensive. Try to find someone who can be trusted, then use the person regularly. Though you may be nervous at first, it is important for your peace of mind. Make that first outing only an hour or two, and try to enjoy the freedom it gives you. The babies will benefit, too, when you are rested and in good spirits.

STROLLERS

A twin or triplet stroller is a must. Many styles are available, including side-to-side, front-to-back, and tandem. Some mothers carry one baby in an infant carrier and another in a stroller when they are very small, but this is

When using the stroller and the children needed bottles, I used the plastic-lined nurser bottles with a special holder with a velcro strap (see Resources, Appendix A). They are lifesavers for babies who throw their bottles. The bottle does not reach the ground; thus no need to wash. It keeps clean and attached to the stroller.

At the park, there were baby swings shaped like a diaper (the only way I can describe it). The swing was totally round with four holes for the legs. My guys have been swinging in the swing from four months to 14 months together. I would put their backs together so they were facing away from each other and they could swing together. They were much happier together, and mom only had to push one swing.
Sharon King, Chester County MOT&T, West Chester, Pa.

Take a walk whenever you can. It will relieve some of your stress, and I haven't met a baby yet who doesn't sleep better after being in the fresh air. Make it as easy as possible. I think of it as a time to regroup, and it's almost like a bit of solitude. Take a bottle of cold water with you (for you) when it's hot out. In the winter, don't worry about the coats and jackets when they are little, just keep their heads covered and keep the rest of them toasty with warm blankets.
Christine Eliseev, Arlington Mothers of Multiples, Arlington, Tex.

less practical when they are larger. Buy the best stroller you can afford, as it will be used frequently – and the weight of two or more children will put more stress on the stroller and the parents. As the babies become mobile toddlers, it can be difficult to keep them in the stroller. Some mothers find a safety harness or wrist harness to be helpful at this stage.

CAR SEATS

Car seats are mandatory from the time you leave the hospital. Insist that each child be buckled in a car seat at all times before putting the vehicle into motion. If you are consistent with this rule from the beginning, the children will become accustomed to it and less likely to complain. Car rides can be lifesavers with fussy or colicky babies, as nearly all babies will be lulled to sleep by the monotonous sounds and movements of the car.

> When the twins were very little, we were able to fool people into not "seeing" them while shopping by putting one baby in a carrier on the buggy and one in a snuggli. For some reason, this cut down on the number of people who actually noticed they were twins...and thus there were fewer question stops. Another trick, if you shop with your spouse, is to each take a baby and go your separate ways with a list in hand. Not only do you get the leg work done in half the time, you don't get stopped and questioned as much.
> *Christie Eagleson, Mobile, Ala.*

When the children become more mobile, keeping them in car seats can also be more difficult. This is not a place to compromise. If you are insistent on this point, they will soon learn that the car does not move until everyone is buckled in his/her seat. If they get themselves out of their seats, pull over to the side of the road until they are back in.

DEALING WITH THE PUBLIC

Be prepared to be a spectacle when on outings. Multiples naturally attract the public's attention. A million questions may be asked. You have to develop a personal style and attitude about these intrusions on privacy. Avoiding eye contact and moving along works well. Some parents have resorted to signs for the strollers, such as: "Yes, they are twins," and "Yes, I have my hands full!" Older siblings frequently are overlooked and often feel left out of all the attention. Be sure to add a nice comment about how big brother or sister is a big help.

SPECIAL TIPS FOR GROCERY SHOPPING

Grocery shopping alone with twin infants can be a challenge. Here are some tips from Jane Vaughn of Central Jersey Mothers of Multiples, Bordentown, N.J.:

- Don't do it on a rainy day, as it is too hard to keep them covered in and out of the car.
- Be prepared with the things that will calm your kids. Feed them right before you go, so they will be content.
- Put all the baby supplies and your purse needs in a backpack — leave room for baby coats, hats, etc., and wear as light a coat as possible, preferably one that can fit in the backpack.

> **D**on't waste time in the checkout line bending over your shopping cart over and over, lifting one jar of baby food out at a time. When shopping, pick up a cart and a shopping basket. Load all of your baby food jars and bottles into the basket and then slide it onto the rack under the cart. When checking out, simply set the basket with all the jars and bottles onto the belt in one motion.
> *Kelly A. Sampedro, Camden County MOTC, Camden, N.J.*

- Put the shopping list, coupons, and your wallet in a fanny pack along with anything else, such as a small toy, that you might need to have quickly accessible.
- Park near a cart with a built-in car seat across the toddler seat area and a rack under the cart body. If you can't find a spot near one, ask a passer-by to be a good neighbor and bring you one. **Don't** ask them to watch your kids while **you** do it!
- Put one child in the built-in seat. Use an old receiving blanket on the seat so the child's skin won't have to touch it. Take the other baby out of your car in its car seat and put the whole car seat in the body of the cart.
- On the way into the store, pick up a small-handled shopping basket and carry it over one arm.
- As you shop, put the heaviest items in the rack under the cart body. Put into the cart around the car seat small items that can't be easily crushed. Put light items in your basket.
- At the register, get bags with handles and hold as many of them in your hands as you can while pushing the cart. Some of it can fit under the cart. You can also ask to drive up for your groceries and let the store personnel pack them in your car for you.
- Be patient. It's not easy, and you usually can't buy everything you need in one trip. But it's a productive day out of the house.

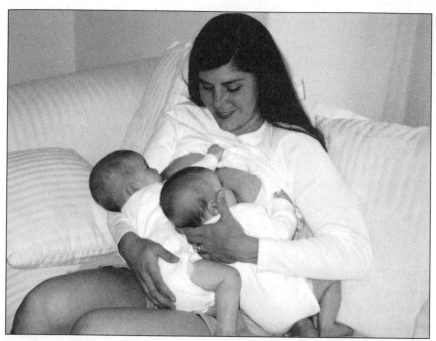

"Spoons" position for nursing, with one baby's head resting on the other's abdomen

Football hold for nursing, mother supporting each baby's head with their bodies resting on pillows under each arm.

DEVELOPMENT

It is always exciting when the babies begin to sit up. They will often start to actively notice each other as separate individuals. Some parents notice that certain twins will not be as fascinated with mirrors as a single child might be. They are accustomed to seeing another baby staring back at them! Dangling toys or those that can be manipulated will be entertaining and stimulating for the babies at this stage. Make sure that toys are soft and cannot become weapons when thrown.

Late infancy is definitely an "oral" stage. The babies will explore everything with their mouths. It is especially important to watch for small objects that can be choked on. Crawling will begin in some babies, though others just scoot around on their stomachs. Other babies never crawl and go from rolling to standing up against furniture. As the babies become more mobile – and, ideally, before – it will be important to baby-proof the home.

Highlights from NOMOTC's 1990 Medical Survey & 1988 Bottle and Breast-feeding Survey

- Mothers feeling that their doctors were the most helpful professional in answering questions about early care of multiples - 21%
- Those feeling that there were no professional persons who were helpful - 44%
- Mothers acquired information about early care of multiples from:
  - Books - 44%
  - Parents-of-multiples clubs - 23%
  - Doctors - 16%
- Mothers who felt that their doctors were supportive of breast-feeding - 76%
- Number who breast-fed twins - 83%
  - Nursed the multiples separately - 62%
  - Fed the babies on demand - 72%
  - Experienced opposition to breast-feeding multiples - 58%
  - Experienced opposition to breast-feeding singletons - 20%

Five factors influenced mothers' decision to breast-feed twins:
1. They didn't want to treat the babies differently simply because there were more than one.
2. Breast-feeding was seen as beneficial to the babies.
3. It was convenient.
4. Mothers felt the bonding attachment would be greater.
5. It was less expensive.

The average age of weaning was eleven months.

CONCLUSION

The end of the first year brings with it many changes. The multiples have grown from helpless infants to mobile toddlers, and you can have pride in all your accomplishments during that year. Do take time out to enjoy each stage of childhood to its fullest. And maintain your sense of humor. As Valerie Chaisson of Albany, N.Y., says: "Enjoy those babies and treat them as individuals right away. I loved holding them while they were sleeping — try it! Make sure that you let them climb all over you when they are big enough. There's nothing like it, especially when they drool or puke on you. It comes off, so laugh about it more than you cry about it!"

7

"Oh, Aren't They Cute," Part II
TODDLER/PRESCHOOL

When I think of life with triplets I have it broken down into stages. When I take the time to enjoy those stages and not rush through them, I have found blessings along with the challenges. One of those stages occurred shortly after we packed up the cribs and introduced our toddlers to beds. It was the first real freedom they had as toddlers. The challenge was how to teach them to stay in their beds each night. The sleepless nights had begun again! One night I was finally enjoying a peaceful sleep when I heard the sound of a quacking duck. At first I thought I was dreaming. Then I heard the laughter of three children. It was three a.m.! I have often wondered how long they were awake and playing on their own. Needless to say, that was the only time I was thankful for noisy toys. Still, bedtime is a treat with multiples. I can read three different books, say three prayers, give three kisses, and receive three hugs. Not long after they are asleep on most nights I find them all snuggled in one bed. At first I thought I had failed the sleeping challenge and then realized they have the blessing of friendship and are best friends for life.

Dawn Keller, Thompson Station, Tenn.

The toddler and preschool years constitute an exciting time full of surprises. After your babies have passed their first birthday, you will begin to see rapid physical, intellectual, and emotional growth. Researchers have proven that these years set the course for future learning and social development, so this is a crucial time for stimulation of all of your children's developing abilities.

WALKING

One of the most important milestones for parents and their toddler multiples occurs when the children take their first steps. Most parents of multiples look forward to the day when they will no longer have to carry two or more increasingly heavy infants. You can be certain that those first steps are imminent when your children begin to pull themselves up alongside furniture and use these support surfaces to aid them in their efforts to walk.

Some toddlers will walk as early as eight months, while others may not take their first steps until 14 months or even later. It is important to remember that not all co-multiples will begin to walk at the same time, as their individual development may vary considerably.   However, the first toddler to walk will generally enhance the non-walker's willingness to attempt those first, shaky steps. If your babies are not walking by age 15 months, this should be discussed with your health care provider.

Your babies' first step is a giant leap for independence and autonomy, but it is also a signal that life in your home will change drastically. When toddlers begin walking, it is important to "child-proof" your home. You may even want to do this before they begin exploring in the crawling stage. (See "Child-Proofing" later in this chapter.) Be sure to never leave young toddlers unattended once they begin walking. Keep bathroom doors closed, as well as doors to other rooms you wish to keep "off-limits." If you are taking your toddlers outdoors without a stroller, you may wish to purchase harnesses or employ the assistance of an older neighborhood child. It's a well-known principle that multiple toddlers will not walk (or run) in the same direction!

TALKING

During the second year of life, speech begins to develop quite rapidly. Encourage your toddlers to communicate with you verbally when they want something. Anticipating their needs will prevent them from developing strong speaking skills. Talk to them whenever you are in their presence. Comment on everyday events; talk about family and friends; offer details about clothing and toy items. Always use the correct name for objects and avoid using "baby talk" with your children. Sometimes the most frequently used word in a young toddler's vocabulary is "NO!" since it is so often heard at this stage. This is normal for all children and also indicates your children's growing independence.

According to statistics, about 40 percent of multiples develop a language all their own which is referred to by some researchers as "idiolalia" or "twin talk." Additionally, some twins and triplets develop a habit of completing each other's thoughts and sentences. They may develop a language of their own, or they may mimic each other and appear to understand each other. Twins will frequently be quicker to respond to spoken words than other children, perhaps because they are so often striving to get in the first word! However, in the race to get words out the toddlers often omit consonants as well as ends of words.

Language can develop more slowly in multiples for several reasons. If your twins were born prematurely, there may be a delay in beginning to speak. However, studies show that most children born prematurely have language skills equivalent to other children by age five or six, all other factors being equal. More to the point, studies show that parents tend to talk less to each twin than to a singleton child. While the singleton child's main model for language is the parent or older sibling, a twin or triplet's speech model is often the co-multiple, who speaks just as immaturely.

IMPROVING LANGUAGE DEVELOPMENT

As a parent, the best way to improve your children's speech development is to talk and read to them on a frequent basis. Always try to model correct pronunciation of words in spite of any silent language between them. Since the children will model their speech after the parent, it's important to use correct language, including "please," "thank you," and "you're welcome."

The bedtime story is a time-honored ritual in many homes which not only helps children to fall asleep but also aids in language development. Read to your children as often as possible, not just at bedtime. Add voice inflection and drama where indicated in the story. Buy books as well as toys for holidays and birthdays, thereby stressing their importance to the family. Reading to your children should begin by age one. It is a fundamental means of developing communication skills.

It's important, also, to notice if the less dominant twin is allowing the co-twin to speak for him. This will result in a less vocal child. Insisting that each multiple speak for him/herself will aid in language development and bolster self-confidence.

If you have a concern over speech or language development on the part of your children, you should check with your health care provider and with your local school district about available testing for preschool-age children. The earlier a problem is identified, the better.

TIPS TO AID LANGUAGE DEVELOPMENT
- Speak frequently to your children.
- Make each child speak for himself.
- Don't anticipate needs which aren't verbalized.
- Use correct pronunciation; avoid "baby talk."
- Read daily to your children.
- Have books available in your home.

MEALTIME

After age one your toddlers will begin to be introduced to a variety of solid foods. Establishing healthy eating habits begins now! While "gracious dining" may disappear from your household for several years, there are ways to make mealtimes enjoyable for the children and bearable for you.

Multiples should be progressing to independent eating by their first birthday. Allowing them to eat by themselves can be extremely messy, but this gives them the opportunity to experiment with different foods. Self-feeding also allows the children an opportunity to improve their fine motor skills. Give your toddlers spoons to hold even if they are too small to use them. Protect the floor with a plastic tablecloth or dropcloth which can be hosed down and hung up to dry after the meal. Newspapers are another good choice. Make sure that your toddlers are always seated in highchairs at mealtimes, and place yourself between the children so they are unable to reach for each other's food.

> For the under-the-highchair mess, place a couple of newspaper sheets under the chairs. They easily pick up and are thrown out instead of the shake-out/clean-out of the shower curtain or dropcloth.
> *Christie Eagleson, Mobile, Ala.*

NUTRITION

Your toddlers will be much more active now while growing at a slower rate than during their first year. Good nutrition is essential to maintain their energy level and body development.

By one year of age your toddlers should be consuming one cup of solids and eight ounces of liquids at each meal. Sometimes snacking or a series of six small meals may work better for your children if they are unable or unwilling to eat large amounts of food at one time. In this case, offer small portions of nutritious snacks during the day. Do not allow the children to drink large amounts of sweet juices between meals. These will fill them up and contribute to pickiness and poor eating at mealtimes.

HEALTHY SNACKS
- celery & carrot sticks
- banana & apple slices
- melba toast
- marshmallows
- raisins
- unsalted pretzels
- dry cereal (not sugar-coated)

Give your children whole milk until the age of two, unless directed otherwise by your health care provider. Growing toddlers require the extra fat in whole milk for proper brain development.

PICKY EATERS

Some toddlers can be picky in their food selections. It is best to let them pick and choose the foods they prefer from nutritious food that is offered to them. Some children at this stage seem to get into "food fads," eating only one type of food for a few days. In this case, you should simply continue to offer a variety of foods. It has been shown that children will obtain the nutrition they need over the course of a week if allowed to choose from a variety of nutritious foods and if not pressured. This does not mean that the parent should become a short-order cook. The parent's job is to supply nutritious food when the child is hungry.

CHOKING HAZARDS

Watch out for foods that a very young child can easily choke on. These include nuts, whole hot dogs, hard candy, and whole grapes. A child may not be able to make any sounds if he/she is choking. If the child is coughing and getting air, leave the child alone to clear the airway himself. **Do not strike the child on the back.** The Heimlich Maneuver should be used on the child if choking is apparent. This is done by placing the hand on the upper abdomen and giving six to ten rapid thrusts. Taking an infant/child CPR class will give you proper instruction on this maneuver and on resuscitation. It may save a life.

GOING OUT TO EAT

Many parents do not even attempt going out to eat until the children are older, but Becky Hames of San Diego, Calif., came up with a solution. Her girls were fussy while waiting for their food in restaurants and then did not eat the food that was served. The Hameses decided to feed the twins immediately prior to going out to dinner. This way the kids could eat something they enjoyed, like macaroni and cheese or spaghetti. Then the Hameses would go out to dinner. After the couple ordered for themselves, they ordered dessert for the twins (such as ice cream). They asked that the dessert be brought out when their dinners were served. They found that this would accomplish several things: 1. They didn't have to worry if the girls didn't finish their food (although they usually did). 2. The food for the girls was not very expensive, so they didn't worry if it wasn't finished. 3. They were able to eat in peace without having to hound the kids to eat their dinner. 4. This arrangement provided the kids an opportunity to feel that going out to dinner was a treat for them, too.

> **M**y wonderful day care provider made this suggestion for eliminating sibling squabbles. We have "Sam day" on odd days and "Rachel days" on even days. On Sam's days, he decides which couch he sits on, where he sits in the van, who goes first for a haircut, whether we play Monopoly® or Clue®, whether we have elbow macaroni or twists, etc. On Rachel's days, she makes the decisions. Those with more than two children can mark a wall calendar labeling each day with a child's name. And, by the way, the thirty-first of the month is my day!
>   *Janet L. Hurwitz, MOT&T,*
>   *Valley Forge, Pa.*

PLAYTIME/DISCIPLINE AND FIGHTS

By the time your multiples reach their first birthday, it may seem that their toys have taken over the house! Doting relatives and friends may have showered your children with identical toys on each holiday and birthday. At some point you will realize that having two, three, or four of every toy is definitely not the way to go! Buying toys that are in the same category, such as two different kinds of trucks in different colors and styles, will help. The children can then enjoy the similar toys but still feel that they have their own unique possessions. Larger toys that are meant to be shared, such as block-building sets or a toy kitchen, can be purchased for all of the children to play with and will stretch your dollars. Large items such as bicycles should be purchased for each child. While twins, triplets, and quads enjoy having their own unique possessions, they can also learn socialization skills by enjoying shared toys.

One of the delights of having multiples is watching them play and interact together. During these early play times, your children are getting to know each other and developing a close bond unique to their situation as multiple birth children. Sometimes you will see them actively engaged in a joint activity; at other times they may be engaged in "parallel play," sitting side-by-side but not actually interacting. It's also interesting to note that multiples learn to play together earlier than singletons. While multiples are much more accustomed to sharing and taking turns, this is not to say that they will play happily together all of the time! There will be plenty of fights.

BITING

Biting seems to be a stage that many multiples experience. Some toddlers resort to hitting and biting to get their way or to get their parents' attention. Biting may also increase during periods of teething. Your toddlers do not fully realize that they are inflicting pain on another person. Though the marks look very ugly and the behavior seems so primitive, the wounds are rarely serious. Approach this just as you would any other undesirable behavior. Separation, distraction, and withdrawing attention will work best. Undue attention to the behavior may escalate it. Biting is definitely a stage, and most children outgrow it.

To stop biting behavior, I used lemon wedges (kept in the refrigerator for fast retrieval). When a biting incident occurred, I took the biting twin to the time-out corner and said, "No biting!" I laid him down on his back and squeezed the lemon into his mouth at the same time. He only bit one more time after this. This worked because the consequence was related to the behavior.
Melody Roy, Gold Country MOMs, Auburn, Calif.

FIGHTING

For the most part, children should be allowed to resolve their own conflicts without interference. A parent will have to intervene, however, if the fighting becomes dangerously physical. The best methods are to remove the offending toy (no one wins), to separate the toddlers, or to distract them with another activity. When they are very young, use as few words as possible to get the point across. Do not give lengthy explanations for your limits. You might simply say, "We do not hit," or "Biting is not allowed," or "I will not let you hurt your brother." These short remarks, made while you are separating them, should be sufficient. Let the children make choices for a new activity, but be sure to offer two acceptable choices. If your toddlers are having a bad day, change the mood or atmosphere. Put on a favorite video or CD, go outdoors for awhile, let them speak on the phone with a grandparent, or let them simply play in the bathtub (under your watchful supervision).

The first and last piece of advice I give to any person looking after my kids is if the situation gets to the boiling point and it looks like it might get worse, "Divide and conquer!" I have a four-year-old boy, a three-year-old girl, and two-year- old twin boys. I put two of them in one room, two in another, and then I relax. When my composure is regained, I first deal with the smaller one or those who are more wound up.
Julie Sovia, MOTC of Rockland County, Orangeburg, N.Y.

Irritability and constant fighting may be a sign that your toddlers are tired and in need of a nap. Too much stimulation can also cause tantrums to develop. Chris Fulmer of South Dade POMC, Homestead, Fla., shares her tip for stopping the fighting: "When my children would fight over a toy or possession I would give them a minute to settle the argument on their own. If they would not compromise I would put the TOY in time-out for 10 or 15 minutes, then make a big deal out of bringing it out of the closet and establishing a schedule of turns for the rest of the day. It must have been effective because the first word for both of them, after 'mama' and 'dada', was 'turn'!"

TANTRUMS

Temper tantrums often appear at this age and are generally the result of exhaustion, frustration, or a desire for attention from the parent. If you notice that your children have tantrums when they become exhausted, establish a strict routine for activity and naps.

When tantrums occur, try not to give in to the behavior. Giving in will usually increase the problem and establish a conduct of behavior. If tantrums occur in a public place, calmly remove the children to the car or home saying as little as possible. When tantrums occur at home, simply leaving the room is the best method.

> **W**hen our twins were about three, they had a nasty argument. I scolded them firmly and told them, "You are sad when you argue." I reinforced this when they argued again, and they seemed to be listening to what I said. We have not had further problems with arguing.
> *Florence Meinders, Pella, Ia.*

On special days, such as holidays and birthdays, continue to follow your daily schedule, planning party times after the children's usual nap time. This will save you and your guests from the embarrassment and upheaval which two or more tired toddlers can create.

BREATH-HOLDING

Some toddlers hold their breath in order to gain attention. This is particularly common during the latter part of the first year and the early months of the second year. This will almost always follow vigorous crying, then gasping. Your toddler may turn blue or pale and then become limp. Although this behavior is alarming, the child will begin breathing again spontaneously on his own. This is usually a short-term problem, and the child will often outgrow it within a year. The key to this behavior and all discipline at this age is to minimize conflict. Let the child make choices, and explain your reasons for limits.

SHARING

Toddlers and young children will not naturally want to share something that is precious to them. All the children should have at least one possession that is uniquely theirs and does not need to be shared. If you respect this and they know that they do not have to share the one item, they may be more willing to share other items. Multiples actually learn to share sooner than singletons. After all, they have had to share their parents from day one!

CLEAN-UP

Some parents make clean-up a game. Donna Marinack of Shawano Lake Area MOTC, Wis., puts all the toys that need picking up in a large pile in the middle of the room. Then she has the first child put away all the green things and the next pick out all the items of another color until all the items are put away. This makes the clean-up go more quickly, and they have fun with it. As they get older, you can use a reward system, such as is used by Laura Mervosh of Nassau County MOTC, Westbury, N.Y. Laura gives her children bingo chips as a token when they have accomplished a certain task. She keeps them for the children in a special purse which each has. The children decide on a low-cost item they want to earn, and once they have earned a specific number of chips, they get the prize.

> **A** kitchen timer is a great tool for helping to share toys. I select one child to play with the toy in dispute, and the other child helps me set the timer for 5 minutes. When the timer goes off it's the second child's turn with the toy, and the first helps me set the timer again. The timer helps them understand that they will get a turn.
> *Lisa Cowden, MOMs Society, Littleton, Colo.*

WEANING FROM PACIFIERS

One suggestion is the "cold turkey" method, which means having the pacifiers disappear one day when you think the child is ready. Ann Marie Mitchell of Parents of Twins and Triplets Organization, Nashville, Tenn., has another method that is more gradual. She starts giving the child the pacifier only during sleep times (naps and bedtime) for the first one or two weeks. Then she cuts out the nap time and gives the pacifier only at bedtime for one week. She then leaves it off altogether. She was surprised at how easy this was, and it has been successful for other mothers of multiples she has shared it with.

CHILD-PROOFING

Before your toddlers reach the walking stage, it's important to begin to assess the possible hazards in your home which need to be safeguarded. Electrical outlets, easily opened cabinets containing medicines and chemical cleaners, bathrooms, and flights of stairs will become high-danger areas for inquisitive toddlers. Getting down on your hands and knees and looking at the home from your toddlers' eye level may give you a better perspective of the many dangers lurking in each room.

You will soon notice that certain toys that will be perfectly safe for a singleton can become dangerous weapons when wielded by twin or triplet siblings. Soft, plush toys are preferable for children up to age 18 months. Regardless of the dating on most toys, be aware that multiple toddlers require strict supervision during the early years so that they do not injure each other with their toys.

> My toddlers kept pulling over the clothes hamper and diaper pail. Our solution was to purchase a large, deep storage bin with the lid removed. We placed the clothes hamper and diaper pail inside the storage bin, which was wedged tightly between the changing table and the dresser (so the kids can only access one side).
>
> Susanna Samick, Bellaire Area MOM, Houston, Tex.

Some studies confirm more injuries in multiples than similar-aged singletons. This is because the combined weight of multiple toddlers can cause dangerous situations which would not occur if they were alone. Many children at this age have been injured when pulling large pieces of furniture or large toys upon themselves. It's also important to realize that most young multiples will assist each other in their mayhem, so try not to have available any items which can help them to do so.

Some families have found it necessary to bolt furniture — particularly shelving or cold air vents — to the walls. Some types of furniture, such as glass-topped tables, might be avoided altogether during these early years. Remember: Two or three toddlers together can often accomplish what one alone would never dream of!

Playpens are fine for small toddlers if they will stay in them. The reverse is so often true, however, that some families have even resorted to putting objects such as the Christmas tree into the playpen to keep them safe from the children. Large yard corrals make wonderful outdoor pens in which the children can play safely. Putting an expandable fence or baby gate at the top and bottom of stairs and padding pointed table edges can help safeguard against nasty falls. If it's available, some parents have found it easier to segregate an entire room that has been carefully child-proofed.

Use of commercial devices for protection can also be a lifesaving investment. In the living areas, edge protectors for sharp table corners and the edges of a hearth can prevent that first ride to an emergency room for stitches. You should also be aware that dangling cords and drapes can choke a child. Clips which hold them securely in place are found in any hardware or drapery store.

The bathroom is definitely one of the most dangerous areas in your home for curious toddlers. All medications should be kept in a locked cabinet. Your toddlers should never be left unattended in the bathtub even for a minute! The toilet can be dangerous if one of your toddlers becomes upended into it with his head under water. Toilet seat locks are available to prevent tragedy. A first-aid kit which contains syrup of ipecac should be kept handy and refilled as needed.

> **W**e were fortunate to have a spare bedroom on the first floor of our home. After the boys were no longer happy in a playpen we moved all of their toys into this empty room, put safeguards on all the electrical outlets, and bolted down the air vents (after one of the boys removed the cover and started to climb down it!). A baby gate secured the doorway. They had hours of fun in there, and the mess was confined to one room.
> *Martha Eicker, Twice as Nice MOMs, Chicago, Ill.*

Just remember that danger and multiple mischief can loom anywhere in the house. All of the commercial safeguards in the world cannot replace the watchful attention of a loving parent or caregiver.

SLEEP PROBLEMS

During the toddler years your multiples may experience sleep problems for a variety of reasons. For example, when one of the children awakens and cries, it sometimes disturbs the sleep of the others. While some parents find that separate bedrooms can help the situation, other families lack the additional bedroom space or their young children may resist sleeping apart. Illness or temporary separation due to hospitalization or the like may also result in sleep problems for the remaining multiple(s).

Stressing consistent routines and regular bedtimes will usually help to establish good sleep patterns. You should establish an evening routine which might include a bath, teeth brushing, a bedtime story or favorite video, and a few minutes of quiet talk at the bedside before turning out the lights. Many young children prefer a small night light, and this is perfectly acceptable. Avoid offering a baby or toddler a bottle to aid in falling asleep. The milk's sugar content, combined with the lack of saliva during sleep, can produce very serious dental decay in the front teeth. Some toddlers have special stuffed animals, blankets, or other toys that they become attached to. These so-called "transitional objects" can help the children to go to sleep and are soothing to them. Some toddlers use pacifiers. If a child needs one of these items included in the bedtime ritual, by all means use it. All children will eventually outgrow the need for these security items, and everyone will sleep better in the meantime.

Once your toddlers climb out of their cribs, it's time to proceed with a youth bed or twin bed. You may worry that your peaceful evening hours will be disrupted at this stage, as the children are able to wander around at will rather than being confined to a crib. Again, stressing consistent bedtime routines and always putting the children back in their beds will help greatly. Many parents feel that keeping the children in a crib for as long as possible is helpful. Some parents just leave the side of the crib in the lowered position as a transition. Toddler beds that use the crib mattress also make a great transitional bed between a crib and a twin-sized bed and are built lower to the floor.

> **W**hen it's time for naps and nighty night, we keep a duffle bag on hand and use it to carry all of the babies' teddies and dollies that they take to bed with them. We carry it both ways, upstairs to bed and downstairs to play. They have fun putting everything into it.
> *Kathie Ricci, Berkshire MOT, Lee, Mass.*

Some children take to crawling into the parents' bed at night. You will have to develop your own method of dealing with this, but certainly an occasional night in the parents' bed is not harmful. Harm does come, however, if this behavior disrupts the parents' privacy over long periods of time. Do not let a demanding toddler ruin your marital intimacy. Your child will not be harmed by your insistence that he sleep in his own bed. You may have to put up with some fussing and resort to keeping your door closed to stop this habit, but it can be changed.

NIGHT TERRORS

Your child may be experiencing another type of sleep disturbance called a night terror. This is a different type of night awakening than a nightmare. The child will cry out but is not fully awake. The child sometimes screams as if terrified, may not seem to recognize the parent, has his or her eyes open, and may get up out of bed. Night terrors may be precipitated by a lifestyle change such as moving to a new home or starting preschool. The child will often experience the night terror about an hour after going to sleep. Do

When going from a crib to a bed, try just the box spring and mattress on the floor (with the frame). This way the child gets the "feel " for the bed without having so far to fall out.
Patti Lyon, Albuquerque MOTC, N.M.

not try to awaken the child. Gently leading the child back to bed and soothing him back to sleep will help. These episodes can be frightening and confusing for the parent, but the child will not remember the episode nor be frightened as he or she is in a deep stage of sleep at the time. Most children will outgrow these episodes, but if you are concerned please contact your health care provider.

NAPS

Most toddlers under the age of four will benefit from a period of sleep during the day. By all means continue the nap schedule which your children followed during their first year of life, and set your own daily schedule around your toddlers' nap time. If your babies were erratic daytime sleepers, you should try to establish an afternoon nap schedule as soon as possible. Many mothers lie down with their toddlers and enjoy the benefits of an hour's rest each afternoon. Once established, regular nap times generally make the dinner hour much more pleasant, as a cranky toddler can be most irritable during dinner preparation. If the child protests that he isn't tired, insist that he lie down for some "quiet time" regardless. Some mothers tell their children that it is "mommy's nap time!" Be firm with relatives and friends over the importance of maintaining the schedule since you are the one who has to live with these children, whatever mood they might be in!

TOILET TRAINING

Between the ages of 18 months and three years, mothers of multiples are eagerly awaiting the day when their children will be toilet trained. This is a big step toward greater independence for both you and your children. Same-sex multiples usually learn this task at the same time because they will mimic each other as they learn. Opposite sex multiples may be ready for toilet training at vastly different times. In general, boys tend to be ready later than girls. The most important fact to remember is that toilet training cannot take place until the child is physically and developmentally ready. This is not a step that can be rushed! If one child doesn't seem interested or ready, concentrate your efforts on working with the one or more who do have an interest and are ready.

You may find it helpful to reward your toddlers when they use the toilet instead of soiling their diapers or underpants. Positive reinforcement can be very helpful. Treats such as candy, dry cereal, or special privileges are used by some parents. Your children may simply

SIGNS OF TOILET TRAINING READINESS
Your toddler:
- Stays dry for several hours at a time.
- Dislikes the sensation of being wet.
- Asks to be changed when diaper is soiled.
- Goes off alone to the toilet.
- Shows an interest in the toilet process.

> It is hard to know if your children will prefer a potty chair or the big potty, so buy a potty chair that has a seat that can be moved to the big potty. It is all right to resort to bribery if it makes them use the potty! Sometimes it helps to let a child be naked. Mine loved applause after success. Try to never, never yell at them. There is no way you can make them use the potty if they do not want to use it.
> *Diana Jones, Bay Area MOMs, Baldwin City, Tex.*

respond to the lure of special "big girl" or "big boy" underwear. Many parents of multiples also find that they need two potty chairs if training more than one at a time, as the other multiple will often want to use the potty chair at the same time. You may wish to have a favorite book or stuffed toy close at hand while your child sits on the potty chair. Using cloth diapers or training pants rather than disposable diapers or paper "pull-ups " can make the process easier, as the child can then feel the wetness more easily.

You need to remember that there will be setbacks in this process and that there is never a place for punishment or ridicule. This will only set up a power struggle between parents and children. Keep in mind that many factors can influence the progress of toilet training. A bad cold or other debilitating illness will set back the child's progress. Exhaustion or emotional upset can also be a cause of accidents during the early stages of toilet training. Sometimes very young children are simply too wrapped up in their play, and before they even know it they are unable to reach the bathroom in time. Be sympathetic to your children's needs as they change on a daily basis.

Allow your child to take part in helping to clean up accidents, but do this in a non-punitive way. Let your toddler know that you have confidence that he/she will remember to use the potty chair next time. Above all, try to keep things in perspective. If both you and your children are becoming frustrated, stop and wait for a few months. When you try again later on, it may be easier for all of you.

Nighttime dryness does not necessarily happen at the same time as daytime training. The child will often continue to be wet at night for much longer. Initially, using thick training pants or paper pull-ups for "nighttime pants" will keep the bed dryer. Use a liner on the mattress to protect it. Start restricting nighttime drinks and fluids to prevent accidents at night. Getting the child up to use the toilet when you go to bed can help prevent nighttime accidents. As with toilet training, do not punish the child for bed-wetting accidents. Teach the child how to clean up the sheets and where to put the wet ones in a matter-of-fact manner. Older children can clean up by themselves. Bed-wetting is often an inherited trait, so if you or your spouse were bed-wetters, it is probable that some of your children will be also. There are medications available to help the child if this continues to be a problem into the school-age years.

Highlights from NOMOTC's 1989 Potty Training Survey

- Number of respondents using two potty chairs - 58%
- Those using both toilet and potty chairs - 69%
- Those using the toilet only - 13%
- Parents using verbal praise - 85%
- Parents using a reward system (candy, stickers, toy) - 85%
- The majority of the multiples averaged five to ten pairs of training pants per day.
- Summer and spring were the most popular times of the year for toilet training.
- Twins A and B were trained at fairly close times, especially in the case of identicals.
- Identical males were trained earlier than fraternal males, who trained the latest.
- Girls were often trained at 25 to 30 months, generally before boys.
- Day training occurred earlier than nap or night training.

OUTINGS AND TRAVELING

Toddlers love their independence and may balk at being put into a car seat for car trips. You must be insistent on this issue, however. Make sure they know you mean business. Remember: The car should not move if everyone is not buckled in. Set a good example by using your seat belt, too. Having special toys that are available only in the car can make the car trips more manageable. Susan Lovaglio of Rockland County MOTC, N.Y., keeps a "Magna Doodle®" in the car for each child. This keeps the crayon mess out of the car. Many suggest keeping a spare diaper bag packed in the trunk at all times with a change of clothes, toys, wipes, and diapers. Keep an extra potty seat in the trunk for emergencies.

LONGER CAR TRIPS

With small children it is helpful to travel during the night so that they can sleep on the trip. Keep their routine the same, suggests Elizabeth Brumfield of South Palm Beach County POMC, Fla., such as the bath time ritual and putting them in their pajamas. Then it is into the car seats and off they go! She and her husband alternate driving and sleeping so one is always rested. During the daytime, keep snacks and juice handy along with some new toys to entertain. Cassette tapes of favorite sing-a-long songs are helpful. Small travel games are fun for older children. Each child should have a backpack or bag that he or she can pack with any of his or her favorite toys — their choice! A pillow for each child is also a good idea. Celeste Jeffway of Hampshire County MOTC, Northampton, Mass., says that if it is affordable, a TV-VCR unit with individual headphones can make a long trip bearable. Penny Smith of Cape Fear MOTC, N.C., puts an auto clothes bar above the twins' car seats and hangs toys on it. It keeps the kids occupied, and she doesn't have to search for dropped toys while driving.

> **W**hen going on a camping trip, pack the children's clothing in ziplock bags - including socks, outfit, t-shirt, and a diaper or pants. This way, when you go to the bathhouse, all you have to do is grab a bag for each child.
> *Lisa M. Lothringer, Southeast Suburban MOTC, Carleton, Mich.*

AIRLINE TRAVEL

Make sure you have essential items with you as a carry-on for the flight. A wheeled bag or a backpack will be easier to maneuver with small children in tow. Have the kids chew some gum on the way up and down to keep ear pressure equalized, or have them drink some juice from a juice box or bottle. Liz Gratz of Coastside MOTC, S. San Francisco, Calif., suggests taking along Play Doh®. Besides its normal use, it doubles as a drawing marker holder so the markers don't fly all over the place. Having some inexpensive wrapped small gifts is great and gives the kids something to do. Take along some healthy snacks and water, as the kids may not like the airline fare. Ordering the fruit plate can be a better choice than the kid's meal. She also suggests not getting on the plane until the last possible moment.

SHOPPING TRIPS

As with infants, it is sometimes difficult to take toddlers shopping with you and actually accomplish anything. When they start being able to climb and run away, it can be a daunting task indeed. Some parents use wrist straps to keep their multiples at bay, while others rely on the straps in the strollers. One must be careful that toddlers don't overturn the stroller or a grocery cart by standing up. Most carts now have straps to secure one child, but not two. Bringing an extra strap along to buckle the second child into the body of the cart can prevent an accident. One single mother, Kim Hoff of Pairs & Spairs, Newman Lake, Wash., devised a method of keeping her twins in the stroller. Her solution is to dress them in overalls. She ties a string with a clasp on one end of the stroller and hooks the other end to the loop on the back of the overalls. If she happens to get distracted by one twin, the other cannot run off. She also feels more reassured that no one can snatch one or both of the boys if she gets distracted, and the boys cannot reach the strap and undo it themselves.

HEALTH ISSUES

Now that your children have reached the toddler years, you are probably getting out more often in public and mingling with other mothers and children. While this is important for your multiples' social development, you will also experience an increase in the number of illnesses they contract. Additionally, multiples will often catch each other's illnesses. Studies show that children in day care will contract more illnesses than those who stay at home.

EAR INFECTIONS

One of the most common problems for toddlers is chronic ear infection. This is an infection of the middle ear behind the ear drum. Germs which normally drain in the Eustachian tube are trapped and cause a pressure and fluid build-up in the middle ear space. (See chart for symptoms.) If the eardrum ruptures, pus may drain from the ear. Although this will actually relieve some of the pain by reducing the pressure, the child should still be examined by your health care provider. Ear infections are usually treated with antibiotics for 10 days. Some untreated ear infections can result in hearing loss and delay in language development. It is important for your child to have a follow-up visit with the doctor after finishing the antibiotics. Keep the appointment even if your child seems to be over the infection.

SYMPTOMS OF EAR INFECTIONS

Toddlers will often:
- Pull on their ears.
- Have difficulty sucking or swallowing.
- Have a fever.
- Experience difficulty sleeping.

OTHER COMMON ILLNESSES

SIGNS OF DEHYDRATION

- Decrease in urination or number of wet diapers.
- Child becomes less alert.
- Child exhibits excessive thirst and dry lips.

Small children often run high fevers with simple viral infections. These may appear suddenly and can be frightening, but they are usually no cause for alarm. A rectal temperature will be higher than an oral or an axillary (under the arm) temperature. If your child has a fever, such as an oral temperature greater than 100.5 degrees, you will need to increase his/her fluid intake by about 10 percent. Always check with your doctor to see what medications are recommended for fighting fever in children.

Your toddlers may also experience nausea, vomiting, or diarrhea caused by infection in the intestinal tract or as a symptom of another illness. You should treat the symptoms with clear liquids and watch for signs of dehydration. Call your health care provider if the multiple is experiencing any of these symptoms or if the child is unable to keep any liquids down. Additionally, abdominal pain along with the nausea and vomiting may signify a more serious illness and should be investigated by your doctor.

Your multiples will often share their illnesses, so you will need to develop extra resources to assist you in dealing with two or more sick toddlers at the same time. Be sure to make a simple chart to keep track of any medications given and record the time and temperature of each child when you take it. Make notes of frequency and type of bowel movements for each child as well as food or fluids which have been consumed. You will be very tired after losing sleep at night, and errors, especially in giving medication, can be serious or even fatal!

When an emergency happens and you are a parent of multiples, remember the other children as well. I have had to take my son to the hospital and be faced with the question of what I should do with his twin sister. If at all possible, have a reliable source that you can trust to take that twin. I found that my mother was the best in this particular case, and that in turn gave me the time I needed with my son who was getting stitches.
Shanna Olson, Aurora, Colo.

When giving your toddlers medication, always use a matter-of-fact approach. Mixing the medicine with juice or grinding up pills and mixing them in applesauce, pudding, or ice cream may make it easier for your children to swallow. If only one of your toddlers is sick and on medication, you may want to offer all the multiples something from the spoon. Be sure that the sick child receives the last spoonful with the medication! (No one ever said that mothers can't be tricky!)

DOCTOR'S APPOINTMENTS

For your convenience, you may wish to make doctor appointments for all of your multiples on the same date. Even if only one is sick at the time, your health care provider may see early signs of illness developing in the other toddler(s). Consider taking another adult along for assistance. A relative, neighbor or member of your local parents-of-multiples club can assist in cutting down on distractions and allow you to concentrate on listening to the doctor.

Another perspective on this is given by Denyel Galle-Mattia of Westside Suburban MOTC, Spencerport, N.Y.: "If possible, take your children to the doctor separately. This way the doctor and you can concentrate on just the one child. You will also have special individual time with this child. When I take them together, the one I can't hold is crying and it's hard to talk about concerns. If a baby has a reaction to a shot, you can take care of it better if only one is sick.

Every single time I go into the doctor's office, the secretaries, nurses, and the doctor tell me how wonderful it is that I bring them separately. They wish all their mothers of multiples did the same. Another alternative is to have a helper and have the children go into separate rooms."

During your visit be sure to ask questions about your toddler's condition, and bring along the information which you have charted during the early course of your multiple's illness. Further, even when your toddlers are experiencing cold symptoms, you may continue with the scheduled course of immunizations which started during infancy.

DEALING WITH HOSPITALIZATION

Families with multiples often face the stress of having one child hospitalized, whether this is for scheduled surgery such as taking out tonsils or an emergency hospitalization for an injury or illness. While much of your time and attention will be devoted to the hospitalized child, you also will need to consider the effects of the separation on the multiple sibling(s) remaining at home. At this age, toddlers cannot fully comprehend what is being told to them about their missing sibling. Remember that your child at home will not only be missing his or her sibling, but he/she will also miss the time spent with parents who are now occupied at the hospital.

In your toddler's "grief," his or her behavior may deteriorate. For example, the toddler who was previously potty trained may start wetting the bed again. He/she may roam the house all day long looking for the missing sibling and refusing to be drawn into play activities. Other undesirable behaviors such as temper tantrums or breath-holding spells may return as a result of feelings of jealousy and resentment over the attention which the sick multiple is receiving. The child at home may have difficulty falling asleep or experience nightmares, especially if he or she is not used to sleeping alone in a room. You will need to recognize that all of these behaviors and regressions are directly caused by your child's grief.

Once the hospitalized toddler is home again, you may still experience repercussions. The toddler left at home may think that the ailing multiple "took" his mommy away. He may shriek, hit, or push anytime attention is paid to the sick sibling and not to him. Be patient, and above all please remember how scary the whole experience must be for all of the multiples.

A few tips that will help you through this experience are:

- If the hospital allows it, take the children at home to the hospital.
- Parents should take shifts at the hospital so that they can spend time with the child(ren) at home also.
- Try to keep the usual routine at home as much as possible.
- Reassure the child(ren) at home and at the hospital that the separation is only temporary and soon you will all be home together.
- Encourage the child(ren) at home to draw get-well cards or make small gifts for the sick child.
- When time allows, spend some special time alone with the toddler(s) not hospitalized.

MULTIPLE ISSUES

During the toddler and preschool years your children will pass through many developmental stages. With each birthday, you will notice that life is becoming easier and the initial workload of raising multiple birth infants is only a fading memory. Still, there are issues which will be unique to the fact that you are raising multiples, and these need to be addressed.

By the age of three your children will begin to recognize themselves as twins, triplets, or quadruplets. Talk with your children about being multiples, and let them ask questions. There are several fine books written for preschool children which will answer some of the questions they may have. Check your local library, or contact NOMOTC for a bibliographic listing of multiple-related children's literature.

Relatives or strangers may call your children "the twins" or "the triplets." It's important that you insist that they refrain from referring to your children in this way. They need to develop individuality, and being referred to as a unit is not beneficial. If your children are identical or look-alike fraternals, assist your family and friends in identifying them correctly. Point out physical or personality differences which will help them recognize each child and refer correctly to each by name.

From the time your multiples are very little, set aside time to spend with each child separately. If possible, try to take one child alone when you run errands. If one awakens earlier than the other from a nap, spend a few minutes talking to that child or cuddling on

Letting toddlers help with "grown-up" tasks improves their cooperation and develops motor skills that will be needed in school.

the sofa or in a rocking chair. Be sure to take separate photos of each multiple in addition to photos of the set. During these preschool years, you may also want to move away from dressing your toddlers in matching outfits. By age four, your children will have their own favorite colors and other preferences which should be taken into account when purchasing clothing. You may wish to limit look-alike dressing to special occasions. Remember that dressing your toddlers in matching clothes will make it more difficult for others to tell them apart.

SCHOOL ISSUES

Many everyday activities prepare children for the fine motor development needed to master writing. Have your children participate in such activities as playing with blocks, stringing beads or cereal onto yarn, or rolling out cookie dough. All types of craft materials, including drawing paper, preschool scissors, paste, crayons, and pencils, are wonderful toys for preschoolers. Save old catalogs and magazines for cutting and pasting. These types of materials develop fine motor skills and encourage the children's budding creativity. Children can also prepare for academics by attending a play group to learn inter-personal skills important for developing self-control and cooperation.

Enrolling your multiples in preschool or a neighborhood play group is extremely beneficial if your children's intellectual or motor development is delayed due to extreme prematurity or any of a variety of physical conditions. Also, if you notice that your toddlers are becoming completely dependent on each other, or if one multiple dominates the other, you should consider introducing them into this type of environment, which will assist in their socialization. If it is difficult for you to find separate time with each multiple, sending the children to preschool on alternate days may be a workable solution.

> **M**y children go to day care three times a week. I need to be organized in the morning to get out of the house on time. The night before, I pick out their clothes, coats, hats, gloves, socks, and shoes. I also make sure their diaper bag is packed with their food, bottles, thermometers, diapers, any medicine they might need, and notes for the babysitter. This way, in the morning we have breakfast together at a leisurely pace knowing we are ready to leave the house without forgetting a thing.
> *Maria Patrick Rokicsak, MOTC of Rockland County, N.Y.*

Choosing a preschool or nursery school for multiple toddlers may be very difficult. Many will not accept children if they are not toilet trained. Some have limited space, especially if a parent wants the children placed in the same class. Expect tears and leg grabbing for the first few weeks. However, multiples do have a built-in advantage when it comes to separation from the parent — each other. This may help their transition to preschool.

Check out various schools before enrolling your children, and discuss your multiples with the staff. Some areas now have co-ops for families with multiples, where care is exchanged equally with another family. Local parents-of-multiples clubs often have established play groups or co-ops, and they certainly offer a large number of children like your own! Above all, seek out what is best for your family.

CONCLUSION

Having multiple toddlers and preschoolers is an exciting time full of surprises. Keeping an open mind and trying new ideas will help you through this time. Enjoy the many different activities and challenges which arise, because the toddler period will be over much too soon. Caryn Fresco of Tidewater Mothers of Multiples, Virginia Beach, Va., shares her philosophy on raising multiples: "Having multiples is certainly a blessing, but sometimes we have to be reminded of that. I have a few favorite sayings I'll share:

1. This, too, shall pass! (No matter how rough things get, I know it won't last forever!)
2. Don't sweat the small stuff! (Only pick the most important battles. If it won't matter one year from now, don't worry about it.)
3. If it doesn't kill you, it will make you stronger!
4. God won't give you more than you can handle, so SMILE!"

Happiness is an ever-ready playmate.

8

THE SCHOOL YEARS

It seemed like just yesterday that I was changing diapers, sterilizing bottles, and wondering if my sons would ever master the mystery of toilet training. Yet here I was buying school clothes, arranging for those required pre-kindergarten physicals, and generally keeping my fingers crossed that these two small miracles would somehow become scholars and blend in with an entirely new group of peers. In the previous five years I had learned a lot about the development and care of multiples. Would their teachers be as wise? Would our school system understand their unique needs as multiple birth children who shared a strong emotional bond and yet functioned as two very different individuals? I have to admit, I had a lot of questions in my mind as I walked them to the door of their classroom on that first day of school.

Martha Eicker, Chicago, Ill.

By the time children reach school age, parents generally heave a sigh of relief after passing many developmental milestones. Bottle or breast weaning and toilet training are only faint memories. Many of the physical problems which premature multiples face are now resolved. Parents can enjoy the luxury of family outings which require less strategic planning. The children are more settled and into a daily routine, are able to handle their own physical needs with less supervision, and are beginning to take on small chores assigned to them.

STARTING SCHOOL

Many parents have mixed feelings about the beginning of kindergarten for their children. It can often be bittersweet, the happiness that they are growing and maturing mixed with the feeling that mom or dad may no longer be the most influential person in their lives. Parents who had their children enrolled in preschool may already have dealt with these issues but can still feel that now this is the "big time."

> **W**henever we take a trip (long or short), I play educational games with my twins. When they were younger, we would sing the alphabet or look for a certain color car or truck. As they grew, we would begin looking for a certain letter of the alphabet and make that sound and say a word that starts with that sound. Now we play the alphabet game. We look for signs along the road, and starting with "A" we find every letter in order. The first one to "Z" wins! This is especially good on long trips.
> *Darlene Aucoin, Acadiana MOM, Port Barre, La.*

KINDERGARTEN READINESS

Determining when your children are ready for kindergarten should be based on more than their chronological age. Some of the expectations for incoming kindergartners include any or all of the following abilities: managing buttons and zippers on all items of clothing, tying shoelaces, proper bathroom hygiene, and memorization of home address and phone number. Additionally, the children should be able to recognize and print their first and last names correctly using lower case letters with a capital letter at the beginning, recognize basic colors, count to 10, and draw a reasonable figure of the human body, naming all the basic visible parts. Letter recognition is helpful but not essential, as this is generally included in the kindergarten program.

Children who are unable to carry out these tasks may be considered for later enrollment or may need special intervention programs prior to beginning kindergarten. Generally, many school districts give "readiness" testing which provides general indicators for success in kindergarten. Children who are not ready to take part in a structured classroom situation, or lack skills needed to begin reading, often need to postpone kindergarten enrollment for an additional year.

SCHOOL READINESS FACTOR

- Month of birth
- Home environment
- Sex of children
- Effects of premature birth
- Socialization experiences
- Physical & emotional maturity

...OR NOT

Many factors can contribute to a lack of readiness for kindergarten. These may include premature birth, sex of the child(ren), and lack of stimulation from outside the multiple group (i.e., from parents, older siblings, neighbors, etc.). Physical, emotional, and academic maturity may vary greatly among children at this age, and the presence or absence of any of these factors should be considered seriously before a decision is made to enroll children in kindergarten.

Five-year-olds with late spring or summer birthdays may do poorly when competing with their older counterparts, even though the age span may vary by as little as six months. Boys tend to mature more slowly than girls. The issue of school maturity takes on special considerations for parents of multiple birth children. Ideally, all of your multiples will be at the same level of maturation. Then the decision is simply when to enroll them.

However, when there are large differences in maturity within a set of multiples, parents need to give kindergarten enrollment considerable thought. Discussions with the children's pediatrician and other appropriate health care professionals will help you to arrive at the best decision.

> When bathing my sons I let them play with stacking cups. They learned about filling the larger cup and using two or three smaller cups to fill the larger one. This is a math concept that many children have a difficult time with in school. Let your children learn while they have fun. Playing with coins as soon as they are old enough to keep them out of their mouths can help them learn to sort by size and color and count by one, five, 10, 25, etc., before you know it!
> *Donna Miller, Greenville MOMs, S.C.*

Additional testing can be performed at the local school district, and this may help define each of your children's readiness levels and provide objective facts upon which an informed decision can be made.

School officials should be made aware of any unusual circumstances, such as prematurity and any health complications associated with it, medications which your children are currently taking, and recent emotional disturbances in the home which could cause changes in the children's behavior. Some complications of premature birth may linger, such as delayed language development and problems with motor control. These may be viewed as factors which would delay school enrollment. However, there can also be strong arguments that these factors may improve with the stimulation of the classroom and the special services (i.e., speech therapy, gym and music classes, guidance counseling) which the school can provide.

WHEN SOME ARE READY AND SOME ARE NOT

Parents of multiples often face the difficult decision of starting one multiple in kindergarten while the other(s) remain in a preschool program for an additional year. Many important considerations need to be looked at in these circumstances.

1. **The Multiples' Relationship** - How close is the multiple bond between the children? How will they be affected by a separation? How will a continued difference in grade levels affect their perception of each other over the course of their school years? Will separation at the kindergarten level allow the immature child a chance to advance more rapidly?

2. **The Sex and Type of Multiples** - Are the children same-sex or different sex? (Remember: Girls normally mature earlier than boys). Are the multiples identical or fraternal? Identicals tend to have a stronger bond and are more dependent upon each other at an early age, so the grade separation throughout the elementary and high school years may have more serious consequences for their relationship.

3. **Health Factors** - Is there a specific medical condition which puts one of the multiples at greater risk for school failure? Are there medical, rehabilitative, or psychological treatments available to improve the condition and allow the child to succeed in school along with peers of the same age?

4. **Enrollment Options** - The decision is basically whether to enroll the multiples at the same time or at separate dates. That is, should the children be enrolled together in kindergarten at age five, even though one is clearly too immature to succeed? Or should both be held back for another year, even though one child is clearly ready to perform successfully at this grade level? Or should one be enrolled at age five while the other multiple(s) wait another year before beginning kindergarten?

Given the complicated issues facing parents of multiple birth children, the decision regarding when to enroll your multiples in kindergarten can be quite daunting and upsetting. No one decision is right for everyone. Each situation must be examined carefully with each of the factors listed above taken into account. Getting professional advice from medical and school personnel will be of great assistance. Ultimately, however, the parents should have the final word. Parents who are sensitive to their children's personalities, strengths, and special needs should feel comfortable when tailoring the school system to fit their personal situation.

PLACEMENT OF MULTIPLES IN SCHOOL

When parents of multiples are ready to enroll their children in school, a decision must be made regarding their placement in the same or separate classrooms. Regardless of the decision made, the most important fact to remember is that placement is always the parents' decision.

SEPARATING MULTIPLES IN SCHOOL

There may be reasons to separate your multiples, depending on individual circumstances. Factors that affect your multiples' growth and development will help you make the best decision for your children's success and happiness in school. According to *Placement of Multiple Birth Children in School*, a publication from NOMOTC, there are several considerations which might suggest a need for separate classrooms:

- Constant "togetherness" is hindering the development of social skills in one or all of the multiples.

When making the decision whether to separate or keep multiples together at a new grade level, ask the previous teacher's opinion. Ask specifically whether one child dominated another, if one was more aggressive or compliant, and whether one child would not be capable of functioning without the other. As a teacher and parent, I believe it is important not to make one decision for an entire group of people. The decision should be based individually on each multiple's circumstances and not on what happened previously to another set.
Karen Viggiano, South Hills of Pittsburgh MOM, Pittsburgh, Pa.

- Insensitive comparisons have led to feelings of inadequacy in one multiple.
- A child's problems are attributed to the fact that he/she is a twin/triplet.
- The multiples form a "power unit" causing disruptive behavior.
- The multiples exploit their relationship to cheat or play tricks.

> I'm a single mom with seven-year-old twin boys, and the best advice I can give is to never put them in the same class because they will shy away from everyone else. Don't try to make them unique, because the more you do the more they become dependent on each other. They will figure out on their own that they are two different people.
> *Tasha Gonzalez, Ossining, N.Y.*

- One multiple appears to resent the lack of privacy resulting from sharing a classroom.
- One multiple is a constant distraction to the others.
- The female multiple is overprotective or "mothering" the male co-multiple(s).
- The multiples WANT to separate.

KEEPING MULTIPLES TOGETHER IN SCHOOL

There can be equally valid reasons for you to insist that your children remain in the same classroom in the early grades. According to *Placement of Multiple Birth Children in School*, some of these are:

- Major emotional upheavals have occurred in the family (death, divorce, a move, etc.).
- Only one classroom is available.
- There is a danger of unequal education because two different teachers employ different methods of teaching.
- The multiples are at or near the same skill level in a skill-based classroom.
- The multiples WANT to be together.

> My 12-year-old male twins are in sixth grade and have shared classes in kindergarten, fourth grade, fifth, and part of sixth. I have found that sharing classes has given them reinforcement in learning the material and has allowed us to conduct homework review as a "study session" for both boys. The boys have actually become more independent while sharing classes as they seek to create their own personas for both the teacher and classmates. Consider the option of placing your children in the same class.
> *L.K. Buckner Inniss, Alpharetta, Ga.*

Above all, you need to observe and listen to your children. In the early grades, forced separation is unwise if the children express a strong need to remain together. At the kindergarten level, young children may feel more secure about separation from the parent if they are allowed to remain with their sibling(s) in the classroom. Most multiples will indicate a willingness to separate in school when they are emotionally ready.

CONVINCING THE PRINCIPAL

At the time of enrollment you should discuss your multiples' placement, and the reasons for your preference, with appropriate school personnel (principal and guidance counselor). Surprisingly, many so-called policies for separation of twins and multiples prove to be unsubstantiated and certainly not supported by any research. Providing the principal with NOMOTC's booklet, *Placement of Multiple Birth Children in School: A Guide for Educators*, and NOMOTC's position paper, *Guidelines For The Education of Multiple Birth Children*, will help you if you encounter resistance from the principal or school board for your point of view. They can give you the background and ammunition to support your preference. Many parents have been successful in changing school policies when using these support materials and arguing their cases in an intelligent and reasonable manner.

EDUCATING THE TEACHERS

The materials mentioned above can also enable the school staff to meet the needs of multiple birth children in their classrooms. Teachers have little to no formal training about the unique traits of multiples. Teachers should avoid making comparisons between the children or treating them as a "unit" with little attention given to their individual attributes. Parents can assist their children's educator by informing him or her of the differences between identical siblings so that each child is more easily recognizable. Dressing multiples in different clothing and alerting the teacher to differences in the multiples' personalities, learning styles, and personal preferences will enable him or her to respond to each child as an individual.

SCHOOL PROBLEMS

It is common for kindergarten and primary school children to be anxious about leaving their homes and parents during the first weeks of the school year. Many times the children will be initially excited, but then a day or week later show anxious behavior. They may fuss and dawdle while dressing and eating breakfast. Tears and complaints of stomach aches are not uncommon. You should be aware that your children may experience a sense of loss due to their increased separation from you and, in the case of multiple birth children, from the other sibling(s). Reassuring conversations which let the children express their concerns and also establish a plan for when and how they will return home are essential in the early days of the school year.

Sometimes children will exhibit extreme reactions when you take them into the school building. They may cling to you, cry, scream, throw tantrums, or cling to the door handle in an effort to prevent you from taking them into the classroom. Although it is very distressing, most often this behavior ends as soon as you leave the building. It is best to leave promptly with a firm promise to return when the school day ends.

Some children complain of morning stomach aches or other physical ailments. If there are no symptoms of fever, diarrhea, or vomiting, it is probably safe to take your child to school. When these complaints are repeated daily over a long period of time without fever or other signs of illness and the pediatrician has given your child a clean bill of health, you should consult the teacher and/or school guidance counselor for assistance. It's always best to deal with school phobias quickly and firmly in the early years of school before they become an ingrained habit leading to chronic absenteeism.

You can prepare your young children to enjoy the school experience by recounting your own school days in a positive, happy manner. Multiple birth children can assist each other in overcoming fears by spending homework time together and sharing in telling the news of their day at the dinner table.

TIPS TO EASE SCHOOL FEARS

- Always speak reassuringly and positively
- Establish a plan for traveling to and from school
- Share your own positive school memories
- Leave the school grounds promptly after the child enters the building
- Refuse to give in to tears and complaints of illness
- Share school news at the dinner table

HANDLING HOMEWORK

For many children homework becomes an obstacle to success in school. If good habits are established in the early school years, children will develop the skills and attitudes needed to handle homework successfully. It's important to establish a daily routine as soon as the children's school system begins to require homework. Decide on a time and place for doing homework, then be faithful to this routine.

> **M**y girls would come home, and by the evening everything would be all over the house: shoes, books, pencils, etc. They had until their bedtime to claim their stuff. Unclaimed items disappeared, and they had to buy back the items: shoes = 25¢, etc. As they got older, money was very precious to them and some of their items, too.
> *Tina Russell, Twin City MOMs, Winston-Salem, N.C.*

Multiple birth children have the added advantage of a built-in "study buddy." If the children are at the same skill level they can take turns reading assigned material, discussing possible responses for written work, and quizzing each other as they prepare for tests. In the early years parents need to be involved in the homework process, making sure that all of the children are participating equally. With multiples there is the danger that one child will exert too much control, ridiculing an incorrect answer or not allowing the other sibling to have a turn answering questions at all. At no time should a child be allowed to complete written homework for his sibling.

DEALING WITH VARIED TEACHING STYLES

During homework sessions you and your multiples may become aware of differing teaching styles if the children are in separate classrooms. It's important to recognize each teacher's style as valid, and to avoid unflattering comparisons of your children's teachers. If your children seem to be progressing satisfactorily in each classroom and are happy with their school experiences, this can provide you with an opportunity to teach your multiples about the value of individual differences. At the same time, many parents of multiple birth children may experience problems when there is a vast difference in teaching styles between teachers in their children's separate classrooms. If one child is falling behind or seems unhappy with the classroom setting, you should schedule a conference to discuss these problems with the teacher. Never allow the situation to go on without some effort to resolve it.

DIFFERING ABILITIES

In the early grades you may notice that one child is more advanced academically than his or her co-multiple. Differences in abilities can be expected in boy/girl sets, since girls mature intellectually at an earlier age than boys. However, even identicals may have different academic abilities. Many difficulties can arise when children have very different abilities. One child may be placed in an advanced class while one may require remedial instruction in reading or math. Report card grades may vary significantly. There may be social or behavioral problems with one child in the set.

It is generally best to be honest when discussing any learning difficulties which arise within the set of multiples. The children will be aware of their different levels of achievement, and they need to develop healthy, compassionate attitudes towards each other despite those differences. If a medical condition is the cause of learning problems, this should be fully explained to all of the children. If special testing identifies a particular learning problem, it should be addressed openly in the family so that the children do not attach any feeling of shame or embarrassment to it.

LEARNING DISABILITIES

There are a variety of different learning disabilities, which can be diagnosed through special testing. Two of the most common problems affecting elementary-age children are attention deficit disorder (ADD) and dyslexia.

ADD

Children diagnosed with ADD (or ADHD) commonly show signs of short attention span and impulsive behavior. They may also exhibit hyperactivity, which includes behaviors such as jumping up and down out of seats, making jerking motions, waving arms or legs, and so on. All children exhibit this behavior on occasion, so parents and teachers must ask themselves if the behavior they are concerned about is persistent and if the child exhibits such behavior in most settings. If either parents or teachers express a concern that this condition exists, parents should first consult their pediatrician or another health care provider. A doctor will know the medical signs of ADD and can rec-

SYMPTOMS OF ADD
- Short attention span
- Impulsive behavior
- Hyperactivity

ommend sources of information or a psychologist for further testing. According to federal law the school is responsible for providing an educational diagnosis. Two primary federal laws apply to the education of children with ADD: the Individuals with Disabilities Education Act (IDEA) and Section 504 of the Rehabilitation Act of 1973.

DYSLEXIA

Dyslexia is a medical term connoting an inability to read. Some children with this disorder reverse letters (b for d, p for q), numbers (6 for 9), or the order of letters in words (tar for rat). (Reversals are common and accepted as developmentally appropriate throughout the early primary grades.) However, reversals are only one possible indicator of dyslexia. Research points to several factors which may hamper development in reading, including awareness of how sounds connect to letters, prior knowledge and experience, and visual/spatial skills.

In the case of both ADD and dyslexia the affected child can be successful if the condition is identified early and if he or she has a supportive family, a strong self-image, and a proper remedial program.

RENTENTION

If learning problems are so great that one of the children is failing, the school may consider retaining that child in the same grade for an additional year. Parents and educators should move with extreme caution when considering retention of one or more children in a set of multiples. Psychological and social considerations involving the nature of the multiple bond must receive equal weight with academic considerations. The effects of school retention are much greater on a multiple birth child since it may alter the sibling relationship in a profound manner. These effects can range from mild loss of self-esteem and confusion over the status of the siblings in the multiple-birth grouping to a deeper sense of loss of identity with the co-multiple(s) and feelings of anger and rejection.

On the other hand, there is a definite need to separate the multiple birth issue from the issue of what is best for the individual child. As a result, the question of retaining a multiple birth child is highly complicated and needs to be approached with full consideration of all the possible benefits and injury resulting from the decision.

Psychological counseling is highly advisable during the decision-making process. If retention is unavoidable, counseling services should be made available to all of the affected multiples. Parents may request a copy of NOMOTC's position paper *Guidelines for the Education of Multiple Birth Children* to assist school districts in making appropriate decisions affecting multiple birth children.

The school years are most often a time of exciting growth and development, but parents of multiple birth children need to be aware of the special issues and challenges they may face. An open and honest attitude toward the value of each individual family member will promote a healthy atmosphere in which the children can explore their own strengths and talents.

HOME SCHOOLING

Another option to consider for your multiples is home schooling. This is becoming more common. It can allow for an adjustable and flexible schedule that suits a busy family. The multiples can remain close, and school placement is not an issue. Special-needs and gifted children can both do well in home school. There is the freedom to speed up or slow down the material for the different needs of each multiple.

Academic scores are higher nationwide by 30 to 37 percentile points for home-school students across all subjects on standardized achievement tests, according to *Home Education Across the U.S.* by Brian Ray, 1997. Even at different grades or health concerns, twins can still socialize together through home schooling. Universities not only accept but seek out home-school students and offer them scholarships (Harvard and Texas Tech, for example).

> The delight in discovery and sense of accomplishment are similar: first steps walking, first words, learning to read and write, calculating arithmetic, successful science experiments, and goals set and achieved. You don't want to miss those special moments in your twins' lives.
> *Margie Downey, North Dallas MOTC, Dallas, Tex.*

Resources are available on the market for curricula from pre-K through high school. The cost is usually 10 percent of a private-school education. Money saved through home education rather than spent on private schools can be saved and used toward skyrocketing college expenses. Parents choose the books with as little or as much structure as fits their teaching styles and their multiples' learning styles. Standardized tests are also available. Many home schoolers pool their resources for science labs, physical education, and sports teams. Most local school boards recognize home schooling. You can obtain more information and a list of state and local organizations and laws in your state from the Home School Legal Defense Association (HSLDA) and by attending regional conventions. (See Resources, Appendix A.)

CHILD DEVELOPMENT IN THE MIDDLE YEARS

The elementary school years are times of exciting change and growth. As children move out of the home into the larger school community they begin to change and develop in a variety of ways. At this time the special bond between multiples will become both a comfort and source of security as well as a challenge and, at times, an obstacle to overcome.

During the years from six to 12, all children develop at very different rates physically, emotionally, and intellectually. Fraternal sets can manifest these variations in development which would normally occur in the general elementary school population. One child, for example, may reach 90 percent of adult height by sixth grade while another child of the same age may be significantly smaller. Typically, this smaller child will show an enormous spurt of growth in the first two years of high school. The rate of growth and physical development in identical sets is usually more uniform.

> **No** matter how harried or how stressed you are, never be too busy to offer a hug to your multiples. It gives your kids a boost, and I've found it also helps Mom's morale.
> *Mary Adcock, Hutchinson Area MOMs, Hutchinson, Kan.*

Children of this age also begin to mature emotionally. They will be gaining social skills during this time. However, it should be noted that these rates of emotional and social maturation may also be very different. One child in the set may be popular and have a lot of respect from his/her peers, while the other seems to lag behind, self-conscious and timid in the presence of new classmates.

Body image is of extreme importance to children at this age. Children who consider themselves clumsy, uncoordinated, too small (or too large), for example, may find it difficult to interact with classmates. At the other extreme, children with poor self-images may overreact, becoming the class clown or playground bully in an attempt to secure a place in the classroom "society."

Parenting at this age requires good observation and sensitive approaches which help the child to communicate feelings without embarrassment. You may find that the best approach is to share your own childhood memories as a way of reassuring your son or daughter that the experiences associated with growing up are indeed universal. It's also important that you reassure children lagging in development that they have many positive qualities. So-called "late bloomers" need constant assurance that they are loved and valued for who they are, as well as for who they will most certainly become. Frequent family meetings which allow an exchange of ideas, and family meals during which the children are encouraged to share the news of their day, are highly beneficial ways of staying in touch with children during these crucial years.

EXTRACURRICULAR ACTIVITIES

Many parents of elementary-school-age children find they spend more time in the family car than anywhere else. Today children have more after-school activities than ever before. Sports programs, sponsored by school districts and city recreation departments, provide year-round schedules. Piano lessons, band practice, scouting programs, and a multitude of other activities vie for family time and finances. Unless you approach the school years with clear goals for your family and children, it will be easy to get overly caught up in the myriad activities which are promoted in the school and community.

You should consider what is most beneficial for both the children and the family when enrolling in extracurricular activities. Sports such as tennis, biking, or swimming, which can include the entire family and benefit the health of the children well into their adult lives, may be better alternatives than highly competitive team sports. Enrolling children in activities which further develop their own natural talents (music or art lessons, drama class, scouting programs which promote leadership skills) can also have lifelong advantages.

Out-of-school activities have the added advantage of allowing parents to promote the *unique, individual talents* of each multiple. Certainly there is no reason to enroll all of the triplets in piano lessons if only one expresses a desire to learn to play! If one of the twins is too small and uncoordinated to play Little League baseball with his brother, how much wiser it would be to enroll him in an appropriate activity where some measure of success and self-esteem is guaranteed. Parents who praise all of their children for their own talents and allow them the opportunity to develop these talents also reinforce the positive aspects of the multiples' relationship. These children are more likely to grow up respecting each other and valuing each other's unique gifts.

COMPETITIVENESS

A high degree of competitiveness is a natural trademark of children during the middle years. To some degree, sports and school programs encourage this, but those who have watched even young children at casual play know that winning is something to be highly prized. Multiples at this age are in competition with each other! Who is the tallest? The strongest? The fastest? The smartest? The most popular? Who gets his dinner served first? And on and on. Children need guidance at this time as they struggle with the values which will determine the quality of their adult relationships. Some families encourage healthy competitiveness: Who is the kindest? The most helpful? The friendliest?

Throughout these middle years parents provide the guidance which assists the multiples as they move through new experiences in school, develop social relationships with children outside the multiple set, and interact with other adult authority figures. The goal is twofold: to assist the children as they develop their own unique personalities and talents and to preserve the special, priceless multiple bond which is uniquely theirs.

EXERCISE AND HEALTH

During school years children acquire the health habits which will influence their well-being for the rest of their lives. Establishing good habits of nutrition and exercise are vitally important. Fortunately, school curriculums now provide parents

I always tried to give them their own special time with me alone. I would take my son food shopping while my daughter was with my husband. Then I'd take my daughter to the manicurist one day for a special "girls day."
Robin Rabinowitz, Nassau County MOTC, Merrick, N.Y.

with ample support in both of these areas. Science and health classes routinely include units on nutrition and drug awareness, and physical education classes have become more focused on teaching activities that benefit individuals for a lifetime.

NUTRITION

Good nutritional habits begin at the infant stage, but it is never too late to introduce healthy eating preferences into a child's life. Children at this age learn best when they are helping. Schools and museums have learned that "hands-on" spells success, and this can become a good learning method in the home as well. Involving the children in the cooking process from start to finish is the best way to educate them to make wise food choices. Families can begin by shopping together, examining the nutrition labels, and doing price comparisons (another great learning activity). There are many cookbooks available for children at this age, and they make excellent gifts! Adult supervision is essential, and kitchen safety and hygiene should be continuing lessons.

Many children at this age continue to be "picky eaters" despite all of their parents' efforts. The temptation may be to give children snacks so they won't "starve," but this usually results in an overweight child who continues poor eating habits into adulthood. Very small portions with the restriction that dessert comes after these are finished may encourage the poor eater to at least sample different foods.

At the other end of the spectrum is the "good eater," the child who finishes everything on his or her plate and often asks for seconds. Unless this child is engaged in sports or other physical activity, there is the potential for encouraging overeating and obesity. Salads and vegetables make for healthy refills. However, parents may want to ask the child if he/she is really hungry before refilling the plate.

In all cases, it's best to avoid confrontations at the dinner table. Family meals should be social events which stress time spent together in a relaxing and supportive mood. Children should learn that food is vital for their physical health while love and good company around the table are necessary for the health of the human spirit!

EATING DISORDERS

Today there are additional nutritional concerns for parents of pre-adolescent children. Most researchers agree that the number of individuals with anorexia nervosa is increasing, and recent estimates

SYMPTOMS OF ANOREXIA NERVOSA

- A refusal to eat
- Large weight loss
- A bizarre preoccupation with food
- Hyperactivity
- Exercising to extreme
- A distorted body image
- Cessation of menstruation

suggest that out of every 200 American girls between the ages of 12 and 18 one will develop anorexia to some degree. While most anorexic individuals are girls, about six percent are adolescent boys. Occasionally the disorder is found in children as young as eight years old. Parents should be concerned if they become aware of any of the symptoms of anorexia.

Individuals with anorexia nervosa frequently come from white, middle- to upper-middle-class families which place emphasis on high achievement, perfection, and physical appearance. An adolescent patient is typically described as a "model child" and a "good student." It is not uncommon for pre-adolescent girls in the middle grades to be preoccupied with body image. Preteen girls may feel self-conscious about their as-yet-undeveloped bodies. They may resort to secret dieting in an effort to attain the thinness of pop entertainment stars currently in vogue. Younger boys may diet to lose pre-adolescent "baby fat" in order to qualify for a sports team. In either case, parents need to be watchful and share concerns about their children's nutrition with their pediatrician or health care professional.

Parents should also be aware of their own attitudes about body image and dieting. Children who are constantly hearing parents talk about the newest fad diet, how unhappy they are with their own bodies, and watching every calorie will grow up with some of the same ideas about themselves. Parents need to avoid making comments about their children becoming too chubby or fat, even in jest. Using food as a reward or making a child feel that food is equated with love and comfort should also be avoided. Encourage exercise as a way to feel good and have fun, not solely as a means to lose weight.

EXERCISE

Proper nutrition should be combined with regular exercise to develop strong, healthy bodies in growing children. Limiting television viewing and computer game time will free up valuable after-school and weekend hours for more physical activity. Noncompetitive sports which encourage the active participation of all the children enrolled in the program are best for children in the early elementary school grades. Active participation allows for development of motor coordination and skills while providing a much needed opportunity to burn up excess energy in an appropriate manner.

When the emphasis is on playing for fun instead of points scored, every child is a winner. In the case of multiples, parents may also have to choose different sports which are appropriate for each of the children's skill levels and abilities. Other concerns arise when multiples play on opposing teams and game-time competitiveness spills over into family time. Some leagues may have self-imposed rules which do not allow siblings to play on the same team, and parents will have to negotiate what is best for their family. Whatever choices are made, the emphasis should be on fun and healthful exercise.

FRIENDS AND PARTIES

During the elementary school years children develop crucially important social skills which will help in later adult relationships. Multiple birth children are often greeted as "celebrities" in the primary grades. However, they soon come to realize that their ability to make and keep friendships depends on their own personalities, just as with singletons. Depending on classroom placement, they may have a set of mutual friends or they may each have separate friendships. Same-sex multiples often develop a core of mutual friends based on shared interests and activities; boy/girl sets more commonly have separate friends.

My twins are 12, and this year we planned the perfect birthday parties. We took my daughter to our time-share condo, which is about 40 miles from our home. I took frozen pizza, pop, munchies, and a birthday cookie. The girls spent their time sitting in the hot tub, doing their makeup, and watching movies. The next day we took our son and three of his friends to the local "gaming" parlor for laser tag, pizza, and a birthday cookie. I didn't have to clean my house before or after, and the cost was minimal with coupons. Everyone was happy, and both twins said it was the best birthday ever!
Kathleen Dautremont, Des Moines MOMs, Ia.

From time to time it may be noticed by parents that one multiple's friendships are creating friction between the children. One child may feel left out and may begin to experience some degree of loneliness when he or she is not included in the activities of the co-multiple.

Typical of this experience is the situation which arises when one child receives a birthday party invitation and the other does not. When this first occurs, usually in the lower primary grades, it's important for the parents to respect the needs of both multiples. Acknowledging the fact that the multiples' lives will move in separate directions as they mature is the first step in helping the multiples develop individual lifestyles. While the disappointment and sadness of the uninvited multiple should be acknowledged, it is unwise to insist that this child be included in the party, particularly if the birthday child is not a friend of both multiples. The child needs to be gently guided to the realization that not all life experiences will be shared. On the day of the party, the uninvited child might have a special friend come to play, or this may be a time for the child and parent to enjoy some time alone together. At the same time, parents should not be uncomfortable in acknowledging the co-multiple's excitement about the party invitation. This child needs assurance that it is all right to enjoy separate experiences, and he or she should not be made to feel guilty about discussing the pleasure experienced during the party. As the multiples mature, this type of situation will become less and less of a problem; in fact, by adolescence most multiples indicate a strong preference for individual friends and activities.

BIRTHDAY PARTIES

A 1989 NOMOTC research report on parties indicated a variety of different ways that parents of multiples plan their own children's birthday parties. Out of over 1,000 parents who responded, 69 percent indicated that they plan only one party for the multiples; 78 percent sent out one invitation from all of the children. If children are enrolled in separate classrooms, parents may wish to allow each child to invite a set number of friends. If the multiples are inviting children who are friends of only one multiple, parents should not expect the guests to bring two gifts.

Always make each of your twins his or her own birthday cake on his or her birthday. It will make each feel special to have his or her own and not have to share just one cake. Make sure that each child gets his or her own birthday card, and encourage family members to do the same.
Colleen Rohling, Cedar Rapids, Ia.

Approximately one-third of the parents served two or more birthday cakes, while another third prepared only one cake. Some parents solve the cake problem by serving cupcakes. In most cases, "Happy Birthday" was sung once, followed by candle lighting for each of the multiples. Some multiples, however, enjoy having the song sung twice, so each can have his/her own moment in the lime-light and have the song include only one name. Creativity and planning are the keys to successful party planning. Multiples will enjoy their special day if they understand that the love of friends and family is what makes this celebration so wonderful.

ADOLESCENT ISSUES

Adolescence is an exciting and challenging time of life for children and their parents. As the children enter middle school, parents begin to notice a number of behavioral changes which may be startling and worrisome. These changes are simply signs of the child's growing maturity and independence. Increasingly, children at this age will spend time alone in their rooms or on the telephone with friends and classmates. Parents may feel a growing separation from their children as conversations become more guarded and children exhibit a reluctance to share feelings and information about their friends and activities.

It's exactly at this time in children's lives when parents must keep the lines of communication as open as possible. Parents who are willing to become good listeners and actively involve themselves in the school and extracurricular activities of their children find that there is a greater degree of closeness during the adolescent years. At this time children begin to further develop their own personalities, examining lifestyles and opinions which may be different from those of their parents. Current studies show, however, that the great majority of adolescents and teenagers continue to accept parents as their first and most important role models. In surveys, adolescents repeatedly acknowledge their desire for limits and clear rules, most often equating rule-setting with parental love and concern.

Multiples often face a "stormy" period in the relationship at this time in their lives. Identical twins and same-sex fraternals, in particular, may indicate dissatisfaction with the fact that they are multiples and express frequent hostility toward each other. Children who were close and loving in earlier years suddenly become moody and openly aggressive toward each other. The level of fighting and arguing may increase dramatically at this age. Anything and everything will become a point of contention.

Adolescent behavior of this type needs to be understood in

terms of two primary influences which are interacting at this stage of life. First of all, hormonal changes are directing the physical development of the child's body, and they also affect emotions in dramatic and rapidly changing ways. The typical adolescent may have frequent mood swings, exhibit unwarranted moodiness or depression, overreact to normal situations, and cry frequently. Parents need to acknowledge the changes occurring in their adolescent children. Discussion of these physical changes will help to assure the children that what they are experiencing is normal and appropriate for their age level. It's also important to teach adolescents mechanisms for handling depression and anger in ways which promote good mental health. School guidance counselors, teachers, and the family's doctor can be of assistance.

Another influence determining adolescent behavior is the child's increasing need to achieve adult independence. While all children at this age struggle with separation from parents, multiples face an additional challenge: separating from their multiple(s) while at the same time trying to maintain the special bond which exists. It is precisely this struggle for independence which lies at the root of most problems between the adolescent multiples. Parents can assist their children and help them to maintain healthy relationships with each other if they follow some simple guidelines:

> When asked what was the best thing about being an identical twin, my daughter answered, "She is always there." When asked what was the worst thing about being a twin, she then answered, "She is ALWAYS there!"
> *Mary Griggs, Michiana POMC, Mishawaka, Ind.*

- As much as possible, allow the multiples to handle their own problems and work out solutions without parental interference. Provide limits for appropriate behavior and forbid physical fighting or any behaviors which cause bodily or emotional harm.
- Allow the children to express their individuality in dress, hairstyles, room decorations, and any other creative aspect of their lives. Respect reasonable choices and insist that they respect each other's choices.
- Avoid making comparisons.

With compassion, understanding and a lot of dialogue during

these confusing years, most multiples will eventually work out a mutual relationship which balances their close bond with a respect for each other as individuals. By the early adult years most multiples will have a closer relationship and may resume joint activities and friendships.

PUBERTY

As has been noted before, children develop at different rates, and parents may have some clue regarding the onset of puberty if they think back to their own adolescence. Experiencing puberty early (such as the third to fifth grades) usually runs in families. These children need strong support and guidance until their peers begin to catch up with them. They may be confused, upset, or ashamed of their developing bodies. They may be exposed to ridicule and name-calling at school.

My experience as a therapist working with adult twins and children who are twins has made me aware of how important it is for parents to spend time with each twin child separately from the other. It is important for children to be introduced to hobbies, interests, and experiences unique to who they are. It is fine for multiples to be interested in the same things and additionally to be introduced to different experiences. Quality time with a child is a lasting gift; quantity of time can be flexible.
Dyhanna Noble, Billerica, Mass.

Most children can be expected to enter puberty between the ages of 11 and 13, earlier for girls and later for boys. As voices deepen and bodies grow at swifter rates, hormonal changes will produce sudden mood swings and seemingly irrational responses to common situations. Both boys and girls are intensely aware of the changes occurring in their peers, and those who may lag behind need assurance that their own biological timetable is unique and unchangeable. Identicals can be expected to develop at close to the same rate; fraternals' development can vary greatly, whether they are the same or different sex.

Ideally, parents have already begun to provide sex instruction to their children. Questions should be answered honestly and correctly. Parents should not be ashamed to admit they don't have answers to all of their children's questions. Excellent books available in the children's section of local public libraries can assist parents in this important task. In the case of multiple birth children, this education can begin as early as they start to notice each other's bodies (age two or three) and ask questions about their status as twins, triplets, etc.

By adolescence, parents should be open and honest in transmitting their values regarding sexuality. Children will be receiving information from their peers, the entertainment media, and classroom instructors. Parents need to reinforce these messages with their own value system. At this age, children should also receive sound information about sexually transmitted diseases, the AIDs virus, and the dangers of using alcohol and recreational drugs. School districts and local health care professionals can provide age-appropriate informational materials and programs to assist parents.

Later problems may be avoided if parents set clear guidelines with their adolescent children about issues such as dating, driving, and attending parties. The reasons for parental rules need to be clearly spelled out, and consequences of disobeying the rules should be clearly outlined. Consistency is the key to success with adolescents, so it's necessary that the rules and the consequences remain firm and unchanging for all of the children in the family.

Many times multiples will feel an intense loyalty to each other that can be dangerous if one member of the set is engaged in self-destructive behavior (drinking, underage sex, use of illegal drugs, etc.). The co-multiple may be aware of the behavior but reluctant to bring it to the parents' attention. This is less likely to happen if parents educate their children from a very early age to distinguish between annoying "tattling" and "responsible reporting." Parents need to know when their six-year-old is speaking to strangers on a regular basis just as much as they need to know when their sixteen-year-old is smoking marijuana. The children should be taught to understand that reporting the dangerous behaviors of their co-multiple(s) is a potentially lifesaving action.

CONCLUSION

Despite the many serious issues which arise during the school years, this can be an exciting, happy time for the family. Good relationships can be maintained with a sense of humor and mutual respect. Encouraging adolescents to become involved in school and community activities, and becoming involved as parents in those activities, will provide much-needed "common ground." Frank and honest discussion will provide guidelines and values on which the children can base their own decisions. Sensitivity to the special needs of school-age multiples will help them to develop their unique and wonderful personhood while maintaining that very special multiple bond.

Highlights from NOMOTC's 1999 Survey of Educators

One percent of educators surveyed were aware of a written district policy regarding placement of multiples. Eleven percent were aware of a "word-of-mouth" policy. Other figures included:

- Educators believing that multiples should be separated if two equal classrooms were available and the multiples were working at the same level - 43%
- Those feeling separation should not depend upon twin type - 82%

Almost all the educators surveyed felt that the parents and school should work together to make placement decisions, and they felt that each child should be considered individually. But there was significant divergence in other figures.

- Those educators feeling that a change in room assignment should be made if the separation had a direct effect on school performance - 82%
- Multiples not asking to sit together, nor allowed to do so - 45%
- Educators believing that if one multiple is failing, the other(s) should not be retained - 50%
- Educators recommending special tutoring and other measures for the failing child needing retention - 92%

Almost all educators surveyed felt that if only one multiple was ready to begin kindergarten, both children should wait another year. There were other interesting figures:

- Educators feeling that multiples did not have more learning disabilities or speech problems than singletons - 50%
- Educators feeling it would be acceptable to refer to the multiples as "the twins" or "the triplets" - 29%

Their observations on telling identical twins apart were intriguing:

- Adults at school having difficulty - 75%
- Other children having difficulty - 25%
- Educators feeling that dressing identical twins alike compounded the problem of identifying the children as individuals - 81%

9

ADULT MULTIPLES

With the blink of an eye, time merged: the growing years, school activities, anxieties of youth, the dating scene. During the young-adult years, we weathered the challenges of college choices, career decisions, serious loves, eventual marriages, and the beginnings of new families. Now these once helpless babies have blossomed into adulthood and taken their rightful place in the world. As parents we continue to nurture, to love, and to struggle with the reminders that they are now in command of their own lives and must make their own decisions. As we reflect back on the years, however, we consistently see that indescribable bond which is a permanent part of their birthright. This is so very apparent to those of us watching from the perimeter. That bond is unconsciously and automatically shared between our twins. And we smile and silently pray they will continue to be there for each other, as always.

Edna Coburn, Tucson, Ariz.

Being a multiple is a life-long "occupation." People continue to be interested in twins and multiples even after they are grown. The news media, books, television, and movies usually portray twins as oddities, even as adults. They are either accused of murders they didn't commit but their identical twin did, or are dressed alike and walk, talk, and act as a unit. News magazines delight in featuring twins who have unusual lives — conjoined twins, twins separated at birth and then reunited, twins who marry twins, and twins with diametrically opposed personalities: the good twin/bad twin set.

Twins and multiples grow up just like the rest of us, and most go on to lead normal, if not ordinary, lives. However, there is a bond with the co-multiple that is special and unique. It is a bond that is stronger than the parent-child bond and stronger than the normal sibling bond. Research has indicated that identical females tend to have the closest relationship, followed by female fraternals, male fraternals, and finally opposite sex fraternals. In fact, a 1998 research study by clinical psychologist David C. Hall showed that 90 percent of identical twins felt they were closer to their twin, while 61 percent of fraternal twins felt closer to each other, than to their mother. This can continue to affect the multiples' lives through old age, whether they acknowledge it or not. The challenge in becoming productive adults is successfully separating not only from the parents, but also from the co-multiple(s), at least to the degree that they are not too dependent on each other.

COLLEGE

Sometimes the first real separation that a multiple may experience is going away to college. Not only is there a decision to be made about whether or not to attend college, there is the decision about going to the same college or a different one. Sometimes one multiple wants to attend college and another doesn't.

Deciding on a college becomes a monumental task in some cases. One must wade through not only different types of colleges and the decision on what to major in but also, in addition, the decisions of the co-multiple(s) which will enter into the mix. The multiples will need to weigh their closeness with each other with outside interests for a future career. In many cases, the decision is to attend the same school. Conversely, one set of triplets went to three different colleges spread out over the whole United States. The mother lamented that her phone bills were astronomical!

A 1992 NOMOTC research survey titled *Multiples and the Pursuit of Higher Education* showed that 74 percent of the multiples interviewed had made a mutual decision to attend or not attend the same school. While 33 percent of the respondents chose to attend the same college all of the time, those who separated listed various reasons. Some saw the opportunity to separate from each other as a growing experience. Others cited divergent interests or the need to get away from the mutual competition.

The decisions do not stop there. Next may be the question of whether or not to room together (in the case of same-sex multiples). There often is a trend to be in different rooms the first year, but this can change later. The multiples may miss having each other to share ideas with as well as the familiarity of being with someone they are used to. In general, the decision may be easier for fraternal multiples than for identicals. Fifty percent of the respondents to the above-mentioned survey roomed together while attending the same college. Of those multiples who chose to attend separate colleges, 33 percent admitted they found it emotionally difficult to be separated from each other. Most mothers of the responding multiples, however, said that the separation during college helped their multiples to grow as individuals.

Parents will be experiencing some stress, as well, with the thought of financing a college education for two or more students at the same time. This can be a major factor in deciding where to attend college. Investigating your state university system should be a top priority. Many states offer grant programs to families with more than one child enrolled in that system. Middle-income families will often qualify for state grants when they have two or more children enrolled in college at the same time. State grants are not the same as student loans, and they do not require pay-backs after graduation. Many multiples also enroll in local junior college programs that enable them to fulfill many undergraduate requirements before moving on to higher-tuition universities. High school college-admission counselors may have additional information about universities which offer special discounts to multiple-birth children. And finally, state parents-of-multiples organizations frequently offer college scholarships to member families. At any rate, it is advisable for parents of multiples to plan well in advance for the college years, either by setting aside separate college funds in a high-interest certificate of deposit or by investing in special state-sponsored college fund programs. Be aware that your children's savings accounts will affect their qualifying for state and federal loans. In most cases, it is better to keep college savings in the parents' name.

Even when together in the same college, multiples may for the first time have a life in which no one close to them is aware that they are twins. The physical expanses of college and university campuses, the varying class schedules, and differing dormitories will contribute to this phenomenon. An identical twin will often experience meeting many people who call him or her by the co-twin's name. Most deal with this occurrence by just nodding and waving; it can take more time to disclose the existence of a twin than just to pretend to be he/she. Adult twins at this stage in their lives find that maintaining a sense of humor about the physical resemblance will help them and others to enjoy whatever confusion arises.

JOBS/CAREERS

It is not uncommon for identical twins to enter similar careers. Some may choose the identical career and work together, but this is not the norm. The frequency of fraternals entering the same fields is not much different from that of any other siblings raised together. Identical twins reunited after being separated since birth will often find themselves in the same line of work. Sometimes they will live no further than 20 miles from each other and have frequent encounters with people who mistake them for their unknown twins.

> My set of identical girls planned different careers when they entered college. One studied the aviation-transportation field while the other aspired to become a teacher. Currently, however, through many different circumstances, they are both in the air travel field, one employed by an airline and the other working in corporate travel.
> Linda Simpson, Valley MOTC, Kent, Wash.

Starting a career is usually the final step in a multiple's independence from the other(s). Unless the multiples work in the same job, they will develop their own friends, activities, and lifestyles. NOMOTC's higher education survey found that only 15 percent of the respondents secured jobs in the same or related fields of interest, and 65 percent of the mothers of these multiples noted far less competition between their children once they were out of school and working.

LOVE AND MARRIAGE

As multiples begin dating, a whole new world of possibilities, and sometimes problems, opens up. In same-sex twins there can be rivalries and jealousy. Even in boy/girl sets there may be a tendency to be protective of the co-twin. Sometimes potential dates are attracted by the twinship itself and the novelty of it. When one multiple is more popular and goes out more than the other(s), it can leave the one(s) left behind feeling resentful. Twinship can also be very intimidating to would-be suitors. Multiples sometimes unknowingly limit the possibility of marriage by doing everything together and living together. Some sets of identical twins never marry and continue to live together, dress alike, and work at the same places of business throughout their lives.

When one twin marries and the other doesn't, there are often feelings of jealousy. The single twin may feel abandoned, much like a divorcee. The married twin can also feel emptiness. The twins can be very supportive of each other, and usually they remain congenial even amid jealous feelings.

A husband or wife of a twin will need to realize going into the relationship that he/she may never be quite as important as the co-twin. Recognizing the twin bond, knowing one will forever share his/her twin spouse, can help the transition to go more smoothly. In a 1991 NOMOTC research study titled *Survey of Marital Jealousy Due to Twin-Sibling Relationship*, 85 percent of the multiples responding indicated the spouse was secure enough to feel unthreatened by the closeness of the relationship between the co-multiples. At the same time, however, 36 percent of the multiples admitted to confiding in their co-multiples before confiding in their spouses on certain issues.

Survey of Marital Jealousy Due to Twin-Sibling Relationship, NOMOTC, 1991

- 85 percent felt his/her co-multiple's spouse understood the special multiple bond
- 10 percent felt his/her co-multiple's marital status had an effect on his/her own marriage
- 67 percent felt closer to his/her co-multiple and the co-multiple's spouse as his/her own marriage progressed

Spouses of multiples are not always understanding. They may not get along with the co-multiples or their spouses. This situation can be very stressful for the multiples, dividing their loyalty between their co-multiples and the spouses. Sometimes the disgruntled spouses will successfully come between the multiples. This can lead to entirely different lifestyles or locations in opposite parts of the country. Many multiples continue to touch base on a regular basis despite negative feelings on the part of loved ones. Sometimes this takes the form of elaborate schedules, compromises, clandestine meetings. Sometimes it breaks up marriages.

In the above-mentioned study, only 10 percent of the respondents indicated that their spouses were jealous of the co-multiple(s), while another 10 percent felt the co-multiple(s) were jealous of the respondents' spouses. Seven out of ten respondents recognized this jealousy prior to marriage or within the first six months following the

wedding. While most felt that this jealousy caused little or no problem in the marriage, the majority attributed it to shared past experiences with the co-multiple(s) and to the fact that they confided in
each other.

Spouses of multiples can also become competitive with each
other, especially spouses of same-sex or identical twins. This can take
the form of "one-upmanship," competing lifestyles, being the first to
become parents, or flirtation with the other's spouse. However, most
multiples' unions are happy, healthy, and include respect for the co-
multiples' lifestyles and significant others.

BECOMING PARENTS

Married multiples can often become parents within a few
months of each other. Identical twins have been known to deliver
their babies within hours or days of each other. When one identical
twin is pregnant and the other is not, many times the twin who is not
expecting a baby feels abdominal pain or has a sense that something
is wrong when the co-twin goes into labor.

Sometimes a twin experiences a miscarriage while the other
carries her baby to full term. This can be stressful for both twins. One
may feel guilt for having a healthy baby, while the other mourns and
may feel envious.

GENETICS

The genetics of twins' children can be interesting when one
parent is part of an identical set. The progeny of the identicals will
share one-half of their genes in common, thus being closer genetically than typical cousins. When identical twins marry another set of
identical twins, all of the children of both couples will genetically be
like siblings. Some of the children of each couple may look remarkably similar. This is not the case with fraternal twins.

Fraternal twins have the same chance of having twins as their
non-multiple siblings do. If twins "run in the family" all the children
have an increased chance of having twins, although the boys will pass
the trait to their female offspring, not their wives (See Chapter 3). It
is not known if identical twins have an increased chance of having
twins themselves, as the cause of identical twinning is unknown. It is
generally thought that they do not.

Having your own set of twins, if you are a twin, will give you no special advantages in parenting, since being a twin does not necessarily mean you will know how to rear them. However, you might be more attuned to the twin bond and other psychological issues.

Sometimes grandparents may show favoritism to the twin grandchildren over a grandchild who is not a multiple. This can be a source of tension among the grandchildren, and grandparents should be wary of this.

TWIN BOND

As mentioned earlier, the twin bond is usually very strong and lifelong. One doesn't stop being a multiple when adulthood is reached. This can be special or an intrusion, depending on the relationship and personalities of the multiples.

One manifestation of the bond is a type of E.S.P. unique to multiples. Stories abound about twins who are separated but can feel discomfort or a sense of fear when their twins, unknown to them, have had accidents or are experiencing pain. Often they will phone their twins just as their co-twins have been about to do the same. Many show up at social functions in identical outfits they had purchased separately.

All in all, the special bond that multiples possess is a positive thing. Most multiples enjoy the experience and wouldn't change it for the world.

SEPARATION

As mentioned above, separation of twins can be psychologically damaging. The death of one of a multiple set can be devastating. Nancy L. Segal, Ph.D., is a professor of Developmental Psychology and director of the Twin Studies Center at California State University. She has written extensively about the prolonged mourning and lifelong sense of incompleteness that possesses surviving twins. She has testified in court cases regarding the special circumstances of twins losing co-twins and how this can be worse for them than losing parents (See Chapter 12, Special Topics).

Cases of twins separated at birth have been extensively studied. When reunited many years later, most of them admit to a feeling that "something was missing" in their lives. Many have remarkably

Twins graduate from school — but not from each other.

similar gestures, movements, and body carriage. A large number have gone into similar careers. It is felt that identical twins reared apart become more similar in actions and lifestyle than those reared together. This might be explained by the latter's striving for individuality and the need to carve out one's own niche in a family unit. There is usually not room in one family for two aggressive, assertive, and outgoing individuals, for example. Most of the time this divergence in personality is not a conscious decision but results from the normal growth and craving for separation from the co-twin.

Some individuals find out later that they were part of a twin pair in-utero in which the co-twin did not survive. Many admit to feeling that they were incomplete or that their lives were missing something. Some have dim memories of interactions with the co-twin. Elizabeth Noble, author of the book *Having Twins*, has studied this phenomenon and interviewed numerous twins about it.

It is not unusual for twins who have lost spouses in their golden years to move back in together and recapture their twin-ness. They may fall back into the habit of dressing alike and doing everything together. They seem to truly enjoy one another's company.

CONCLUSION

Issues about being a multiple don't end with adulthood. The twin bond is usually lifelong and can be very strong and very gratifying. Most twins and multiples feel fortunate to have soul mates to share their lives with.

10

STAY-AT-HOME PARENTING

It is much more than seeing each child's first step. It's being there to answer their questions and to impart your values while doing so. It is discovering each child's innate individuality by taking the time to observe how that child learns about the world. It is building the foundation of trust to support each child in the future. And there is the joy of sharing experiences, some that only mom will be able to remember in the future. Of course, it is even more exciting and challenging when the babies come two or more at a time. Then you get to watch your children build a unique relationship that only multiple-birth children get to share.

April Anderson, Fair Haven, N.J.

As previous chapters have shown, the birth of twins, triplets, or higher order multiples is accompanied by many challenges for the doubly- or triply-blessed parents. Not the least of these challenges will be the day-to-day task of meeting all of the children's physical, emotional, and intellectual needs during the all-important first five years of their lives. If both parents are working outside the home prior to the children's birth, it will be wise to plan for child care well in advance of labor and delivery.

MAKING THE CHILD CARE DECISION

There are several valid reasons why many parents of multiple birth children decide to leave their outside employment in order to devote themselves to full-time parenting. To begin with, the cost of day care for multiple infants may actually be as great as, or greater than, any earnings received from the second parent. Premature

> I think the hardest thing about working was splitting myself between the male-driven corporate world and switching back to baby time at home. I found myself telling my children they came first, but I felt that my behavior contradicted that. Now that I'm at home I really treasure every moment that I'm spending with them. Since it was my choice to stay home, I feel I have a lot more patience than I might have otherwise — because I asked for the job!
> *Marianna Chrisman-Keller, Mid-Peninsula, Calif., POMC*

infants will definitely require parental care over an extended period of time, and if prematurity or complications of delivery have resulted in any long-lasting medical conditions, the cost of expert child care will certainly be excessive. Beyond financial or medical concerns, many parents simply wish to avail themselves of this very special time in their lives. Having a "hands-on," active role in the daily care, nurturing, and upbringing of their children provides them with rewards and challenges which bring joy and fulfillment to their lives.

NOMOTC's 1997-98 *Survey of Stay At Home MOMs* confirms this position. Overwhelmingly, parents who responded to this survey (all of whom were mothers) felt that their priorities were in order, that children are more important than those things which working outside the home can bring, and that children need time, not "stuff." These parents also felt that their children were happier because they had a parent at home with them. About one-half (570) of the survey respondents also said they chose to stay home because it was too stressful trying to balance working a separate job and parenting at the same time. Fatigue and the prohibitive cost of day care were other major factors influencing their decision.

Be sure to spend some time discussing child care options with your partner. While a mother may wish to return to work after a reasonable period of maternity leave, be aware of the various circumstances (prematurity, medical problems) which can arise from the multiple pregnancy. Prepare a plan which will enable you to cope well with the birth of your multiples. Be creative and tailor your child care plan to the unique circumstances of your own family. Will the stay-at-home parent be mother or father? Are there opportunities for in-home employment, part-time or flex-time scheduling? Do you have a support network of relatives and friends who can relieve you for short periods of time? During your pregnancy, explore these questions thoroughly and develop a parenting plan with which you are both comfortable. See Chapter 11 for further discussion.

FINANCIAL CONSIDERATIONS

The NOMOTC *Survey of Stay-at-Home MOMs* also indicated that for many of the respondents (615) being a stay-at-home parent has had a negative financial impact on the family. A total of 319 members indicated that the reduced income had caused marital stress, and 94 said that it caused stress in dealing with their children. About ten percent of those completing the survey said that they lacked money for essentials, while 680 reported a lack of money for "extras." Although many said they missed the extra income, they also indicated a realization that the financial sacrifice is small compared to the rewards.

I am a stay-at-home mother of three including my 18-month identical twin girls. I can't imagine leaving them and going to work, although I realize some parents have no choice. I think that sacrificing the extra money I could be making is definitely worth being at home and raising my children. It's a true blessing to watch my children grow and learn new things each day.
Cheryll Mason, Murfreesboro, Tenn., POTC

Initially, it may seem very difficult for you to face a significant drop in income at the very time that your household is doubling (or more) in size. When either you or your partner makes the decision to stay home as your children's primary caregiver, you will need to review your financial plan and prepare a new budget. The good news, however, is that by leaving the work force you have just eliminated one of your biggest potential expenses — child care. And there is more good news! Other expenses such as vehicle maintenance, gasoline, clothing, dry cleaning, and eating out will also be significantly reduced. Your two (or more) new tax deductions will further reduce annual tax expenses. You may wish to consult a CPA or tax preparation agency to see how your changing circumstances have affected your tax liability and how you can optimize your tax situation.

During the first few months into your new routine as a full-time parent, you will be very busy with your infants. Still, this is a good time to take a look at cost-trimming measures in all areas of your life. Begin to plan menus, shop thriftily, and cook and freeze dinners made from scratch. Avoid purchasing convenience foods, and when possible purchase staples in bulk.

This is a good time to take some basic sewing classes. Sewing children's clothing can bring huge savings. Purchasing children's clothing at outlets, discount stores, garage or parents-of-multiples clubs sales is a wise policy during the preschool years. Your multiples will outgrow their clothes every few months, often before the clothing itself is worn out. Save your dollars to purchase shoes, again every six to eight months as your children's shoe size changes.

Infant multiples will introduce some new expenses into your budget. Breast-feeding will eliminate the high formula costs of feeding two or more infants. The cost of cloth and disposable diapers is fairly similar. If you are considering cloth diapers, figure at least one wash load per day for the first six months for twins and triplets. Calculate the cost of soap, water, and electricity. If you find that disposable diapers are more practical, purchase them from discount stores in bulk. Once your infants have graduated to baby foods, cook and puree your own fruits and vegetables. Freeze them in ice cube trays, then store the cubes in plastic freezer bags. This is much more economical than purchasing canned baby foods.

When Sue Grammer of MOMs of Houston, Tex., mother to boy/girl twins, left her fifteen-year career in biomedical research to spend more time with her then toddler-age twins, her household income dropped by 50 percent. There simply wasn't enough money to spend on "entertaining" the kids. Sue found that "county parks were free on weekdays, and pitching a tent in the front yard was almost as much fun as Discovery Zone." She enrolled her twins in free lessons at every gym in town and finally asked for a few weeks of gymnastics lessons as birthday gifts from grandparents. She checked out the bookstore and library

> As a stay-at-home MOM, my biggest challenge is to survive each day with the family "intact" and hopefully for each of us to have something "good" to remember. Many mornings are spent painting pictures at the kitchen table. My three little ones: big sister, three and a half, and twins, two and a half, gather at the table. I pass out paper, small plastic cups to hold water, brushes, and paints. They "create" multiple masterpieces and occasionally announce the need for fresh water or paper. While they paint, we sing and I load the dishwasher or throw in a load of laundry. When finished I have new "artworks" to hang up, and they are eager to bring their paints and brushes to the sink to wash up.
> *Debbie Ciardi, Rare Pair, Norman, Okla.*

storytimes and linked up with a group from the parents-of-multiples club who went to the beach every week.

Creative parents who use community resources to their fullest need not spend fortunes to bring culture, knowledge, and entertainment to their children. Take advantage of free concerts, free museum and zoo days, holiday parades, fireworks extravaganzas, visits to the firehouse...the list goes on and on.

GETTING ORGANIZED AND MANAGING YOUR TIME

If you have been used to a regular working day schedule, you may find that your first few months as a stay-at-home parent lack focus, planning, organization, and a sense of accomplishment. Time management practices will be as vital in your new role as they were to your workday routine. Your particular schedule and practice of time management will vary depending on the number and ages of your children, their (and your) outside activities, and any number of day-to-day occurrences which will affect your life and your household routine.

The benefit of my staying at home is that I'm able to raise my children. I can be there when they fall down, and when they're walking, and when they're in trouble. As they grow, I can volunteer in PTA. The negative part is that it's very stressful being at home all day long and not having an adult conversation outside the home.
Olivia Watson, Great Valley POM, Tracy, Calif.

Your children will thrive on a schedule, and multiples especially benefit (as do Mom and Dad) from set naptimes and bedtimes. Begin in the morning by establishing a regular time for getting up, showering, dressing, and preparing to begin your daily chores. You will be most comfortable if you allow yourself one hour for personal care before the children arise. Be sure to shower and dress each morning; looking good will help you to feel good about yourself, and this is vital when you are house-bound with small children. If your children are extremely early risers, establish a morning routine for them which allows you some personal time. If they are infants, this may mean providing a quick diaper change and bottle or breast-feeding, followed by quiet time in their crib or playpen. Toddlers will usually be content with a snack and a video or quiet activity which requires little supervision.

Here are a few examples of how you can simplify household chores and make your life run more efficiently:

- Learn how to do two or more tasks at once. The sooner you adapt to the concept of multi-tasking, the easier your household and child-rearing responsibilities will be. Some examples of multi-tasking with multiples include: nursing both babies at the same time; using one spoon and dish to feed both babies; bathing the children together or, better yet, getting in the tub with them and taking care of your own bath at the same time. If you prefer to shower, make the most of your time and scrub the shower while you are in it and then bathe yourself when you're done.

- If you don't have a cordless phone and can afford it, get one. You'll be amazed at what can be accomplished while talking on the telephone. For example, you can fold the laundry, unload/load the dishwasher, dust the furniture, empty the trash, or even feed two babies while you are on the phone.

- If your children are old enough, involve them around the house. Toddlers can lend a hand at picking up their toys, putting their dishes in the sink, putting their clothes in the hamper, or throwing away trash. Older children can take on more responsibilities such as making their beds, watering plants, or feeding pets. These small chores help you out while also teaching your children responsibility. Patti Beemer of Colorado Springs MOMs, Colo., mom to identical teenage boys, says that "the children need to have a stake in the household regardless of the parents' work status. It allows them to learn vital life skills such as cooking, laundry, cleaning, while giving them an appreciation for the parent's labors."

- Get your children organized. Toy clean up doesn't have to be a nightmare for you or your children. Do what day-care centers do; sort toys into large plastic totes or baskets. Take a photo of the sorted toys with the tote or basket and tape it on the front of the container. This will help your young children to remember what goes where. The same type of sorting method can be done with shoes, socks, hair ties/bows, and arts and crafts.

- You will find that you may spend as much time in your car as you do at home. Make the most of "wasted" time by planning ahead and having tasks available that can be done while you are out and about. If you plan ahead and bring needed supplies along, you can read mail or write out checks for bills while in the doctor's waiting room (a place you will visit often with multiples!). If you are the passenger in your car, use the driving time to balance your checkbook or answer letters. When running errands, plan your stops in advance so that you can arrange the quickest and most efficient manner of getting from point A to point B and home again.

- When you're at home, keep a things-to-do list nearby and tackle one or two items while your children are at school or in bed for a nap or for the night. Have "no-brainer" projects that can be done while watching television (like mending or pasting and labeling photos). Be aware of how much time you spend watching television and, if possible, try to occupy yourself with some useful chore or rewarding hobby while enjoying those evening sitcoms.

These are only a few ideas which can help you to better organize and manage your time. You'll come up with many more of your own ideas along the way. Remember also that you may have already learned some time management principles in the workplace which can be scaled down and applied to organization and management of your home and family. There is no doubt that keeping a busy home organized, on schedule, and running smoothly requires flexibility and organizational skills which many employers would envy.

BECOMING YOUR CHILDREN'S FIRST TEACHER

The most important role of the stay-at-home parent is that of initial educator. From the moment of birth your multiples are learning skills which are vital to success throughout their lifetimes. Overcome the temptation to allow them to entertain each other for the greater part of the day while you busy yourself with household chores. Without the influence of adult speech and behavior patterns, your multiples may not acquire age-appropriate language and social skills. Indeed, some twins who are left to entertain themselves for long periods of time without adult interaction have been known to develop a particular type of twin language called "idiolalia" (see Chapter 7). Multiples who rely solely on each other for social interaction may lack the ability to make friendships when they reach school age.

You do not need to engage in structured learning activities with preschool-age multiples. Plan at least some time out-of-doors each day. Fresh air and exercise will be beneficial for both the children and you. Engage your multiples in activities with other children their own age. They need to become able to relate to other people. This may be as simple as short encounters with other toddlers at the local playground, or you may choose to enroll your children in a play group or preschool program.

Especially if your multiples were born prematurely or have particular developmental delays or physical disabilities, you will want to spend time on specific exercises or physical tasks which promote small or gross motor coordination. Coloring, cutting with a safety scissors, washing dishes, stringing beads, and using a cookie cutter are excellent and entertaining methods of developing crucial physical skills in all children, even those within the normal range of development.

Read to your children daily, beginning in the first year of life. Research has proven that children who are read to frequently are better students and more capable learners. In the car, use driving time to teach colors, numbers, shapes, and letters; at the grocery store examine textures of fruits and vegetables, describe smells, or begin to familiarize your children with money. In other words, use the ordinary, everyday events of your children's lives as learning experiences which broaden their horizons and equip them physically and mentally for the elementary school years.

You will also find special "teachable moments." For Sheron Wallace, Colorado Springs MOMs, Colo., mother of five children including boy/girl twins, these are "times when the children are interested in a subject and ready to learn something. These moments aren't pre-set; they just happen." As a stay-at-home parent, you are there for those teachable moments instead of relying on a day care provider to offer the necessary guidance or information. This becomes crucial in the lives of your children when the subject matter is something that you would like to have exclusive guidance over (for example: moral, religious, or sexual issues, drug education, etc.).

Some stay-at-home parents decide to teach full time in the home (home schooling). There are advantages and disadvantages to this. There are commercial materials available to aid you in this. For a full discussion, see Chapter 8.

STAYING INVOLVED IN THE OUTSIDE WORLD

When you first bring your multiples home from the hospital, you will experience a brief period of frequent visits from family, friends, and neighbors who are thrilled and excited with the birth of your children. These visits will be a welcome diversion from constant infant care and a new routine which does not allow you to leave your home very often. After a month or two, you may notice that visits are fewer and farther between. You may get lonesome for adult companionship while your spouse is at work, or you may begin to experience typical symptoms of "cabin fever": irritability, boredom, and a general feeling of fatigue. If your multiples are already toddlers, you may feel like you're losing touch with the world outside your home or that you are no longer contributing to it.

One of the best ways to squelch those feelings of inadequacy is to put some of your talents to work outside the home. As a parent of multiples, a great place to start is with your local parents-of-multiples club. It is there that you may have already been receiving support and encouragement for the issues and challenges that you are facing as a parent of multiple birth children. As time goes by, you

**NOMOTC STAY AT HOME SURVEY
(1059 respondents)**

- 652 felt they had some free time
- 593 missed outside contact with adults
- 687 felt isolated some of the time
- 906 were able to go out on a regular basis
- 273 had help to go out
- 752 had extended family members nearby

can provide that same support to other parents by choosing some level of involvement in your local, state, or national organization. Keep in mind that as a parent of multiple birth children you have been afforded a unique opportunity to assist others in a similar position. Without the experience and support of "veteran" parents, many families of multiple birth children would be struggling with overwhelming issues. If you have not already joined a local parents-of-multiples club, it's not too late. Contact NOMOTC's Executive Office for the club nearest to you, and join a support network which reaches out to all 50 states of this country. If you already belong to a local club, consider serving on a committee, running for a board position, or even volunteering at the state or national level.

There are many other worthwhile organizations which can use your part-time volunteer efforts. Contact your local church or

> I served as president of my local club when my children were still of preschool age. I enjoyed speaking to new and expectant MOMs on the phone, and I could do this during the children's naptime or while I was ironing or doing some other "mindless" household task. It left me with a warm feeling of helping someone else out while at the same time easing my own longing for adult companionship during a long day of child care.
>
> *Martha Eicker, Twice as Nice MOMs, Chicago, Ill.*

school and volunteer your special talents. Singing in the church choir, decorating for special holidays, teaching an art class, or running an after-school program can be an invigorating experience in your weekly routine. You may wish to become involved with a crafters' organization or the Girl/Boy scouts, or volunteer for occasional special activities with local and community charities. Take a look at Resources, Appendix A, of this book for a list of other support groups, or contact your local Chamber of Commerce or public library and ask if it has a listing of non-profit groups and organizations in your area.

Unlike in the workplace, you alone can determine how much time and commitment you are willing and able to put into outside activities. You may wish to take on a responsibility which can be managed at home during your occasional free time, or you may schedule an evening or weekend volunteer commitment during the hours when your spouse is available to handle child care. The decision is yours, but whatever it is you will feel physically and emotionally better for committing some of your time to an outside interest.

Earlier in this chapter financial considerations were discussed. As your babies become more independent, or once you have established a firm routine which includes set nap and evening bedtimes, you will find that you have time to indulge in hobbies or interests which allow you to express your unique talents and abilities. If the family budget has become strained due to reduced income, you may want to consider turning your hobby into a profit-making enterprise. Whether you bake, sew children's clothes, dabble in desktop publishing, or have some other particular talent, this would be an excellent time to start your own home business. Many mothers of multiples have even used their unique parenting experience to produce and market products which assist other parents of multiples.

All parents would do well to remember that before they were someone's mom or dad they were individuals with unique talents and interests. Make it a point to schedule some time alone — perhaps time to take part in a hobby or social activity, perhaps simply to get needed rest and relaxation. The working spouse should be willing, and even eager, to relieve the stay-at-home parent in the evening or on the weekend, so that child care does not become a seven-day-a-week job. Time spent alone, away from the family, will help you to regroup and recharge, and make you a better parent in the long run.

> **R**emember to nourish your spiritual self. The day-to-day demands of twin parenting can leave you drained physically, emotionally, spiritually. Renewal of your inner strength pays dividends in your family life and in being able to deal with the constant giving which mothers of twins are asked to do. Stay in connection — or re-establish connections — with a faith community which nourishes your soul.
> *Lisa McKinney, Mesquite, Tex.*

Daytime child care can be a problem if you lack extended family members in your immediate area and are unable to afford nanny or professional sitting services. There are other options, and they should be explored fully so that you can take advantage of the services available in your community.

Local park district or city recreation classes and exercise programs are usually inexpensive, and many offer free child care in an adjoining room while you attend the class. This is a wonderful way to enjoy some personal freedom while also receiving the physical benefits of healthy exercise. Many churches and libraries also run moms-and-tots programs, many with babysitting services. Your local community newspaper is a rich source of information regarding ongoing community programs such as these.

A local parents-of-multiples club is, once again, an excellent source of support. Many clubs already have organized daytime social events or small "coffee groups" for mothers of young children. Many clubs have organized babysitting services on a cooperative basis. If yours doesn't, feel free to suggest it and offer to organize the participants.

Cheri Campbell of Northern Virginia POMs, Alexandria, Va., parent of three young children including 21-month-old twins, feels that the bond established with her children early in life is the best. However, while she loves staying home with her children she feels that they need to know other authority figures besides mom. "I don't want my children to think that I will always be around to spoil them," Cheri says. She strongly suggests that children grow up in a larger environment than just their home. This "other environment" may be as unstructured as a neighborhood play group or as disciplined as an established preschool program. Certainly a two- or three-day preschool program will allow you needed time off from child care responsibilities, while at the same time allowing your children a chance to mingle with peers and cope with other authority figures.

Whatever choice you make, being a stay-at-home parent doesn't mean that your children can't be provided with child care by someone else now and then. Getting away by yourself is vitally important. It will help you to keep your sanity and make you a better parent.

Community Sources of Child Care
- Parents-of-multiples clubs' babysitting co-ops
- Church-run moms & tots programs
- Park district or city recreation adult programs which include free babysitting
- Summer camps and Vacation Bible Schools
- Park district or city recreation preschool programs
- Neighborhood adolescents and teens

TIME WITH YOUR SPOUSE

Before babies made four, five, six, or more, there were just the two of you. Many couples find that the birth of their multiples puts a strain on their marriage. Thirty-nine percent of the respondents to a NOMOTC *Single Parent Survey on Divorce* (1992) felt that the added emotional stress of having multiples contributed to the breakup of their marriages. Another 22 percent reported that the added financial stress was the cause of their divorces. Seventy-five percent of these divorcees found their marriages beginning to deteriorate when the multiples were three years of age or younger. Obviously the strain of sleepless nights and crying infants, as well as mounting bills and laundry, can test the healthiest of relationships.

During the first difficult weeks and months, both parents need to be patient with their new situation and each other. Remember that infants grow and children do not remain babies for long. While scheduling time to be with your spouse may be extremely difficult at first, it should be a priority just like any other important activity. Sometimes this may mean an early breakfast before the children arise. It may be an hour or two on a weekend afternoon while the children sleep.

As soon as possible, we established a regular bedtime for our infants. By seven p.m. they were bathed and in their cribs. Whether they were tired or not, the three or four hours after that was "mom and dad's time." This lasted until they were about eight years old. Then we let them stay up until eight o'clock. Of course, once they were adolescents we had to flee the house in order to get quality time together!

Martha Eicker, Twice as Nice MOMs, Chicago, Ill.

Time together doesn't have to equate to big expense. With multiples, there's not much money left over for date nights, much less a babysitter. If you are fortunate to have family living close by, take advantage of their offers to stay with your children. When the multiples are babies, encourage these family members to come in pairs or even threes, so that babysitting does not become overwhelming and distasteful. Likewise, if you hire teenage babysitters you may wish to employ two sitters for the first six months. An economical move would be to swap babysitting services with friends or neighbors whom you trust.

When planning date nights, be creative and keep the plan simple. As parents of infants you may just enjoy a quiet stroll around the neighborhood. Time under the stars can certainly help to get things back in perspective when you return to your demanding babies. A round of miniature golf, a piece of pie and a cup of coffee at a local restaurant, or a quiet chat in a neighbor's backyard are great inexpensive ways to enjoy some time away from the children. If your budget allows for it, think back to all of the activities you and your spouse enjoyed together before the children arrived. Take in a movie, enjoy a romantic dinner, and if you are really blessed with reliable child care go on a couple's retreat or enjoy an overnight stay at a local hotel.

Andrea Singy of Colorado Springs MOMs, Colo., mother of fraternal twin girls, doesn't get out a lot with her husband, Jacques. When someone does offer to babysit, they jump at the chance to enjoy a date. They also always take Sundays for themselves. Andrea says, "Sunday naptimes are sacred, and my husband and I always spend them together." She also says, "We try to talk for a little while before going to sleep at night. It's not always feasible, but it's a little time for us. We hold hands in bed and discuss things (usually how cute our children are!). But it's nice to be able to boast and brag to the one person who finds you can't say enough and never rolls his eyes!"

The best thing that parents can do for their children is to have a loving and happy relationship between themselves. There are many things which you and your spouse can do to keep your marriage relationship strong and healthy. Just remember to revisit some of those things that you enjoyed B.C. (Before Children), and schedule time alone during your otherwise hectic days.

FINDING THE MEANING AND THE JOY

Just about the time that you begin to feel that you've gotten a grip on your new routine as a stay-at-home parent, you may begin to ponder the meaning and purpose of your new role. There will be days when you find little personal satisfaction in a routine which offers few tangible or verbal rewards, and certainly no public recognition, for a job well done.

> I have never heard anyone say she regrets staying home, but I have heard many say they regretted not trying.
> *1998 NOMOTC Survey Respondent*

These are the times when you need to sit back and look at those aspects of parenting which are most rewarding in themselves: a calm and sleepy baby nestled at your breast before naptime, toddlers snug in your lap for storytime, a sweet smile from your children after you have "doctored" a small wound, and that unexpected "Mommy, I love you!"

Andrea Singy summed it up well when she said, "The best and the worst parts of being a stay-at-home parent are exactly the same: being with your children all the time. What a joy it is to always be with them when they wake up from naps and are ready to rush out and get to their job — playing. And to always be there to pick them up when they cry and to laugh with them when they succeed is beyond wonderful. But how incredibly exhausting it is when one or both of your babies is sick and there isn't enough of you to go around. Or when you really need to get something done, but you have two leeches on your legs, begging to be picked up."

As you reflect upon your time as a stay-at-home parent (or as you contemplate leaving the workforce to become one), remember that some days may be harried, but at the end of each of them your heart will be full. Staying at home has its particular joys. You'll watch your children evolve and grow before your eyes each minute, hour, and day that you spend rearing them. This will be the most rewarding and fulfilling career that you will ever have!

With proper organization, good time and money management, opportunities to share your talents outside the home, moments alone, as well as quality time with your spouse, you'll see yourself grow as a person as well. You'll have no fancy nameplate on the door, no certificates on the wall, no paycheck in your pocket. But you'll know and feel your worth each time one of your children looks up at you with the gaze that only a small child can give and says, "I love you."

Highlights from NOMOTC's 1998 Stay-at-Home Parents Survey

- Most respondents (998) stayed at home because they wanted to be their chil dren's main caregiver.
- Other reasons for staying home included:
  - It was too stressful trying to balance working and parenting.
  - It was too fatiguing to work and parent.
  - The cost of day care was too high.
  - The other spouse had requested this arrangement.
- Most respondents (615) reported a negative financial impact on the family. However, many felt that the sacrifice was small compared to the rewards.
- Although most respondents were satisfied with their decision to remain at home, a small percentage had significant amounts of negative feelings which included depression, a high amount of stress, and a general feeling of unhappiness.
- Advice from respondents to this survey included:
  - Get some help, especially when the multiples are young.
  - Set aside time for yourself.
  - Join a parents-of-multiples club.

With multiples, you can have your own parade.

WORKING PARENTS

After 14 years of marriage and several years of juggling our careers with on-again/off-again fertility treatments, I was finally pregnant. Lying on my back waiting to see our baby's heartbeat for the first time, my mind wandered. It was easy to imagine adding a baby to our busy, two-career lifestyle; we had watched friends hardly miss a beat as their family grew from two to three. I mean, how hard can it be? My major concern was the new job I had started two months ago and how to break the news to my new boss. As the technician rubbed jelly on the ultrasound probe and the doctor got started, I imagined showing my first black-and-white baby picture to my friends at work. "OK, your tubes are clear, we just have the two in the uterus." "Two what?" I asked, thinking that it seemed a little early to see two legs or two arms. "Two heartbeats — two babies," he answered. Suddenly, being a working parent didn't sound so simple after all!

Susan Grammer, Houston, Tex.

CAN WE REALLY HAVE IT ALL?

Parenting multiples is a bit more complicated than "normal" for the first few years. If both parents are working or going to school, life can often seem like a roller coaster careening out of control. On the other hand, when things are going smoothly there is nothing more satisfying than enjoying hugs from happy multiples at the end of the work day, as parents of singletons look on in awe and admiration! Margaret Izard of Katy Area POMs, Houston, Tex., mother of one-year-old triplets as well as retail store manager, web site designer, and VP of her club, says that one of the best parts of being a working mom is "people's reactions to my working with triplets." According to Jennifer Thompson of High Bridge, N.J., mother of one-year-old boy/girl twins and a CPA working a 40-hour week, "There is a certain sense of accomplishment you feel about holding down a job AND raising twins. I work with a woman who has adult twins my age and did not work outside the home when her children were little. She is always saying that she doesn't know how I do it."

You may love your job or want or need the additional financial help. You may be a first-time parent expecting multiples, a career parent already, a student, or a seasoned "at home" parent of multiples wondering whether it is time to rejoin the workforce. Regardless of your situation, there are special issues confronting parents of multiples in the workforce.

FEELING GUILTY

Regardless of how committed you are to being successful working parents, there is bound to be some doubt. Moms of multiples may be especially prone to guilt about rejoining the workforce because they already feel stretched trying to give individual attention to two similarly needy children. Jennifer DeVore of the West Los Angeles MOTs, Calif., mom to ten-month-old identical twin boys, loves her job and feels she can really make an impact as director of marketing and planning at The Los Angeles Times. Even so, she feels that "if money were truly no object, I would be at home with my babies. I feel tremendous guilt about it sometimes."

Remember, you are working for a reason. Either you love your career, you need the income to provide for your children's future and current needs, or both. It is your family's decision and no one else's. As long as you take your responsibility as a parent seriously and provide the best care for your children that you can afford, you can feel you are doing "the right thing."

THE SUPPORT NETWORK

Most working parents who really seem to "have it together" have a strong network for back-up support, ideally consisting of extended family living nearby. It is amazing what sending the kids to the grandparents' house one Saturday a month can do for exhausted parents, a stressed marriage, and a filthy house.

Many working parents do not have extended family nearby, so

they must create their own support network. Friends, babysitters, and co-workers can be a big help to any working parent, but for parents of multiple babies or toddlers, building this network is especially important. This task is often difficult to accomplish, however, because many people who are potential sources of support are terrified at the prospect of being responsible for two or more babies or toddlers. For people who seem eager to help out but nervous about their ability to care for multiples, try hiring a "mother's helper" — a school-aged child too young to babysit independently — to lend a hand.

Emotional support from other mothers of young children and answers to everyday parenting questions can be hard for some working parents to find. Consider the resources available on the Internet. You can research your latest dilemma (nightmares, potty training, separating multiples in school) on parenting websites during your lunch hour.

Of course, nothing takes the place of one-on-one support from other parents of multiples through a parents-of-multiples club. Most meet only once a month and usually in the evening. It can be time well spent, and you can forge relationships with other parents that will last a lifetime.

Some parents of multiples find that their employers or co-workers are prominent sources of the support which allows them to be successful working parents.

My mother stayed at home with her children despite a promising pre-baby career and feels I am making a terrible, horrible mistake by not staying home with my kids. I'm sure this will cause guilt for me until the kids move out on their own.
  Melissa Mackey, CAMOTC, Lansing, Mich.

I credit my in-laws, my mom, and my older children with making it possible for me to work and get the twins to their activities. I know it would have been harder without my family.
  Larrie Plunkett, Wailuku, Hi.

The e-mail twins lists have been great. I don't have time to attend Mothers of Multiples meetings as they are all right at the babies' bedtime, and I like to be at home then. The e-mail lists allow me to get support at work and whenever I need it. Plus it opens you up to people all over the world, so you get lots of different opinions and viewpoints.
  Jennifer Thompson, High Bridge, N.J.

BENEFITS FOR TWO-CAREER FAMILIES

Besides the obvious financial benefits that go along with two-career families, many parents of multiples are enthusiastic about the impact their jobs have had on their emotional health, their marriage, and development of their children. Although they admit juggling two careers is complicated, many say they wouldn't trade it for the world. Among the benefits mentioned were confident, independent, adaptable children, patient parents, and a working partnership in marriage.

> I have the world's best boss. She is the parent of two wonderful almost-adults, and she knows how hard it is to balance work and home. Her priorities are similar to mine, and she has told me to go get the kids or take an afternoon off because they needed me. I don't know how I would do it without the enormous flexibility she gives me.
> *Amy Hsu, Rockville, Md.*

Some benefits to the kids include:

- They have a happy mother! I would be completely miserable if I stayed home full time. (Melissa Mackey, CAMOTC, Lansing, Mich.)
- Better early education with preschool and a mother who has the patience to spend time with them when we are all home. (Danine Rydland, M.D., Martinsburg, W.Va.)
- Confidence — in themselves as they socialize and learn at school and in their parents' love when they return after leaving. A good role model (hopefully) of a successful working mother. A good example of a working partnership in marriage as we both pitch in to take care of kids and house as well as work. (Lohri Phelan, Ph.D., Pomona Valley MOTC and Double Deal MOMs, Anaheim, Calif.)
- A patient mother — I appreciate so much the time I do get to spend with them that I think it helps me to be more patient. And, of course, financial — we will be able to afford college, a bigger house, and a better school district. (Jennifer Thompson, High Bridge, N.J.)

Some of the benefits mentioned for the working parent and for the marriage include:

- It makes me feel good about myself. And the only time I know I have time to myself is when I am working — maybe that's why I enjoy it so much!! (Bobbi Gomez, East Quogue, N.Y.)
- I truly enjoy the work I am doing; I enjoy being a part of an organization beyond my family. The extra money doesn't hurt, either. (Lisa Sageev, Cranford, N.J.)
- I feel more fulfilled and am using the degree that took so long to acquire. My husband and I have a good "working partnership" because it takes both of us to take care of the kids and the house. (Lohri Phelan, Ph.D., Anaheim, Calif.)
- I am fulfilled both personally and professionally. I love being a parent, and I love my career. I feel I have achieved the most important goals of my life: to have a happy, healthy family and a job I enjoy. In the first few months, because caring for twins was so demanding, I couldn't wait for the "break" I got at work. (Melissa Mackey, CAMOTC, Lansing, Mich.)
- My relationship with my husband is probably better because the balance has not shifted from what it was before we had children. (Jennifer DeVore, West Los Angeles MOTC, Calif.)

SHARING THE LOAD

Raising a family while juggling two additional careers demands teamwork from all involved, especially mom and dad. In the beginning the children's responsibilities to the "family team" are few. As kids get older they can pitch in more and more. Have you ever seen the pride on a toddler's face the first time he or she is asked to carry the silverware to the table? Or when he or she is allowed to help empty the dishwasher? In the beginning you may think these chores hinder the cause more than they help, but just think how many toys those twin, triplet, or quad three-year-olds could have scattered throughout the house during the ten minutes they spent with you in the kitchen!

My husband and I had less difficulty with the division of labor after the multiples arrived than we did with our singleton. With our singleton, there wasn't as much work to be done in the area of child care, and my husband would automatically defer to me unless I asked him to do something. With our multiples this hasn't been the case. This is partially attributable to time and learning each other's expectations, but it is also a result of the amount of work to be done with multiples.
Ann Slayter, Twins Family Club, Corvallis, Ore.

Older children can truly feel a part of the "family team" if they have daily responsibilities. Even a four-year-old (with lots of encouragement) can be expected to pick up toys, put dirty clothes in the hamper, make his or her bed, and even bring in the empty garbage cans (on rollers, of course). Put out as many cans as you have kids, and they can race back up the driveway with them! Three- and four-year-olds can also begin to set the table, clear their dishes from the table, help feed the dog, and even fold towels.

Families who work in the yard or tidy up the kitchen together have time to talk about the day's happenings. Washing the car with Dad can be great for "one-on-one" time. And, of course, the faster the chores get done, the more chance the family has to take off on a picnic, hit the tennis courts, or head to the zoo.

GETTING ORGANIZED

One way to help the family function as a team is to get organized! If you are on maternity leave, this is a good time to start. If you are already back at work and feeling out of control, take the time to get it together now, even if it means using a couple of vacation days. Getting organized will benefit the entire family as well as your boss and co-workers.

Many parents of infant multiples are overwhelmed with trying to remember who did what when, who had too few wet diapers, who was constipated yesterday, who slept the right amount last night, and who was up crying half the night. When you add the diapers, naps, and feedings while the parents are at work, it may seem impossible to keep track. You don't want to feed prune juice tomorrow morning to the baby who had loose stools today or bananas for dinner to the one who was constipated at day care. Keep a small notebook in your pocket and record any information which the day care provider gives you when you pick up your children at the end of the day. Try to transfer this information to your home chart as soon as possible.

> We washed windows the other day — I took out all the panes, they rubbed one for 15 minutes with sponges soaked in a touch of vinegar and dish soap while I did the rest. They got tired of it just in time for me to redo theirs and put it back in. Clean windows (in one room at least), happy kids, relaxed mom -- can't beat it!
> Lisa Sageev, Cranford, N.J.

This information may be vitally important when answering a doctor's questions should one of the babies become ill. Charts such as these should be kept through the babies' first year. There are several charts available to record all this information as the day progresses, including one from NOMOTC.

Rebecca Moskwinski of Michiana POMC, Granger, Ind., mother of six, is a physician, a member of the Board of Directors of NOMOTC, president of her local school board, and editor of this book. Her husband is a pharmacist.

To make life more bearable we hired a maid service that comes in once every two weeks. We view it as buying our Saturdays back. It helps us stay more organized because, while the service does the bathrooms and mops, vacuums, dusts, etc., there is very little it can do with clutter. So at least every two weeks, the old magazines and newspapers get thrown away and the boys' toys are all put away. Then for about a half-hour the place looks great. But the bathrooms are scrubbed, the floors are vacuumed and mopped, and the toilet paper roll ends are neatly folded into triangles. I keep waiting for a mint on my pillow, but no luck yet!
Diane Kellogg, Richmond, Va.

Rebecca described some of the methods her family uses to juggle their many commitments. "All the kids have chores that they are expected to do which alternate each week. It is an elaborate system that is charted on the refrigerator. They have daily and weekly jobs to do. It gets the house clean at least once a week! I try to have a place for everything so it at least has some chance of getting put away — lots of bins and storage containers. There is a calendar where all the activities are written down and a white board for messages. The kids have their own answering machine on a separate line (we have teenagers), and we don't feel obligated to answer it. We have a basket where all the forms and school papers are filed. I try to put away or throw away all the mail every day, or it gets out of hand. There is another basket for 'pending' papers. We have a wooden desk that all the bills go in immediately when we get them, and that is where we pay the bills, keep receipts, etc. I have hooks for the coats, a bin for boys' shoes, a bin for girls' shoes, one for the adult shoes, and a shelf in the coat room that holds a bin each for mittens, hats, scarves, and adult winter things. We have to be organized, or it would be chaos in a household this big."

ONE-ON-ONE TIME

One of the biggest concerns of many working parents of multiples is a lack of "one-on-one" time with each child. Many parents use the "divide and conquer" approach to mix their errands and chores with individual time with the kids. Another possibility is to stagger infant and toddler naps on the weekends. Many parents of multiples find that one child takes a longer nap on the weekend or gets up earlier in the morning, and taking advantage of these short periods for one-on-one cuddling, reading, talking, or games can go a long way towards strengthening an individual relationship with each child. "Every few weeks from the time our daughter was an infant," says one mom, "she just didn't seem ready to go to bed when her twin brother fell asleep at eight p.m. It often seemed to happen on a Friday night, so we called her our 'Friday night party girl.' We kept her up, and she played happily while we fixed and ate dinner, showing off, singing, and playing peek-a-boo with her blanket. Her brother was usually the first up in the morning and had his individual time with us then."

Sometimes working parents find it easier to schedule one-on-one time with young multiples than stay-at-home parents do. When one baby is sent home from day care with a mild fever or runny nose, leaving the other in child care and spending some quiet time together with the one sent home can turn a bad day into a special one. One good time for "one-on-one" for some families is in transit to or from a sports game or practice.

> Each night my husband and I take turns getting one twin ready for bed. They have kind of different "routines" and comforting things they like, so it gives us each a chance to cuddle and "chat" with them one-on-one. We also try to have one-on-one time on the weekends — one of us will take one twin out to the store, on errands, or whatever, while the other stays home with the other twin. It's really fun to go out with just one baby and see how easy it is!
> Melissa Mackey, CAMOTC, Lansing, Mich.

MARRIAGE COMES FIRST

Keeping in touch with your spouse can be a challenge when you both work outside the home. The special demands of caring for multiple infants or toddlers can relegate the parents to the back burner for a long time. One mom of young multiples laments, "I am really tired all the time, so I'm not as much fun as I used to be, and our sex life has definitely suffered! I hope it gets better when I stop breast-feeding!"

Some parents feel that every free moment away from child care responsibilities or their jobs is spent taking care of the house, bills, cars, etc. There seems to be no time left to connect with that person who is your partner in life. Add to that the potential for one parent to feel he or she is shouldering more of the burden, along with the lack of time to discuss such issues, and you have a recipe for disaster. The best way to head off problems is to consistently make time for each other and your marriage from the very beginning, even if it is only a few minutes each day and even if something else (like cleaning the house or sitting down to meals with your young children) has to take a back seat.

Many parents of multiples who work similar schedules have found that setting an early bedtime for their children in the infant and toddler years and having dinner together once they are asleep has saved their marriage! One parent can fix supper while the other gets the kids ready for bed. The few minutes together while waiting for the kids to fall asleep and dinner to cook gives them time to catch up on each other's day at work and on the agenda for tomorrow.

Many working parents of multiples find they miss their children so much during the week that they aren't interested in (or are too exhausted to) make an evening date with their spouse on the weekend. Try scheduling each other for a "business lunch"— the business of having a life! Be as creative as possible in scheduling moments alone with your spouse.

> **W**e don't do the couple things we used to — dinner out with friends, movies, lots of weekend ski trips. Because I work, I want to spend all my free time with the kids. But I also think that our marriage is stronger than ever. I think we got to a whole new level as a couple – a place we'd never have gotten without the stressful experience of multiples and bedrest. He is a great dad, and I think we make a great team now. At some point we'll get back to doing more stuff as a couple – I know we'll make it there eventually.
> *Jennifer DeVore, West Los Angeles MOTC, Calif.*

TIME ALONE

Becoming a parent is like taking on a second full-time job. Becoming a parent of multiples and trying to keep a career from backsliding can be both physically and mentally exhausting. Months may go by with no "down time." Working parents of multiples must find a way to squeeze in time to do something they enjoy — whether it is a vigorous workout, learning a craft, playing golf, or just staring into space.

The following are suggestions sent in by some creative parents who found their own special ways to carve out personal time.

- Don't stop in for a quick haircut at lunch. Have a shampoo. It only takes an extra ten minutes and may be a rejuvenating experience.
- If your only time alone is in the car driving to and from work, make the most of it. Bring your favorite tapes, a bottle of water or a favorite juice, and a book or magazine in case you find yourself arriving early in the parking lot at work.
- Sign up for an aerobics class at your local park district or city recreation department; join a book club group or your local church choir. Find time on one evening during the week when you can pursue an activity of your own.
- Reserve time in the evening when your spouse is home to enjoy a leisurely walk, a chat with the neighbors, or a soak in the tub.

WHEN IT ISN'T WORKING

Sometimes being a working parent seems not to work for any number of reasons. No matter how positive your attitude, you might become dissatisfied with your job, lose your good child care, or find that your marriage needs to become a priority.

Some parents of multiples, especially those who have not been able to set up a strong "safety net," find that the demands of parenting multiples — along with those of their jobs — make it impossible to continue as they did before kids. If there is no fun left in your family life (or if you don't have one anymore), consider making changes in your jobs or living situation that will give you more time together.

Lohri and Pat Phelan of Anaheim, Calif., decided that Lohri's long commute to her job was putting too much strain on their family. They moved closer to her work, and a year later Lohri is ecstatic! "When I was commuting, I would come home from work and rush through the motions. I loved my time with my family, but I always had this overwhelming background feeling of stress. Now that feeling is one of calm. I can't say how wonderful it is to have time to go outside and play with my kids before dinner. Or how pleasant it is to let my kids sleep longer in the morning. I didn't realize how the stress of commuting permeated my whole life. Even on the weekends, I felt rushed. Now I actually have time to plan, reflect, relax, live. Life is good!"

Some families make major changes in dad's work situation. Other solutions include a transfer to a new location to be closer to home or a change to a more stable job that has regular hours to be with the children.

If you are planning to return to work entirely for financial reasons, do your homework and make sure it is truly the best choice financially. If you are paying for child care for two or more children, buying expensive clothes for the corporate world, spending hundreds of dollars a month on fast food and convenience foods, and hundreds more for household help, it may surprise you to find you would be better off financially if one parent stayed home! Check out the section on finances in Chapter 10. If you consider this option, however, make sure there is some money left for you and your spouse to splurge occasionally. Burnout is just as painful for a stay-at-home parent.

VARIATIONS ON THE "NINE TO FIVE"

More and more parents are finding unique ways to juggle work and parenting responsibilities. Flextime, telecommuting, job sharing, extended parental leave, and part-time work are increasingly finding a place in corporate America.

Some parents taking advantage of non-traditional options have expressed concern that it is difficult to be taken seriously when they are not actually "in the office" during regular working hours. Times are changing, though, because parents are demanding the flexibility necessary to successfully balance work and family. As more companies begin offering flexible options to their employees, the ability of those employees to remain successful members of the team will become apparent.

PART-TIME WORK

Many mothers would love to work only three or four days a week and have more time with their kids, even though they love their jobs. A part-time schedule has been the answer for a number of satisfied families of multiples.

> The biggest struggle has been the "credibility factor." I have to prove to those above me that I can be a successful, contributing employee even working part-time hours.
> *Ann Slayter, Twins Family Club, Corvallis, Ore.*

Bobbi Gomez of East Quogue, N.Y., has worked a part-time, flexible job as a florist since her twins were born. "I am not a 'burned out' mother," she says. "I am happy to be out in the real world and still have time to do things with my family. I have the best of both worlds! I am very happy with the choices I have made." The Kaufmans of Bethesda, Md., are both attorneys. Beth is concerned about losing her skills if she takes a few years off, so she has worked three days a week since her older child was born. Beth feels that the children appreciate her more, and that she is more patient with the kids when she's home because she has some "adult" time. In addition, she hopes to provide her daughters with a positive role model of a working woman.

WORKING AT HOME/TELECOMMUTING

Lisa Sageev of Cranford, N.J., decided it was time to transition back into the workforce when her twins turned three, and she stumbled onto the perfect compromise. Her local public radio station announced that a new website was looking for a web master, someone who would work from home. The former Montessori teacher has found a new career that can change with the changing needs of her family.

Lisa says she has "the best and the worst of all possible worlds. On the best days I can drop what I'm doing to read them a story, take them to the park, or bake cookies — be the standard at-home mom. Working from home gives me the chance to watch them playing, listen to their conversations, and enjoy their company even if I'm not actively playing with them."

Once her twins are in school she will be ready to work in the office part of the time. One suggestion Lisa has for other parents who work at home is to devote some attention to the kids, first.

When you answer your kids right away, they tend to leave you to work for longer stretches. When they know their needs will be met, they aren't as needy.

Another mom who has worked part-time at home with toddler and preschool twins suggests that when her kids become impatient and demand more attention than usual, she packs a lunch or a snack and heads to a park with a great playground. After they picnic, she works on something easy like proofreading, drafting correspondence, or updating lists of tasks, things she can accomplish with one eye on the playground. With twins, there is never a park with "nobody to play with!"

Deanna Sikes of Houston, Tex., mom to three-year-old boy/girl twins and a six-month-old baby, does Internet research from home. "I only work when I can commit my full attention to it," she says. "The children are either sleeping, having quiet time, or are at an outside activity when I work. My hours are very flexible, and I can work as much as I want to. I enjoy this arrangement because I can still be with the children to raise them. There are disadvantages, though. My work time is limited, and I often put work to the side in order to spend time with my kids when they complain. I am still in the beginning stages of working at home and am learning as I go."

If you were able to talk your employer into trying out telecommuting during your pregnancy, you might be in a good position to continue that policy at least part of the time as a parent. It can actually be easier to work at home with multiples than with singletons once they reach preschool age, because each has his/her best friend right there and is less likely to need mom or dad for entertainment. Most work-at-home moms, though, suggest that a few hours a day of child-care during the workday is necessary to be able to concentrate on tasks which must be completed without interruption.

JOB SHARING

More companies than ever are offering opportunities for job sharing. If you know a mom in a similar situation to yours, the two of you might get together and draft a proposal to your company to share one position. This is often beneficial to an employer, because the part-time positions often come without benefits, a very large part of any salary package.

Often when a woman is expecting multiples, the work/family dilemma asserts itself early in the pregnancy with extra severe morning sickness and fatigue. Some multiple pregnancies are complicated by pre-term labor and complete or modified bed rest. Many obstetricians advise travel restrictions after 16 to 20 weeks and cutting back on work hours between 20 and 28 weeks, and some advocate electronic monitoring to detect pre-term labor. Many expectant mothers, even with relatively uneventful pregnancies in terms of contractions, find that by 25 or 28 weeks they are just too uncomfortable to manage sitting in front of a desk all day.

> I was on bed rest with pre-term contractions for four months. I relied heavily on Marc for everything. Meals, emotional support, entertainment, you name it. I was really a wreck with worry — in and out of the hospital — and he really came through.
> Jennifer DeVore, West Los Angeles MOTC, Calif.

One way to prolong your time at work without endangering your health or the babies' health may be telecommuting, as mentioned previously. It might take a little cajoling and creative reasoning to organize, but in the long run it may benefit your employer as much as it benefits your family. Doing this may enable you to handle your work responsibilities for weeks or months longer than at the office. Another complication of many multiple pregnancies which can be avoided by telecommuting is the lack of civilized-looking and/or comfortable maternity clothes for very large pregnant women!

Because pre-term labor or preeclampsia can come on without warning and you could find yourself in the hospital suddenly, it is a good idea to look into any employee benefits you are entitled to early in your pregnancy. Researching your benefits is tough to do from a hospital bed when you are full of medications used to slow pre-term labor. Many companies have medical leave or short-term disability benefits, and — thanks to the Family and Medical Leave Act of 1993 — all U.S. companies regularly employing 50 or more employees are required to offer up to three months of unpaid leave to any employee with 12 months of service. The paperwork necessary to take advantage of these benefits can usually be obtained from your company's employee benefits office and should be obtained early in your multiple pregnancy. Look into available benefits, collect the necessary forms that you and your doctor will be required to fill out, and keep them at home or have your doctor put them in your medical file.

Be aware of the possibility of leaving work early and make your co-workers aware of this. It will allow all of you to decide on a plan of action to cover this eventuality. Many expectant parents hesitate to alert their supervisors to a situation which may never occur, but it is often better than leaving everyone in the lurch if the worst should happen. Your co-workers might even throw your shower a little early so you don't miss it!

The prospective father of multiples may find that in order for his wife to be able to continue working, he will have to take over most household responsibilities for the duration of the pregnancy. This might be the time to hire outside help for house cleaning and laundry if you can afford it. Dad's priorities at this point should be shopping for healthy food and making sure Mom eats it, along with making sure he keeps himself well rested. Even though dad isn't likely to end up on bed rest or in the hospital, his work schedule will be turned inside out if his wife's pregnancy gets complicated. For this reason it might be a good idea for him to brush up on his employer's family leave policies, too.

RETURNING TO WORK

Most of the issues you will deal with during your maternity leave are covered in other chapters of this book. Whatever age your children are when you return to the work force, however, think about organizing your life BEFORE your first day of work. Get as rested as you can. If you are planning to continue breast-feeding or to pump breast milk after your return to work, see "Breast-feeding," Chapter 6. Discuss household and child care chores with your spouse before you begin work: when, how, and by whom are bill paying, housecleaning, yard work, grocery shopping, and laundry going to be done? Who will get up with the kids during the night, and who will drop off and pick up the kids from the sitter? Will you share time off when the kids are sick, and who will take them to doctor visits?

Sometimes you are faced with dilemmas you have no control over. Some parents report that going back to work when their babies are placed in the NICU helped them to keep busy and not worry as much. For others, it is not so positive an experience. One mom's twins were born at 25 weeks and in the NICU. She felt the experience was very difficult. She didn't feel better or more useful returning to work. Her fellow employees didn't know what to say to her and most said nothing. It was difficult having no one acknowledge the fact that she had just had two babies.

SLEEP DEPRIVATION

Sleep deprivation seems to be one of the greatest problems facing working parents of infant twins, triplets, or more as they return to work. Multiples who don't sleep through the night can keep moms and dads from getting more than a two-hour block of sleep for months on end. Working parents usually don't have the option of a nap while the baby sleeps during the day. Many parents find it preferable to synchronize their babies' schedules before both parents return to work. If you are nursing, you might express enough breast milk for a late evening feeding and go to sleep early, leaving dad to give a bottle of breast milk later. If you are formula-feeding or mixing breast and formula, this becomes even easier.

> I just kept getting up and never stopped to think about sleep when my triplets were infants. Sometimes we would take turns — one staying up until midnight, then the other getting up at four. Once it became more tolerable to have one person handling three infants, we took turns and rotated different nights.
> Margaret Izard, Katy Area POMs, Houston, Tex.

To stay alert on the job a generous dose of caffeine, if you are not breast-feeding, might get you through many days, but when exhaustion becomes overwhelming you are not doing anyone, including your babies and your boss, any favors. Take a sick day (with child care) and sleep! And that means DO NOT clean the house! Some moms resort to "power naps" at their desks or in the car at lunch time. (Don't forget to get a watch with an alarm on it, and set it!)

ROUTINES

All babies benefit from routines, but working parents of multiple infants will find it difficult to avoid them. Parents who must wake their babies and toddlers early in the morning to take them to day care often prefer to dedicate the hours after arriving home to the children and getting them settled early, leaving chores and adult talk until later. Other families, especially those who have nannies coming into their homes before the children wake in the morning, prefer to keep the kids up later for family time and leave before they awaken in the morning. However your family functions best, it is a good idea to make a choice and stay consistent whenever possible. A bedtime routine can make the difference between happy, adaptable kids and cranky kids in the morning. Think of how YOU feel when you are over-tired. A rested child is a happier child!

SURVIVING THE MORNING RUSH AND AVOIDING THE EVENING MELTDOWN

For many families there is no such thing as "down time" during the work week. The time they spend together is also the time they spend trying to get everyone out of the house in the morning and fed and into bed at night. Many parents have found certain "tricks of the trade" to help them streamline the chores which must be done during these hectic times. These "tricks" help them find more "fun time" as a family.

- Getting down on the floor with your kids for ten minutes on arriving home, or starting the morning with a tickling/hugging session can pay off not only because it's fun, but because it might leave you with kids content to play long enough for you to tend to the most important chores.

- Older infants and toddlers love to tear open "junk mail." Sit them down in the kitchen next to the trash can, and you can all open mail together. You might even get dinner started while they "read" theirs.

- Over the weekend, prepare several meals which can be easily reheated. This can reduce some stress of the weekday dinner hour.

- Mix formula in large batches. Make a whole can of powdered mix in the proper volume with room temperature bottled water and pour enough bottles for 24 to 36 hours.

- Color code bottles, clothes, sippy cups, etc. Do this from the start so that all family members quickly learn each baby's color. This will be of enormous help when one child is ill.

- Lay out children's clothing in the evening in preparation for the next day. Pack lunches and set the breakfast table before going to bed.

- Put the laundry away as soon as you fold it.
- One mom of three-year-old identical boys lets her boys share all clothes except shoes. She suggests lots of sweat pants and sweat shirts in the cool months, shorts and T-shirts in the warm ones. She prefers the mix-and-match separates rather than "outfits" that tend to become separated, especially when she is in a hurry to find them!

CHILD CARE

> Since I need to label everything that goes to day care, I had special address labels made with my daughter's and twin sons' names on it ("The O'Keefe Kids — Madelaine, Spencer, Trevin") in four lines. I can circle the designated child's name, if needed. Also, my three-year-old daughter enjoys helping mom get lunches ready by putting the stickers on lunch items.
> *Camilla Joe, Gemini Crickets POM, San Jose, Calif.*

The U.S. government Census Bureau reported in 1995 that 55 percent of women ages 15 to 44 who had given birth were in the labor force. This percentage increased even more, to 77 percent, if the women were older (30 to 44) and the birth was their first. It also reported that 29 percent of preschoolers were in some type of day care. Just remember that you are not alone!

No matter how much you love your job there is a period of adjustment in returning, for mothers especially. Some employers allow staff members to make a gradual return to their previous status. If you don't have such an arrangement with your employer, you might want to arrange for child care to begin a week or more in advance of your return to work to give you and your babies time to ease into the separation. You may wish to take the opportunity to spend a couple of days alone with each of your multiples or spend time by yourself preparing to go back to work. If you cannot ease into the child care situation, consider starting back to work and day care on a Thursday. The family will have two days to adjust to your new lifestyle and then a weekend to regroup.

Begin your search for child care early — as soon as you know you are having multiples. Three months into your pregnancy is not too early to add your name to waiting lists. Remember that you may not feel like trekking around to day care centers when you are six months pregnant. Some parents have found it difficult to find day care centers or family day care situations with openings for two or three infants, toddlers, or preschoolers at the same time. Perhaps you can come to an agreement that if a spot comes available for one child, they will hold it for you for a month or two until another opens up.

When looking into day care centers or preschools, visit the first time unannounced. Get a feel for the situation (Are most of the kids happy? Is the school clean? Are staff members busy interacting with children or sitting in the corner talking?), and then, if you are still interested, set up a meeting with the director to ask your questions. The better you feel about your child care situation, the better you will fare as a working mom or dad. Leaving infants or young toddlers may be especially heart-wrenching. Many parents of multiples worry that, since they find it so demanding to meet the needs of two or more babies or toddlers at once, finding a caregiver experienced enough to do the same will be nearly impossible.

The most important thing you can do to help your children with this transition is not to let them feel the ambivalence you are bound to be experiencing. Let your children know that you miss them and are thrilled to see them at the end of the day, but not that you are devastated at parting! Children will develop their own developmentally appropriate (and entirely unavoidable) "separation anxiety"; don't encourage it by letting them feel yours. Reassure them that you will be back when you have finished your work, and that you will be so happy to see them. Try to present the time away from mom and dad as an adventure. If you seem happy to see the caregiver, they will be more likely to feel the same. Many parents commented that their multiples adjusted to day care more easily than their singleton siblings. Multiples have each other for support.

Once multiples enter school, taking care of their basic physical needs becomes much easier. But parents who work must now find child care for before and after-school, as well as arrange transportation for their multiples to after-school activities. Many elementary schools are now offering after-school care right on the school grounds, sometimes in conjunction with a local YMCA chapter. Also, pick up a locally published parenting magazine to look into after-school care. Most of these publications also run articles on local summer camps well before school is out for the summer.

Many parents admit that the choice of child care was the

most critical issue in their lives with their children. Parents must feel comfortable with their choice of child care in order to concentrate on their jobs, their marriage, and their own health. When children are thriving in their child care situation, parents can relax and enjoy parenting.

WHEN THE KIDS ARE SICK

Many parents find that deciding what to do when children have minor illnesses is a major stressor. Do you send them to day care with a runny nose and save your sick days to take when they really need you? Or do you keep them home? Some couples split the sick day. Either they will alternate days off or each will work half a day when the kids are home sick. Those with nannies tended to let the nanny manage sniffles and colds, but the parents take off for anything more serious. Some employers have "sick child care" opportunities for children with minor illnesses, and many will cover the cost. In some instances children don't have to be enrolled in the on-site child care facility on a regular basis to utilize the "sick care" option.

> **O**ur twins had several colds the first year in day care, but our pediatrician told me that by age six, most kids would have about the same number of illnesses. Pay now or pay later! Each year has gotten better, and the past two years (four and five years old) have been cold- and virus-free!
> *Diane Kellogg, Richmond, Va.*

One of the major drawbacks of day care cited by many parents and physicians is the potential for exposure to germs. It is true that babies born very prematurely or with other health problems do not belong in a group day care situation. As long as a facility has strict guidelines for cleanliness and for keeping sick children out, however, most children do fine, and many parents find that children are sick less often once they reach school age.

CHILD CARE — WHAT DO OTHER PARENTS SAY?

- Karen Dziurzynski of Hamburg, N.Y., says of her identical twin girls, now almost four: "My girls have been in the same day care center since four months of age...I would not change the day care situation for the world. They are so happy there. They are so outgoing and get along with whomever they meet. They are very responsible children and very well-behaved."

- "As infants our twins needed an incredible amount of stimulation," recalls Susan Grammer of Houston, Tex. "At their day care, a university campus preschool, they were surrounded by young adults who were studying child development and were thrilled to interact with the kids constantly. Had they been at home with me, I would have had so many chores to do that I wouldn't have been available to each of them 100 percent of the time, as their caregivers were. Even when they weren't interacting directly, there was always something going on in the room."
- One mother went back to work when her twins were three months old, and since she had no relatives nearby, few friends with babies, and little time to read the parenting/child care books and magazines, the child care providers in the infant room at her preschool provided her with some tips. They told her when to feed certain foods, how to deal with constipation/loose stools, sleep problems, etc.
- Another mother spent a few hours with her babies at the day care they were to go to during the two weeks before she returned to work. The caregivers were able to observe how the babies interacted with her, and she was able to observe the routine in the infant room and get to know the primary caregivers they would be spending their days with.

WORK-SITE DAY CARE

The benefits of day care located at your place of employment are enormous. Parents can concentrate on their work duties better when their children are close enough to check in on occasionally and to get to quickly in case of an emergency. Many employers even provide access to sick-child day care, where children with runny noses and low grade fevers who are not too sick to play all day can be taken care of by nurses while their parents work.

It may be tempting to visit your children during the day, but, depending on your child's personality and developmental stage, you might be better off sneaking a peek from a safe vantage point. Many children are thrilled to be in their day care setting as long as mom and dad aren't around, but putting them through another separation might prove stressful. Talk to the teachers/caregivers and ask how they think your child would do.

The major drawback of on-site day care and commuting with kids is that the parent who travels with the kids often loses the only personal "peace" she or he once had — behind the wheel of a car in traffic! Make sure the hours of the on-site day care center leave you a few minutes on either end to switch gears and recharge. Since the parent who works at the site is usually responsible for both drop-off and pick-up, he/she is at a higher risk for burnout without some time alone. Schedule time a couple of evenings a week when the other parent flies solo during the dinner hour and bedtime hour, and the parent who commutes with the kids goes out for a walk or runs errands alone.

Tips for Commuting with Kids

- Build a library of tapes (kids, classical, jazz, vocals) and talking books.
- Purchase a back seat mirror (available in catalogs) which attaches to your rearview mirror and can be focused on the kids.
- Invest in a comfortable car seat and sunglasses for the kids.
- Carry an extra insulated bag each day with juice and snacks for all of you. Leak-proof cups work well for toddlers and preschoolers. Stick to pretzels and other dry food that vacuums up easily.
- At the end of the day, spend a few minutes getting hugs and kisses and snacks in the hallway or on the school playground before loading up the car for the trip home. Five or ten minutes of "mommy or daddy time" can go a long way towards making the drive and subsequent dinner hour fun instead of chaos.
- Keep an emergency box in the car with non-refrigerated juice boxes, bottles of drinking water, extra sippy cups or bottles, diapers, wipes, paper towels, a couple of bath towels for rain, spit-ups, and accidents, along with a change of clothing.

FAMILY DAY CARE

Many parents prefer their children to be cared for in the home of another family. Every state has licensing laws for family day care. Your librarian can help you to look into the requirements for licensing in your area and to find lists of licensed providers. Spend time in the home before you make your decision.

Melissa Mackey of Capital Area MOMs, Lansing, Mich., is adamant about references. Request references and check them. Do not assume just because someone has good references that this person can run a day care situation acceptable to you. Mackey advises reading between the lines when talking to people listed as references. Visit the provider several times before enrolling your children. Be very observant not only of the provider but of the provider's home and any family members you happen to meet. How do they interact with one another? Are they loving, or is there tension? Are their own children well-behaved, or do their children act like brats when you are there? Is the home clean and safe? Does it meet licensing requirements? What day care experience does the provider have? How does the provider respond to your children or pictures of your children? What is the provider's relationship with parents of children the provider has cared for in the past? What does your gut tell you? Would YOU like to spend a lot of time in this home?

NANNY

When interviewing nannies, follow your instincts, but make sure references are legitimate. Many a parent has hired a nanny, later finding out that her supposed "nanny" experience was just babysitting for a family friend. One way to ease your mind is to use a nanny agency. There are many services which will place a nanny in your home and carry out background and reference checks. They will also replace the nanny immediately if things don't work out, so you will not have to begin your search anew while working. Hiring the nanny a week or more before returning to work will give her time to learn the lay of the land, and your babies or children will have time to get to know her. You can run errands, preparing for your return to work, while assuring yourself that this is the person you want caring for your children every day.

My babies were eight weeks premature. We did not want to expose them to the germs in a day care center or in home day care so we elected to hire a nanny. It is also much easier to have the nanny come to our house, rather than to get myself, my husband, and the babies fed, dressed, and out of the house. I can't imagine how difficult that would be. The third reason we chose a nanny is that it is actually cheaper to have someone come into the house than it is to pay for two infants in day care. It was not that easy to find a nanny to care for two babies. Our current nanny did a lot of soul-searching before she decided that she was up to the task of taking care of two babies!
Jennifer Thompson, High Bridge, N.J.

Many working parents of multiples, when asked what their greatest source of support is, will put the nanny at the top of the list. A nanny can give a child the benefits of being at home while also teaching them that there are adults other than their parents whom they can depend on. One of the negative aspects to having a nanny is that homes with children in them all day take a beating! If you do not want your nanny doing household chores, you might hire someone to come in and clean once a week.

FAMILY MEMBERS AS CHILD CARE PROVIDERS

As of 1999, a total of 43 percent of America's 10.3 million preschoolers received one percent of their care from relatives other than their mothers. Fathers accounted for 18 percent, grandparents 16 percent, and other relatives nine percent. Grandparents, aunts, uncles, and other family members can be wonderful sources of child care if they feel comfortable caring for more than one child of the same age. Some find they cannot do it every day but can help out a couple of days a week. If both sets of grandparents live close by, it might work out to have the children spend half their time at each home. Before embarking on an arrangement involving your much loved family members, make sure all parties are in agreement about basic child care and discipline issues. It's tough to fire a family member without severe repercussions!

> **W**e wanted our kids to be at home. Also, since there are three of them we preferred to keep them together with a caregiver all to themselves. With the oldest going to elementary school, I need before- and after-school care for her, so it makes sense to have a nanny at our house.
> *Beth Kaufman, Montgomery County POMs, Bethesda, Md.*

NO DAY CARE

Some parents arrange their work and/or school schedules so that at least one of them is home with the children all the time. One disadvantage of this arrangement is feeling like "two ships passing in the night." Most couples committed to this arrangement adjust and make time to be with each other when they can. The advantage is cost-free child-care by the person you trust the most.

A FINAL NOTE

Some days your family life will run like a well-oiled machine. You will take on the world with the optimism, clarity, energy, and self-confidence born of successfully juggling multiple responsibilities.

Other days your machine will malfunction. The kids will be sick, one parent will be out of town, the car will break down, the air conditioner will fail, there will be no milk in the fridge and only three diapers left in the closet, and you will have a presentation to give that afternoon. This is the reality of being a working parent of multiples.

The first step in handling these breakdowns gracefully is to admit that they WILL occur. Discuss and initiate back-up plans: back-up child care, back-up help at work, back-up transportation. Most of all, keep yourselves physically and mentally healthy. Maintaining the general feeling of well-being that comes along with taking care of your own physical and mental needs can go a long way towards enhancing your coping skills. Also, learn to recognize indicators signaling the need to make major adjustments in child care arrangements, working hours, living arrangements, household help, or job status. When the bad days overwhelmingly outnumber the good days, step back, prioritize, and make those changes with the confidence that you are doing what is best for your family at this particular time in your lives.

A stored supply of self-confidence and a sense of humor can carry you through the tough times. When all else fails, try to remember how empowered you feel on those days when you have the world in your hands. On those days set aside some time for family fun. After all, isn't that what it's all about, anyway?

Though they look alike and act alike, even identical twins have their own individual personalities.

12

SPECIAL TOPICS

A. A SET OR INDIVIDUALS?

When parents are first told of the impending birth of multiples, they begin to ponder the many issues involved in raising these children. Initially the question of utmost importance may be: How will I identify my children as individuals? While this question seems simple, it encompasses many important aspects of dealing with multiples on a day-to-day basis. Should they be dressed alike? Should they be given rhyming or similar names? Can you expect the same level of physical and social development on the part of each multiple?

To this day the "nature vs. nurture" debate continues to fascinate parents and fuel the research of academics. Many parents of multiples observe subtle personality differences in their children almost from the moment of birth. Indeed, some are aware of their children's individual differences in utero.

Mary Moore Davis of Jackson, Miss., noted the following differences in her infants: "Once born, they began to establish and reveal their personalities. Beth screamed and cried and generally fussed. Laura yawned, stretched, and cooed. My secondary impression was, 'Gee, Mary Beth doesn't like to be disturbed. Laura is pretty laid back.' Three years later, Laura is a more active child, but she doesn't seem to get upset over unexpected changes. Mary Beth, on the other hand, can't stand for something unanticipated to happen."

INDIVIDUALITY

From the moment children are born, they enter the world with many personality traits already established. Whether identical or

Responses to Being a Multiple Survey (NOMOTC, 1996)

- Number of multiples who dressed alike at some point - 87%
- Number of multiples who shared clothing - 71%
- Number of multiples having the same hairstyle when younger - 72%
- Number of mothers who could always tell their multiples apart - 94%
- Number of multiples who engaged in similar activities with their sibling(s) (i.e., music, sports, clubs, etc.) - 58%
- Number of multiples called "the twins" or "the triplets" by friends or relatives - 39%
- Of fraternal sets that looked alike, number pretending to be their multiple - 29%

fraternal, you soon learn to differentiate among your children. For this very reason, it is important that you present your children to family and friends as individuals rather than as members of a set. Yes, there will be a great deal of excitement over the birth of twins or higher order multiples. By all means, send out announcements that spread the news of your unique birth circumstances. Enjoy the gifts of identical infant clothing sets and the exceptional amount of attention that your multiples receive from individuals outside your immediate family during the first few months after their birth.

At the same time, it is important that you begin to recognize your children as individuals from the onset. In the case of close identicals, parents often resort to such practices as painting toenails or fingernails in different colors, or leaving hospital ID bracelets on the babies in order to identify each of the babies from the moment they bring the infants home. This has practical implications if one or more child is taking a specific medication or if formulas differ. It also allows the parents the opportunity to bond in a very specific manner with each of the children.

Watch for specific personality traits that enable you to bond more closely with each child and meet his/her needs. Do not assume that one schedule for feedings, bathing, activity, etc., will meet the demands of each multiple. While a uniform schedule such as that presented in earlier chapters is of benefit to the parents, it may not always meet the unique needs of each infant. An active, fussy child may require more stimulation and physical interaction with the parent while his quiet, more passive sibling(s) may be content with less parental interaction during the first few weeks following the birth.

After the babies come home from the hospital, be prepared for multiple visitors! This is a unique and very special event, and many friends and family members will want to share in the excitement. Take this opportunity to begin to establish your children's individual identities. Point out their unique features. In the case of same-sex multiples, this may be a dimple on one child's face or a notable weight difference. Stress the children's names and avoid referring to them as "the twins" or "the triplets." Talk about the personality differences which you have already noted, and encourage visitors to talk about their own observations or differences among the multiples.

As multiples pass through the toddler and preschool stages, physical and personality differences become more obvious. This is true even in identical sets. Attentive parents will begin to note each child's preferences, and the children themselves will begin to assert their own wishes and demands. At this early stage, one-on-one time with you will help to strengthen each multiple's sense of self-worth. If possible, take only one child on a short trip to the grocery store. When one is having difficulty falling asleep, take that time to cuddle or rock the child apart from the other siblings. If necessary, establish a timetable of "private time" with each child in order to assure both you and the child of a unique time to get to know each other.

To dress alike or not, that is often the question. Certainly infants are oblivious to your clothing choices. However, a strict desire to dress the babies alike can place a strain on a parent. Babies require frequent changing due to diaper accidents or feedings so it may be best to reserve those adorable matched sets of clothing for special outings or visits. By the time most toddlers reach their third birthdays, they will begin to take interest in their clothing. When this happens, you may wish to give the children more freedom in selecting their clothes for the day. Some same-sex multiples will enjoy dressing in identical clothing, while others resist. At this point, you will need to decide if and when identical clothing is appropriate.

Once multiples begin socializing with other children, dressing them in dissimilar clothing will allow their playmates to recognize

> I've found that many mothers of multiples see their decision to dress alike or to dress differently as a reflection of their parenting skills. I don't care if they're dressed alike or not. I would rather concentrate my skills and fill my time with the worry of whether they are getting enough to eat. Although I see the dressing decision in a lighter way, that doesn't mean it's not an important issue to others.
> *Mary Moore Davis, Jackson, Miss.*

each of them more easily. By the school-age years the multiples will be making their own clothing choices. Some younger children prefer to dress alike, and this is fine. You may encourage them to choose similar outfits in different, perhaps their favorite, colors. The children will begin to request different hairstyles by this time also.

In the early years, it is important that you pay close attention to your children's developing talents — their weaknesses and their strengths. Don't necessarily enroll each of the children in the same dance or art classes or the same sport unless all of them exhibit a similar talent or preference for that activity. Scheduling extracurricular activities for multiples can be difficult and time-consuming for working parents, and the temptation to enroll all of them in the same activity can be great. However, these youthful experiences often help children to develop skills and abilities that are useful later in life. Multiple-birth children need the same variety in the choices that are made for them as singletons are usually afforded.

RECOGNIZING THE MULTIPLE BOND

In the case of identical twins, it has been observed that often the children bond more closely with each other than with the parent. Whether identical or fraternal, multiples share a unique relationship. During the school-age years, friends will either be supportive of their unique closeness or try to come between them. You should be alert for situations that are harmful to your children's relationship with each other.

Many times other adults will suggest separating the twins or triplets as a way of encouraging individuality. In the past, school systems routinely required multiples to be placed in separate classrooms. However, this is often painful for very young children who are closely attached to each other. Artificially separating multiples based on the assumption that separation will promote

> When my look-alike fraternal sons were in their freshman year of college, Alan came home one weekend with a pierced ear. Needless to say, his parents were quite dismayed. Alan's father gave him a very strong piece of his mind, and his brother Ed had quite a few strong words on the subject, also. Later, when I asked Ed why he was so upset with the ear piercing, he said, "I was going to get an earring, but now I can't because I'll look just like him!" And here I thought I had one conservative, mainstream college son!
>
> *Martha Eicker, Twice as Nice MOMs, Chicago, Ill.*

individual development is a practice that overlooks the great blessing and treasure that multiple-birth children enjoy. Yes, each child in the set is unique as an individual, but each child is also deeply ensconced in an extraordinary relationship.

Both identical and fraternal twins will experience changes in their relationships as they grow and mature. Many multiples experience greater difficulties during adolescence, a time during which all children begin to assert their own personalities in a variety of ways. You might notice your teenagers moving in different directions, establishing separate friendships, and having more arguments. Boy/girl sets have less difficulty and may remain closer and more protective of each other. Moving on to separate colleges after high school is another challenge for multiples, as they face their first long-distance separation. Regardless of their ages, multiples will most likely want time together and time apart, and you need to be conscious of these needs as they arise.

A 1996 NOMOTC research survey titled *Being a Multiple* found that the majority of responding multiples liked their sibling multiple(s) and enjoyed feeling "special" by virtue of being a multiple. Most had worn similar clothes as children by their parents' choice, but few continued to do that as they grew up. While most multiples felt they were treated the same as everyone else, they reported that when they were treated differently it was usually by teachers and friends.

NOMOTC member Mary Moore Davis of Jackson, Miss., summarized her feelings in this way: "Whether you have been blessed with twins, triplets, or more, an understanding of your children's unique birthing experience will help assist you in understanding each child and his/her emerging self. Identify with your children as the individuals they are, and recognize the special bond of their birth. Encourage the extraordinary closeness that you will find with many multiples. By doing so, you are helping your children understand the amazing circumstances surrounding their births and the importance of their individuality within that grouping."

B. ADOPTING MULTIPLES

Adoptive and birth parents of multiples are both faced with the issue of being "ready" for their overwhelming parenting responsibilities. Whether you have nine months, nine years, or nine days to prepare, you are never quite ready for this awesome responsibility. The day-to-day strategies employed by parents in caring for multiple-birth children are the same regardless of their biological connection. Adoptive parents should be encouraged to utilize all resources for twins, triplets, or more to assist them with their parenting questions.

If the children are adopted at birth, the issues may be similar to those of birth parents. If the multiples are adopted as toddlers or older, past histories will help to define their needs. Many adoption resources are available in these areas and can be used in conjunction with the literature available regarding multiple births.

JOINING A CLUB

Networking with other parents of multiples through a local parents-of-multiples club as soon as possible will prove to be invaluable in helping with the adjustment to being a parent of twins or more. Especially in the cases where the placement occurred very quickly, utilizing the expertise of those who have "been there" will provide you with some tried-and-true solutions to everyday needs. Don't be afraid, because your children were adopted, to reach out for advice, encouragement, and support from the multiple-birth community.

Keep in mind that the decision to share information and details about the adoption of children is your option. Just as preferences about whether to share pregnancy and birth experiences vary from woman to woman, so, too, do the choices adoptive parents make about sharing their experiences. For many, the years leading up to the adoption were so emotionally and physically challenging that they choose not to relive them. Others are eager to share their stories and details of the adoption experience.

TYPES OF ADOPTION

Adoption experiences can and do vary greatly from family to family depending on the way the adoption was facilitated. Adoption agencies provide a service connecting birth parents with prospective adoptive parents. Trained personnel help to ensure that the needs of birth parents are met and the qualifications of the adoptive parents are suitable. In an identified adoption, the agency provides counseling services for all parties after the prospective adoptive parents have found birth parents and an adoptable child on their own. International/inter-country adoption involves connecting children born outside the United States with parents residing in this country. This type of adoption is usually handled by a specialized agency and often involves increased financial costs. These complications may result from the difficulty of meeting the requirements and criteria set by two different governments.

OPEN OR CLOSED ADOPTION

During every adoption event, decisions are made between the birth parents, prospective adoptive parents, and agency personnel regarding the "open" status of the adoption. An open adoption is one in which identifying information is shared between birth parents and adoptive parents. The definition of "open" is variable. It can range from the minimum of exchanging first names of the involved parties briefly meeting face-to-face, to having the birth mother live with the adoptive parents prior to giving birth. Once the adoption has taken place, ongoing contact between the families may continue. Pictures and letters may be sent, or the children may know and see their birth parents on a regular basis throughout their childhood.

A confidential or "closed" adoption is one in which no identifying information between the birth parents and adoptive parents is exchanged, and the records are sealed under court order. This style of adoption can be in compliance with the wishes of the birth parents, adoptive parents, agency, or any combination of these. Background and health information is usually shared between the parties.

TELLING YOUR CHILDREN ABOUT THE ADOPTION

Whether you choose to share information with others outside your family, most experts agree that children who are adopted should be aware of their adoption. There is no magic age at which this information should be shared. Many parents begin using the term "adoption" well before the children know its meaning, just as a birth mother may mention the term "Caesarean" to her child born by Caesarean section when discussing the child's birth.

To explain adoption to children and adults, you should focus on the facts. Adoption is a method of establishing a family, just as is birth. However, families adopting multiples may face additional comments related to their adoptees being twins, triplets, etc. Questions such as "How could your parents give both (or all) of you up?" may be difficult for children to handle. One way to help is to illustrate the benefits to them of being adopted multiples, such as having a biologic connection to each other, something singletons do not have.

ADOPTION TERMINOLOGY

Educate your children and others by using language that is respectful and positive when discussing adoption. Using terms such as *birth mother, birth father*, and *birth parent* instead of *real mother, natural father*, and *real family* treat your family unit with the dignity it deserves. Explain to those who may not understand that the birth parents did not "give up" their children. Rather, they realized they were unable to parent their children and made an *adoption plan* for them. Characterizing adoption as being "the easy way" to become parents implies that adopting a child does not compare with giving birth and diminishes the adoptive family unit. Therefore adoptive parents should not be faced with questions about these children being "their own." Whether conceiving multiples or adopting them, every parent of multiple birth faces a unique and challenging experience. Adoption is a genuine and permanent relationship and should be treated as such.

EDUCATION

Adoption may be an issue in a child's education. If older children are adopted, their past histories will influence their needs at school as well as at home. The connection for children adopted as infants or toddlers may not be as evident. If a child experiences areas of concern related to education (possible learning disabilities, behavior problems, etc.), an honest discussion with school personnel, including the fact of the child's adoption, will provide everyone involved with the complete background necessary to help the child.

Adoption, however, should not be viewed as the sole reason for any problems a child may face. Teenagers experience many new and different problems that may lead to changes in their academic performance. While adoption may be one of the issues a child may be dealing with, it may also be totally unrelated to his/her current school situation. It should not be seen as the major cause of adolescent school problems. Working together honestly and openly, parents, school teachers, and administrators can help children develop to their full potential.

SEEKING OUT THE BIRTH PARENT

Whether or not your multiples decide to seek out their birth parents, this possibility exists in all adoptive families. As adults, adoptees may desire to find their birth parents for a variety of individual reasons. One way to assist your children is to save all information received during the adoption process. Parents who withhold this information from their children due to fear of rejection risk promoting distrust in their relationship. A strong parent-child bond can never be destroyed if the foundation is one of trust and openness. Many adoptive-family support groups can help parents and children with this part of their adoption experience.

With multiple-birth children, searching for their birth families can become more complicated. Sometimes conflicts arise if one of the twins or triplets wishes to search for the birth parents and the other(s) does (do) not. Remember your multiples are separate individuals and may have different needs in this regard, just as in other aspects of their lives. The amount of contact your children choose to have with their birth parents may be one area where their individual preferences become apparent. For these reasons and many more, most experts agree (and many laws require) that the adoptees must reach legal adult status before any search is undertaken. Professional counseling may be helpful in addressing in advance the issues that may surface as well as potential conflicts resulting from the search process.

CONCLUSION

Parents of adopted multiples will face the same day-to-day challenges as birth parents of multiples. These issues will require a resolve on the part of parents to focus on the needs of their children in two areas: as multiples and as adoptees. Through education and communication, adoptive parents of multiples can provide their children with a full appreciation for their lives as twins or triplets. In addition, the opportunity to share the joy of their adoption with two or three children multiplies the love within the family.

Remember: each twin is unique.

Highlights from NOMOTC's 1993 Mothers of Adopted Multiples Survey

- Number of parents reporting infertility as their reason for adopting - 84%
- Adoption vehicles:
  - Private agencies (26%)
  - Public agencies (26%)
  - Private adoption (32%)
  - International agencies (2%)
  - Other (10%)
- Length of time between application and receiving children in home:
  - Six months or less (26%)
  - Six to twelve months (16%)
  - Twelve to eighteen months (16%)
  - Eighteen months to two years (6%)
  - Two to three years (16%)
  - More than four years (10%)
- Adopting couples receiving health information and social background of the biological parents - 77%
- Adopting couples experiencing a genetically predisposed health problem in one of the multiples - 13%
- Adopting couples informed of the possibility of the above health problem prior to the adoption - 50%
- Parents who would assist their multiples in finding the biological parents if their children expressed this desire - 81%
- Parents having friends and family who were encouraging and supportive - 94%
- Parents who would choose to adopt multiples again if age and finances were not deciding factors - 88%

All participants in this survey reported a need to network with other adoptive families of multiples.

C. SINGLE PARENTING OF MULTIPLES

A growing number of parents of multiples are finding themselves in the role of single parents due to divorce, separation, or death of a spouse. A growing number of women are also making the choice to assume parenthood while maintaining their single status. A 1994 report released by the U.S. Census Bureau revealed that one-third of all American families with children were headed by a single parent. The report showed a steady increase from 13 percent in 1970, 22 percent in 1980, 28 percent in 1990 and 30.8 percent in 1994.

Although more than half of black families are headed by single parents, the rate for white families is increasing at a faster rate. In 1994, 25 percent of white families were headed by a single mother. The report also showed that there are 11 million single mothers as compared to 1.7 million single fathers. Single fathers accounted for 16 percent of all white single parents, while black fathers accounted for 8 percent of all black single parents.

Responses to Single Parent Survey (Divorce) NOMOTC's 1992

- Marriage began to deteriorate during multiple pregnancy - 24%
- Emotional stress of having multiples contributed to breakup - 39%
- Financial stress of having multiples contributed to breakup - 22%
- Single mothers needing employment after divorce - 71%
- Single mother receiving regular child support payments - 42%
- Single mother receiving no child support payments - 39%
- Single mother receiving financial help from other family members - 50%

One of the biggest problems for single mothers is reduction in income. On average, women earn less than their male counterparts. The median income for a white mother is $14,000.00, while the figure for black and Hispanic women is $8,000.00.

FINANCES

Many women who have previously stayed home with their young children now find themselves in search of employment. Women with young multiples have the added expense of child care for two or more children. Sadly, it has been estimated that women who divorce and retain custody of their children will lose almost three fourths of their annual income!

While the divorced parent may receive alimony or child support, the widowed parent will not. Hopefully, by planning ahead with life insurance and pension plans, the widowed parent should not be left without money for the future. A financial planner can help the newly widowed parent not only with life insurance and mutual funds but can also give valuable information about health insurance for the family.

> **I** could have continued working full time with a singleton child. Day care for my twins is my main problem in trying to get off any type of public assistance.
> *Anonymous by request*

Never forget the importance of a will! Having a will is an absolute must for any parent, but especially for a widowed parent. In the unusual event of the death of the surviving parent, plans must be laid out for the care and welfare of the children.

Following are some tips which may assist you in dealing with financial concerns:

- Retain a lawyer to help you to obtain the child support and/or alimony which you and your children deserve.
- Retain a financial planner if you are newly widowed to help with life insurance, profit-sharing or pension payouts, distribution of mutual funds, etc.
- Look for day care centers which offer reduced prices for families with more than one child.
- Shop at stores which give reductions for twins or more. Some children's shoe stores give reductions for multiples and some large department stores offer reduced prices on diapers and other baby items for multiple birth families.
- Ask nearby relatives to help out with child care.
- Cook at home more often.
- Cut corners and simplify your lifestyle. Cancel subscriptions to magazines you don't read regularly. Switch from paper to cloth diapers. Buy generic store brands instead of more expensive name brands. Ask family and friends to assist you with household repairs.
- Shop at the local Good Will® or thrift store. Check out garage sales. Many parents-of-multiples clubs have spring or fall sales where you can buy children's clothing and toys at very reduced prices.

In times of great financial difficulty it may also be necessary for you to consider moving in with family or friends, either temporarily or permanently. You may also consider applying for public assistance programs, such as WIC, ADC, food stamps, reduced or free school lunches, reduced or free book rental, and fuel assistance. Your local church or family physician can refer you to social service agencies which will assist you, often free of charge.

CUSTODY ARRANGEMENTS

In the majority of divorce cases, the mother is the parent who has physical custody of the children. The visitation rights of the non-custodial parent are usually decided upon at the time of the divorce or separation.

Joint custody is often the best arrangement for the children, but this only works if both parents live in the same locale. It also won't work if the parents are immature, hostile, or spend half of their custodial time speaking negatively about the other parent.

1992 NOMOTC Divorce Survey

Custody Arrangements
- Mother, custodial parent 80%
- Father, custodial parent   2%

Time Spent with Non-Custodial Parent
- Every weekend 20%
- Every other weekend 17%
- Not on a regular basis 38%
- One month per year 5%
- None, by choice 5%
- None, dad's location unknown 5%

Above all else, try to keep the multiples and all the children together. Breaking up the twin unit will definitely make their adjustment to this major life change even more difficult, as your children, and especially your multiples, find security in being together. Twins being reared apart may make an interesting movie, but this situation also denies them their own special relationship.

It's also important to insist that the non-custodial parent take all of the children during his/her visitation time. First of all, you need time to yourself. Secondly, the multiples also need time to interact with the other parent who will grow in an understanding of their special bond.

KEYS TO SINGLE PARENTING

The number one rule in a single parent household is that the parent is boss. You should make it clear to your children that you have the ultimate authority. Your children are not always going to be happy with the decisions that you make. They may moan and complain, but deep down they're relieved and more secure in knowing there are definite rules to live by. Order and structure are essential in a single-parent home.

MAKING RULES

The two keys to being the boss of your single-parent household are:
1. make the rules
2. stick to them

Make explicit, realistic rules for acceptable behavior and be consistent in expecting your children to obey them. If you are consistent your children will learn to accept the rules and abide by them. If you are inconsistent, they will test you whenever possible. For example, if you let one twin out of doing a chore the other twin is going to complain about doing his or her chores. Pretty soon nothing is getting done around the house, and everyone is bickering. Everyone in a single-parent household needs to contribute to make things run smoothly. You, the parent, need to take charge!

> **W**e separated and divorced when the twins were infants. One of the twins was very easy-going, while his fraternal twin was shy and clung to me. My ex-husband only wanted to take out the out-going twin, but I insisted he had to take both. During the first short visit the shy child cried the entire afternoon. In fact, my ex-husband called after one hour and wanted to bring them home. I said, "No." As he spent more time with BOTH boys together, my shy son warmed up considerably to his dad and now, as pre-teenagers, both boys are very close to their father.
> *Anonymous by request*

TAKING TIME FOR YOURSELF

Single parenting multiples is a daunting endeavor. It will seem like there aren't enough hours in the day to get everything done that you would like to accomplish. After dealing with the children, work, meals, household chores, and school assignments, there often isn't a lot of time left to play with your children or just collapse with a good book. Often single parents feel that they must be everything to each child.

It's not healthy for you to sacrifice yourself completely for the children. Don't make the mistake of living for your children and not for yourself. You won't be happy, and you'll be worn out trying to please everybody else. You are an adult and you need social activities that have nothing to do with your children or with being a parent.

If you sacrifice yourself for your children, you may build up a subconscious hostility towards them which will undermine your relationship. Instead you should be a role model of self-esteem.

Make it a point to get out of the house for at least one evening or one afternoon each week when your multiples are small. You could go to the movies with some friends, take a night class at a college in your town or go swimming at the "Y." Some single parents are only away from their children when they are at work. That is just not conducive to good mental health.

If you don't have friends or family who can babysit, trade off with a neighbor or call the local college to find a good sitter. The bottom line is to take care of yourself. If you are happy and in good mental and physical shape, you'll be a better parent to your children.

BEING ORGANIZED

In order to manage a busy single-parent household with two or more children, you must get organized. Depending on your personality, this may not come easily, but you'll have more time to enjoy the fun aspects of life. Here are some tips that may assist you:

- *Have a good filing system.* Properly labeled and stored

> The twins were very clingy, especially when they were young. Their dad didn't spend a lot of time with them. They were always fighting for my attention. One day I was standing in the kitchen washing dishes, and my two three-year-olds each grabbed one of my legs and started pulling in opposite directions as they screamed, "MY Mommy! MY Mommy!"
> *Anonymous by request*

> Three or four nights a week I took a step aerobics class at a local gym. They had free babysitting, so I took my young twins with me. The physical exercise was good for me, both mentally and physically, and I met a lot of nice friends there. My parents were very critical of me for doing this. They thought I should be with my twins every second that I wasn't at work. I told them that I deserved some time. I thought of it as "my time." I told them that I needed the physical and mental break or else I'd wind up making ashtrays at the local psychiatric hospital! I feel that I was a happier mom and more attentive to my kids because I allowed myself some social activities.
> *Anonymous by request*

files will help you find bills, receipts, and important papers quickly without wasting valuable time. Handle each piece of paper only once and throw away everything that you possibly can.

- *Post a calendar or bulletin board.* Be sure that activities, doctor's appointments, athletic events, etc., are clearly marked. You may choose to color code your calendar using a different color for each member of the family.
- *Designate a message center.* With older children it is important to have a common place for messages which everyone knows how to check when they enter the house. Your teenagers, for example, can let you know that they're at the neighbor's house. Phone messages should also be left there.
- *Delegate as much as possible.* Give your children age-appropriate tasks. At an early age they can begin to fold laundry, set the table, make their beds, sweep the kitchen floor, and so on.
- *Learn to prioritize and accept compromise.* Do the most important things first. For example, do the laundry before dusting; go grocery shopping before washing and waxing the floors. Save up small errands and household repairs for a once-a-month marathon on the weekend.
- *When possible, do two things at once.* You might go through the mail or write bills while watching the evening news. Make those routine phone calls to family and friends while you iron or clean the kitchen counters and sink.
- *Have a place for everything, and keep everything in its place.* This age-old adage holds doubly true for single parents. You can save precious time if you don't have to hunt for hair brushes, staplers, screwdrivers, scissors, envelopes, stamps, etc. Make sure the children know where items are kept and that they return each to its proper place after use.
- *Always prepare for the next morning.* Set the breakfast table, fix

I am a single mother of twin boys with an older daughter. Some days it can be difficult without another adult around. It's easy to give up, but I don't. Through God, my church, my twin family, and going to school to better ourselves, I have come to the realization that I don't need another adult at home. It seems so trivial, the things I used to worry about, but now it's just amazing all the opportunities that I have come across. I wish all the single moms out there to take courage because they won't be babies forever.
  Natasha L. Rustchak, Tidewater *MOMs, Norfolk, Va.*

bag lunches, and lay out clothing, school books and projects, lunch money, notes to the teacher, etc., the night before. There will be less craziness in the morning, and both you and your children are less likely to forget something that you need.

Above all, remember that your sanity and your family's happiness and security are worth more than a spotless house. If you fall into a daily and weekly routine that works for your family and allows you time for relaxation and social activities, you'll know that you are doing well!

COPING WITH A NEW LIFESTYLE

It is important to affirm your children's self-esteem to help them adjust to a new family lifestyle. Many young children mistakenly believe that they are the cause of their parents' separation, divorce, or a parent's death. Reassure them that this is not the case. Talk with your children about the pain and anger that they're feeling and tell them that you are hurting, too. You may wish to enroll in a family counseling program. Many schools also offer special counseling programs for children who have lost a parent through death or divorce.

Many children will interpret the non-custodial parent's absence as a rejection of them. Be sure to stress that the change in living arrangements is a result of problems between the parents and not between parent and children.

Regularly reassure your children that you love them. Be sure to say, "I love you!" often, as this will do wonders for your children's self-esteem. Studies show that children with strong self-esteem will handle a parent's divorce or death better. They are also better able to handle and express anger appropriately.

Find time to talk with your children even though your life may be hectic. Turn off the radio and talk in the car on the way to school or other activities. Eat at least one family sit-down meal at home each day and use that time to catch up on your children's activities. Start new family traditions, such as a "Family Game Night" or movie night. Start Saturday morning with breakfast in bed. Be innovative and involve the children in planning pleasurable activities. While single-parenthood involves a lot of responsibilities, there are also special joys and wonderful times spent with your children.

SUPPORT SYSTEMS

Family and friends will be your most important support system. Don't be afraid to ask for assistance. Often the people who love you want to help, but they just don't know how. Frequently you have to take the first step in asking for help. If you are living far from family, you might consider moving closer to them, as it is important to have someone you can count on in an emergency situation.

> When my twins were 18 months old, I had to rush one of them to the hospital because he was having an asthma attack for the first time. I couldn't reach their father, so the babysitter agreed to stay with my other son while my parents drove in from 100 miles away. My son had to be hospitalized for several days. I don't know what I would have done with my other son if my parents hadn't helped out. I decided right then and there to move to my parents' community.
> *Anonymous by request*

Grandparents can be wonderful people in your children's lives. For one thing, they can give your children a sense of their heritage, and with a lifetime of experiences behind them they have much to teach your children. They also make great babysitters; just make sure you don't take advantage of them. Keeping in contact with your spouse's parents, if possible, will help them to accept the new living arrangements and give your children much-needed contact with both sides of the family. They will often appreciate not being cut out of the children's lives, especially in a divorce situation. If the separation was bitter, however, this may not be possible or desirable.

Other support systems include groups, such as Parents Without Partners, church groups, or your local parents-of-multiples club. For the children, Big Brothers/Big Sisters may offer important role models, especially male role models if the father has passed away or is rarely present in their lives. Male relatives, such as uncles and other male friends, can also be role models to both boys and girls. A Sunday School or a Boy or Girl Scout leader may also provide a positive influence. As a safety precaution, make sure a child is never alone one-on-one with an adult you are unfamiliar with. Group activities are always best.

Consider joining a church or synagogue if you don't already belong to one. You will meet many wonderful people, and many church activities are geared to single adults as well as to children. In times of stress, faith in a higher power can often be quite comforting.

Within NOMOTC's member clubs across the United States, an increasing number of individuals are single parents of multiples. Understanding that raising multiple birth children alone is a difficult task, NOMOTC has a nationwide support services program for single parents based on the concept that interaction with other single parents with common concerns can be helpful and supportive. Single parents may participate in the Pen Pal Program by sending a request to NOMOTC's Executive Office (See Resources, Appendix A). Participants are then matched with other single parents in similar situations. For example, expectant parents, widowed parents, adoptive singles, and divorced parents may be linked with each other.

> **M**y biggest problem as a single mother is lack of time to get everything done. Just as mothers of single children don't completely understand how multiple moms cope, married moms can't understand how single moms survive.
> *Anonymous by request*

NOMOTC's bi-monthly publication, *MOTC's Notebook*, contains a single parenting column. The Single Parent Coordinator writes this column, encouraging and coordinating submissions from other single parents.

Finally, if you are just not dealing with the many stresses associated with single parenthood, consider getting some form of professional help. You may receive all the help that you need in your support group, or you may require a professional, such as a family doctor or psychologist. Seeking the help that you need shows strength and maturity, so don't be afraid to ask for it when you need it.

CONCLUSION

Single parents of multiples often face financial and emotional stresses. Family support and the concern of their fellow parents of multiples are very important. One mom shared her words to live by:

- Keep your sense of humor.
- Try forgiveness.
- Keep a positive attitude.
- Cherish each day.
- This, too, shall pass.
- A little dust never hurt anybody.

- Learn to say, "No."
- Children are God's special blessing.
- Tell your children, "I love you."

When you do not have an ounce of patience left, when your children have been fussy and spilled everything everywhere, just take them in your arms and say, "Thank you, God, for this wonderful opportunity to try to some day mean as much to my children as my mother means to me today." When your children hug you, the stress will magically disappear.

D. DEALING WITH DISABILITIES

For many couples, the joy of a multiple-birth pregnancy may be shattered shortly after the birth of the children by birth defects or disabilities in one or all of the children. Conversely, some disabilities may not surface for months or years after birth. Whatever the timetable, dealing with one or more disabled children within a set of multiples will be difficult and time-consuming.

Multiple births involve a higher rate of birth defects, physical disabilities related to premature birth, and school-age learning disabilities than are commonly found in the general population. Prenatal and neonatal care has improved considerably in the United States in the last few decades. However, an increase in higher order multiple births due to fertility drugs and in vitro fertilization has resulted in a corresponding increase in multiple birth-related medical problems.

Parents of multiple birth children are often faced with critical decisions in the early hours of their children's lives. Many face a lifetime of major medical care and its resulting costs, which have a tremendous impact upon these families. Prenatal costs can be exorbitant if the expectant mother faces long-term hospital-

You will find yourself going through the stages of grief constantly throughout your lifetime. Surely you will be angry at the notion of not having a child who has "perfect" health. Certainly you will be saddened and somewhat depressed at times. Throughout it all, you will at some point come to a time of acceptance. It is during this "lifetime stage" that choices will be made that decide your child's worth, both in your eyes and his/hers.
Mary Moore Davis, MOMC, Jackson, Miss.

ization before the multiple birth. For this reason alone it is wise to investigate health insurance policies before attempting to conceive artificially.

If problems surface soon after birth, there may be mixed feelings of joy and sadness — joy for the healthy multiple(s) and sadness for the child(ren) with medical complications or disabilities. At this time it is especially important to rally family and friends who can assist in helping to care for the healthy infant(s) while the parents' attention is focused on the needs of the baby (or babies) who require special care.

Parents need to be aware of their own feelings about the disability. Initially, a parent will grieve for the loss of the child's normal abilities. Progressing through stages of anger, disbelief, denial, guilt, depression, and fear are all normal. Most parents eventually reach a stage of acceptance, though the feelings of loss can be lifelong. Depression can be common and result from stress, lack of sleep, and being overwhelmed. It can also be due to the postpartum hormonal changes. Parents should try to recognize when they are having trouble coping and seek help from a health care provider. Neglecting one's own health and well-being will lead to burn-out and sometimes resentment and can affect the good care parents need to give to their challenged children.

A 1993 NOMOTC research survey titled *Disabilities/Handicaps in Multiples* explored the relationships between the multiples when one or more in the set suffered from disability. All of the parents responding felt that the multiples' relationship was somewhat close. The healthy multiple tended to be understanding and protective of the co-multiple.

As the children mature, parents need to provide age-appropriate information that will help each of the multiples deal with the particular disability. Be frank and open in answering questions while avoiding stereotypes. For a healthy relationship to develop among the multiples, discussions about the situation should be frank and open. It is important to allow the healthy multiple(s) to experience some freedom, without guilt, to do age-appropriate activities in which his/her challenged sibling may not be able to participate. Also, avoid overburdening healthier children with excessive care-giving to the disabled child(ren).

All of the parents in the above-mentioned study sometimes found themselves "spoiling" the child with the disability. They said that it was sometimes difficult to discipline that child. Whenever possible, set the same limits and expectations as one would for a child who is less handicapped. This will minimize jealousy and resentment on the part of the healthy multiple(s).

Latent effects of premature birth may not emerge until the multiples reach school age. For this reason, it is advisable to maintain a regular schedule of checkups with the pediatrician, as well as hearing and vision specialists, during the preschool years. Early psychological and educational testing may also be desirable if one or more of the multiples exhibits developmental delays. A child may not fit a specific diagnosis for a long time, but this should not delay therapy which can influence how successful he/she will be in the future. Parents must be advocates for their children and sometimes be assertive to get them the best care available.

The Illinois Organization of Mothers of Twins Clubs, Inc., created the Special Needs Assistance Fund (SNAF) to help multiple-birth families with a special-needs or chronically-ill child. Therapies, surgeries, special equipment, and adapting a family home for a physically challenged child can be extremely expensive. Unfortunately, not all expenses are covered by traditional health insurance or other benefit programs. This is where the SNAF program can help.

A recent recipient wrote, "When I saw the amount on the check I started crying, and it brought tears to my husband's eyes as well. The SNAF program is certainly something that IOMOTC should be proud of, and hopefully it will be able to assist other families for many years to come."
Anonymous by request

For many parents, the so-called "invisible disabilities" are the most difficult to deal with. In the case of extremely premature infants who have exhibited no previous physical problems, the school years may pose a challenge. Once a diagnosis has been confirmed (for example, a vision or hearing deficit or a specific learning disability), parents must be strong advocates for their child's needs. Additionally, parents need to be concerned with the social and psychological aspects as they impact the affected child and the co-multiple(s). Good communication is essential within the family, so that the affected child's self-esteem is maintained and the relationship among the multiple-birth children does not suffer. This can be especially important if the children require separation in school because of the disability. Keeping the children together as long as possible can help them to cope with future separations.

Caring for a handicapped child is time-consuming and stressful. When parents are also faced with the daily routine of caring for multiple-birth infants, the workload can be overwhelming. Establishing a support network is essential. Family and friends may be available to help with feedings, babysitting, and traveling to doctor's visits. Parents should make it a point to spend some alone time with their spouses. Respite care and vacations away from the children can help parents become renewed and refreshed and able to face the daily responsibilities of caring for the multiples. Accept without guilt any help offered from family and friends. The children depend on healthy and happy parents for the love and acceptance that leads to a happy and productive life.

Joining a local parents-of-multiples club will also provide additional support, especially in the crucial first years of the babies' lives. NOMOTC provides a Support Services/Pen Pal Program that allows mothers to correspond with other parents of multiples in situations similar to theirs. Some state parents-of-multiples organizations also offer additional help.

Check out federal, state, and local agencies which may provide financial or medical assistance. Early intervention will often help to alleviate symptoms or provide a head start on mastering skills that may be delayed due to the particular disability. Some school systems offer programs which include children as young as one or two years of age. The Internet can be a helpful resource in providing additional information as well as linking parents with other families in a similar situation. Parents of special needs multiples can find a support group at www.onelist.com/subscribe.cgi/specpar, or they can contact Dr. Elizabeth Pector at P.O. Box 5845, Naperville, Ill. 60567-5845 for a list of parents of special-needs multiples, Internet sites, e-mail support lists, and children's books.

Parents' love and support for all of their multiples as the unique persons they are will go the farthest in allowing each to thrive. Parents should honor the bond among the multiples, find support for themselves, and be advocates for their challenged children. In this way, every individual in the family can realize his or her full potential.

E. LOSS OF A MULTIPLE/GRIEF

Death and grieving are not easy topics to think about, let alone discuss. The normal birth-to-death cycle does not always occur in the "correct" order, and parents may face the death of a child with varying emotions: devastation, frustration, shock, anger, denial, and guilt. These are unlike any other emotions imaginable — similar to, yet entirely different from, the same emotions surrounding the death of a parent or spouse. No other event impacts lives as powerfully as the death of a child.

LOSS IN EARLY PREGNANCY

Few pregnant women envision the outcome of their pregnancy as anything less than healthy, happy, and fulfilling. However, statistics indicate that one in five pregnancies ends in miscarriage; a small percentage end with stillbirth; another very small percentage end as ectopic. Multiple pregnancy is associated with an eight- to tenfold increase in the risk of perinatal death and neonatal morbidity as compared to singleton pregnancy, an incidence largely confined to identical twins with one placenta.

MISCARRIAGE

The medical profession may respond to a miscarriage with clinical explanations such as: "This is Nature's way of eliminating a less-than-perfect fetus." Though this may be accurate, it offers little emotional support for the feelings of parents who grieve over loss of the child. Most often the exact cause cannot be found even after pathologic examination of the fetal tissue. This leaves parents without an acceptable and understandable explanation for the cause of death, compounding grief with unanswered questions. Many times there may be improper development of the egg, a factor not likely to be a risk in a later pregnancy.

ECTOPIC PREGNANCY

An ectopic pregnancy results when the fertilized egg implants outside the uterus, usually in one of the fallopian tubes. There may be damage to the fallopian tube as a result, impairing future fertility, sometimes up to 50 percent. These pregnancies are usually lost within the first month, at times before the woman knows she is pregnant.

Mourning these losses can be difficult for the family experiencing the death. Many people don't recognize a fetus as a living being. Friends and family may not want to acknowledge the loss as a death. The tendency is to expect everyone to "get life back in focus," to bounce back to normal within a few days, and go on as if nothing had happened. The inability to see the baby or babies may make it seem less real to all involved, but it is very real to the parents. There are often no memorial services nor formal recognition. Many may be unaware of the loss. Parents must be allowed to talk over their grief and handle it in their own way and time. They should be encouraged to acknowledge the death or deaths in ways in which they feel comfortable.

Recent technology for infertility can create higher-order multiple pregnancies with sometimes six or more fetuses. Occasionally parents are faced with difficult or impossible decisions to terminate one or more of the fetuses to protect the health of those remaining — or risk losing all. There may be a grieving process regardless of the decision made.

STILLBIRTH, PERINATAL DEATH, AND PREMATURITY

Stillbirth is the death of the fetus between the twentieth week of pregnancy and birth. In the United States stillbirth occurs in one of every 80 births. Vaginal bleeding, toxemia, or premature labor may be warning signs. One indication may be lack of movement of one or both babies. Sometimes the cause of the stillbirth may not be found, although it can often be attributed to genetic or congenital defects, umbilical cord or placental problems, or medical conditions of the mother. A perinatal death is a death of the infant in the first week of life. Most often it is due to prematurity.

Premature infants, those born prior to the thirty-seventh week of pregnancy, often encounter severe medical problems. Nearly half of all multiples, compared with only seven to 10 percent of singletons, face the struggles of prematurity. Neonatal Intensive Care Units (NICU), complete with highly technical medical equipment and superlatively trained staff, have made many advances in the recovery and survival of even very tiny infants. During these traumatic times, however, parents often experience a grieving process with all the emotions of an actual death. Amid the chaos is the ongoing awareness that death may happen at any time. Going home to an empty nursery while your babies are still in the hospital can be very stressful. It is helpful to take the time to learn the NICU procedures and terminology and get to know the staff members. Sharing feelings with family members as well as with the medical staff, social workers, and other parents experiencing the same situation can be comforting and empowering. Many hospitals have support groups for parents with babies in the NICU.

Following a stillbirth or perinatal death, parents are faced with the decision of whether or not to see the baby or babies. Many parents who have experienced a perinatal death derive much comfort from seeing the baby or babies, touching them, naming them, and sometimes photographing them. Parents should be allowed to hold the deceased as often and as long as they wish. Saving some memento of the deceased can be very comforting and help in the grieving process. Such items include scans, autopsy reports, locks of hair, and photos of the multiples *together,* whatever their condition. All of these are personal choices, and parents should do what feels right for them and their families. Allowing parents to progress through all stages of the grieving process can aid in the process of letting go and bonding with the surviving infant or infants.

A funeral service for a stillborn infant is also a very personal matter. In Christian faiths sometimes a small, private ceremony is held. A baby of Jewish faith is not recognized until after the age of one month; therefore there is no formal ceremony.

SIBLING RESPONSES

Siblings at home need strong support with an understandable explanation of the situation plus a sense of continuity in their own lives. Extended family and special friends can often provide some strength in this area. Expect questions, some of which may hurt. Expect that the other children in the family may withdraw and say nothing. Some parents are distressed to find that a child can seem unconcerned about the death or seem to take it lightly. This is a normal reaction and does not mean the child is not grieving. Some children are overwhelmed and need to grieve in small doses over time. The subject may dwell in a child's mind. Children need time to think things out to achieve understanding. Questions may surface at inappropriate times, perhaps weeks later. It is necessary that the child witness your feelings of sadness along with an explanation. A shared cry or an extra hug at the end of a discussion may happen and should not be stifled. However, parents should emphasize their comfort in having the surviving child still with them. Statements such as "I have nothing to live for since this child has died!" make surviving children feel unloved and unwanted.

Be truthful in any talks with a child. Use of proper terminology is always encouraged. Someone has DIED, not "passed on." Using confusing terms leaves the child with the wrong impression that the sibling may return later. Grief over the loss may come out in hostility or anger when least expected. Look for regression, but don't punish it. Letters or pictures might help the child to express his or her feelings. Placing a letter or trinket into the casket, if the child feels comfortable doing this, might well be the beginning of a healing process. A memory box that is painted or decorated, therapeutic in its very preparation, can hold pictures or letters to the deceased. The box should be sealed and not read by anyone unless offered by the creator.

The special bond of multiples should not be underestimated. Research suggests that the twin bond is stronger than the parent-child bond. In infancy, the loss may not be realized, but there are reports of feelings of incompleteness that manifest themselves in later life, even with very early losses. At a very early age the child needs to be told he or she was a multiple. If the multiples shared a bed or bedroom, special considerations may be needed. The child may reject sleeping in that once-shared bedroom, demand that lights not be turned out, experience nightmares, not tolerate removal of clothing or toys, etc. Young children often carry a blame or guilt complex about the loss of their multiple mate, and they may feel the death is somehow their fault or that they, too, should have died. Older multiples may experience complete denial and withdrawal from family and friends. There is sometimes role reversal, guilt, hostility, or regression. Sometimes the surviving multiple will become an overachiever in an attempt to accomplish everything the missing child might have done. Strengthen positive memories by talking openly, sharing personal feelings and stories with crying or laughing, and reminiscing about memorable incidents.

The special relationship that multiples have over the years may make the survivor feel an emptiness and the sense of not being a "whole" person any longer. Identify and validate the child's strong feelings. Emphasize the positive legacy left and that life and living must go on. Don't expect the surviving sibling to share all memories. Research has shown that the loss of a co-twin, especially in identicals, can lead to protracted grieving not seen in other losses. The sense of loneliness and profound deprivation can last for years. Many times the child will need professional counseling to aid him or her in the grieving process.

Special groups have been formed for multiples who have lost co-multiples, so that they may share their unique feelings of grief. The Twinless Twins Organization and the Lone Twin Network are two such groups. (See Resources, Appendix A.)

SUPPORT GROUPS

There are many support groups, counselors, and teachers highly trained in children's and adult's reactions to grieving. The National Organization of Mothers of Twins Clubs has a Bereavement Support Coordinator who can contact bereaving families. Helpful information about support groups can be obtained by contacting the Executive Office. *Bereavement* magazine was founded by Andrea Gambill in 1987. Following the death of her 17-year-old daughter, she founded one of the earliest groups of "The Compassionate Friends." The *Bereavement* staff has compiled a national listing of support groups numbering well over 500, as well as booklets on grief-specific subjects. Some groups, such as CLIMB (Center for Loss in Multiple Birth), are for the parents, and others, such as the Twinless Twins Organization and the Lone Twin Network (see Resources, Appendix A), are for the multiples themselves. In receiving support from a group, individuals can begin to realize that they are not alone.

CONCLUSION

No one is ever ready for death, but somewhere along the line some sense will come from it. Grieving, with all its complexities, has no standards to follow; it is a process. Just as each family grieves as a unit in a different manner from another family, so do the individuals of that family grieve differently from each other.

There are no time schedules, no rules telling us how to mourn, no promised adjustment, no simple way to eliminate the hurt. Grieving is painful. It demands attention. There is no way around it. We must go through it to gain an understanding and new purpose, but a healing does come. No one has all the answers, and there appear to be so many questions. If we can take one day at a time, we will be strengthened by the very existence of our children. Choose a rehabilitating path that includes love, and eventually reach out to uplift someone else along the way.

So long as we live, they, too shall live,
For they are now a part of us...as we remember...
(from The Gates of Prayer*)*

Highlights from NOMOTC's 1998 Death of a Multiple Survey

- 25 out of 31 parents reported that the death of their multiple child occurred before the age of one year. Nine deaths were the result of miscarriages.
- 15 sets of parents said that the death had brought them closer together. 10 said it caused a rift in their relationship.
- Although grief was the most common reaction to the death, anger, denial, and other reactions were completely normal.
- The death of a close family member may take years to work through, not weeks or months.
- Networking with others who have suffered similar losses is beneficial.
- It is a good idea to contact a group that deals specifically with losing a multiple (CLIMB, Bereaved Parents USA, Support After Neonatal Death, Twinless Twins, etc.).

F. MULTIPLES AND THE FAMILY

Ask any member of any family blessed with multiple birth children what special circumstances had to be faced, and you will undoubtedly receive many interesting and emphatic answers. The introduction of twins, triplets, or higher order multiples into the family unit also introduces unique family issues which need to be recognized and dealt with.

FAMILY HISTORY OF MULTIPLES

A 1992 NOMOTC research survey documented what many parents of multiples already knew: Multiples do indeed run in families. This survey was filled out by biological mothers and fathers of multiples. The mother's side had a significant number (70 percent) of multiples. This would most likely be due to fraternal twin births, as it is generally believed in the scientific community that identicals are "chance" occurrences and therefore do not run in families. The father's side had a 54 percent incidence of multiples in the family. Additional statistics included:

- 93 percent of the mothers had siblings who had multiples;
- 89 percent of the mothers had other relatives (grandparents, aunts, uncles, cousins) who were multiples;
- 13 percent of the fathers had siblings who were multiples;
- 76 percent of the fathers had other relatives who were multiples;
- 10 percent of the respondents had grandchildren who were multiples.

EFFECTS OF MULTIPLES ON THE FAMILY UNIT

You may already be nodding your head in agreement as you look down the branches of your own family tree for evidence of twins, triplets, or higher order multiples in previous generations. While this is a fascinating subject, the effects which multiples have on the immediate and extended family unit is even more interesting. A great deal of research has focused on this topic, and the results are helpful for families coping with the new dynamics created by the introduction of multiple birth children.

One such study was performed at the Graduate School of Psychology of Fuller Theological Seminary and at the Veteran's Hospital in Loma Linda, Calif. Researcher David Hall presented his findings at two NOMOTC National Conventions. His subjects included identical twins, same-sex fraternal twins, and siblings ages 15 to 25 years. The participants were asked, "Are you closer to your twin than to your mother?" Ninety percent of identical twins responded that they were closer to their twins, while 61 percent of the fraternal twins felt closer to each other than to their mothers. Only 49 percent of same-sex siblings close in age answered in the affirmative. Hall theorized that because of the closeness of identical twins, especially as they grow older, their mothers may feel a sense of loss in maternal relationships with identicals.

Other findings from this study were equally interesting for their long-term effects on the family:

- Identical twins sometimes are in control of the family unit and have a major impact on it.
- More fraternal twins and same-sex siblings are involved in blaming mom and sulking.

- Identical twins have fewer hostile battles with mom.
- Fraternal twins tend to ignore parents more and be more independent from each other than identicals.
- Twins' families tend to have more stress.
- Mothers of multiples need to nurture fathers and act as a communicative link between the father and the multiples.

Your multiples' interaction with the rest of the family may well depend on whether they are identical or fraternal and their sexes (girl/girl, boy/boy, or girl/boy). Identical twins will tend to have a closer bond and may exclude other siblings and even parents from a close relationship. Does this mean that they will not become loving family members? Of course not! It simply implies that the multiples' relationship will be closer than any which they establish with other family members, including the parents.

Many triplet groupings are comprised of an identical pair and one fraternal sibling. The identical siblings will tend to maintain a closer bond regardless of whether the third triplet is the same or different sex. As a parent, you will need to be sensitive to the feelings of the fraternal triplet, making sure that the other two do not shut out their fraternal sibling.

A 1992 NOMOTC Father's Survey indicates that dads are a valuable part of the parenting team in homes with multiple-birth children. In fact, 26 percent of the fathers admitted that they would enjoy raising another set of multiples! More than half of the respondents stated that their lifestyles had changed for the better, and 42 percent would consider becoming a "house-husband" if it was financially possible.

While these are encouraging statistics, many other marriages are adversely affected by the birth of multiples. As Hall's study indicated, mothers need to provide a vital link between fathers and their multiples. A mother who belongs to a local parents-of-multiples club should share the information which she receives from other parents or from books in

1992 NOMOTC Father's Survey

Fathers' help with multiples:
- 92 percent changed diapers
- 89 percent gave bottles
- 74 percent helped bathe children
- 62 percent got up at night to care for babies
- 50 percent occasionally stayed home to care for ill multiples
- 45 percent picked up toys
- 31 percent did the grocery shopping
- 22 percent shared chores 50/50 with their spouses

the club's library. She should encourage him to become an active member if the club allows fathers to join. Engage your spouse in child care, and seek professional help from your family doctor if the stress of caring for infant or toddler multiples is becoming an overwhelming burden.

DEALING WITH SIBLINGS OF MULTIPLES

Most children will react positively to the birth of multiple siblings. A NOMOTC survey of almost 200 singleton siblings of multiples (*Being a Sibling to Multiples Survey*, NOMOTC, 1996) indicated that the majority liked their multiple siblings and enjoyed the special attention multiples brought to them. Almost 90 percent of those responding said that they were close to their multiple siblings, but they admitted that the downside was having to help out more at home because of the multiples' birth.

> The multiples and I were three of five girls in our family. Most of the special attention was because we were close in age. We would all dress alike when we were small. We sang as a group. Even though we are all over age 35, we are still all close today.
> *1996 NOMOTC Sibling Survey respondent*

It's important to prepare your children for the impending birth of the multiples. Explain that life will be considerably different once two or three or more babies are present in your home. If your children are old enough to help, give them a mini-course in infant care. Teach them those tasks which you feel are appropriate for their ages. Toddlers and preschoolers can hold baby wipes and powder and hand them to you as you change the babies. They can also hand you items during the babies' baths. Elementary school-age children can feed babies once they are shown how to do this properly. They may also change babies, but they should never be allowed to bathe them without adult supervision. If you are blessed with a teenager in the home, you are indeed a fortunate mother of multiples and can delegate specific infant care tasks in return for a weekly allowance or special privileges, such as use of the family car.

If you have toddlers or preschool children, you may have to adjust their daily schedules, especially in the early morning hours, to accommodate the needs of the multiples during the first few months of their lives. Young children are definitely creatures of habit, so decide what morning habits you wish them to have and proceed to establish them. Plan ahead to allow time to change and feed the babies first thing in the morning. In order to do this you may wish to establish a routine of having your toddler watch a particular children's program or video immediately after rising in the morning. Or you may want your toddler to play in bed for a specific period of time after he awakens. Whatever you decide, establish this routine before the multiples are born. This will ease your stress level during the first few weeks after the babies' birth, and your older siblings will not associate changes in the household routine with the birth of the multiples.

PROBLEMS BETWEEN SINGLETONS AND MULTIPLES

Sadly, there are times when the stress of introducing multiples into the family does not encourage the development of happy relationships between the children. The 1996 survey also provides insight into the difficulties which arise from being a sibling of multiples. Some respondents told us,

- "Sometimes I wish I didn't have them."
- "My older daughter is seven years old and has had extreme difficulties with feeling left out. She wants a twin for herself."
- "Since my sisters are six and I'm ten, I sometimes feel left out when they play together."

In a NOMOTC survey issued to find out how mothers viewed the blessings and stresses of raising multiples (*Survey for Mothers of Multiples*, NOMOTC, 1986), the most frequent comments from members were related to the difficult adjustment of older singletons when multiples entered the family. Some mothers felt stressed by the older siblings' jealousy, while others were concerned about the limited amount of time available for the older child or children. Mothers with older children were found to have higher overall stress scores.

If you notice your singleton child(ren) becoming sad, depressed, angry, or rebellious, and making negative comments about multiple siblings, it's time to take some action. Talk with other parents in your local parents-of-multiples club. Many of them have probably experienced similar circumstances in their own families, and they will gladly offer advice without being judgmental. Your pediatrician or family doctor is another source of professional help.

Many times singletons are reacting to the overwhelming amount of attention which the multiples receive from other relatives, neighbors, and friends. It's important to be keenly aware of your singleton's feelings during the initial months after the babies' birth. You will probably have frequent visitors bearing gifts for the babies, and your toddler or preschooler may feel jealous and neglected. Your attention has also been diverted from your toddler to the new arrivals, and he/she will be mourning the loss of the special relationship with you. While this is normal when any new baby enters a home, the situation is magnified with the arrival of multiples. Be aware of this, and plan ways in which you can spend time with the older siblings.

> We've worked hard to keep the boys friends so our singleton doesn't feel left out by his brothers.
> *1996 NOMOTC Sibling Survey respondent*

The babies' feeding times are wonderful moments for visiting with your singleton child. While you are feeding one or both babies, spend time talking or singing to your toddler. A three-year-old can cuddle next to you and hold a book while you read the story. Play guessing games, teach the alphabet or numbers, or relate family stories, perhaps about the older child's infancy. The babies will enjoy the soothing sounds of your voices, but your attention and interest will be directed to an appreciative sibling. After you hold the babies for any length of time, be sure to take a few seconds to give some hugs and kisses to an older child. You will need to be creative and find moments such as these during your busy day when you can lavish attention on your other children. Sometimes including them as a part of the "team" caring for the multiples and making comments such as "Boy, these twins sure are a lot of hard work for us sometimes, aren't they?" can make the other siblings feel more important.

DEALING WITH THE PUBLIC

Parents of multiples find that one of the biggest sources of potential problems will come from insensitive remarks and actions by people outside the family. When strangers approach you and your children in a public place and begin to fuss over the multiples, be sure to make them aware of the importance of your singleton siblings. Say, "And this is their big brother. Without his help I could never take care of two babies!" Or you might comment, "Yes, they're cute, but this is their big sister, and she's the most invaluable member of our family right now. I don't know how I'd manage without her!" While strangers may not be interested in these comments, your singleton child will experience a very necessary burst of self-esteem as he or she becomes reassured of your love and his or her own value in the family. If strangers persist in insensitive remarks, feel free to walk away and then explain to your child that these people are acting in a rude manner which is unacceptable to you.

> **W**hen my sons were one year old, we were walking with them and our three-year-old daughter at an outdoor art fair. One of the exhibitors, a photographer, asked if she could take their picture. We agreed, and then she proceeded to push our daughter out of the picture! We were horrified and hurt for our child. Immediately we pushed the boys' stroller away from the photographer. The picture was never taken, but my daughter was confused and hurt by the experience.
> *Martha Eicker, Twice as Nice MOMs, Chicago, Ill.*

Attention from strangers was the second most frequent source of stress listed by the 1,500 members who responded to the previously mentioned 1986 survey. While some parents found attention in general to be stressful, many more reported particular concerns with strangers who believed they had a "right" to comment on the multiples' likenesses and differences. Others were tired of strangers' personal questions about the pregnancy and birth of their multiples and even about future family planning!

THE EXTENDED FAMILY

Grandparents, aunts, uncles, cousins – all will share your joy and excitement after the birth of your multiples. In fact, they will bask in the reflected glory of your accomplishment as they pass around photos at their places of work and call their own special friends to share the news. Before you are besieged by an army of relatives, it will be wise to consult with your doctor. If your multiples have been born prematurely, only limited visitors may be welcome for several weeks after the babies come home. Mothers who have spent several months on bed rest may be feeling weak and need more rest and periods of exercise to regain strength. At the very least, you will wish to maintain a schedule with your infant multiples that allows your family some type of comfortable routine.

As the parents it is your prerogative to establish visiting hours in your home. Be sure all potential visitors are informed of these (perhaps in the birth announcement) and that you remain firm in adhering to them. Just as important, never forget that an extended family living nearby is the most important support system during your children's early years. Joint research surveys for grandparents and parents of multiples confirmed the importance of the grandparents' relationship with their multiple grandchildren. Forty-eight percent of parents who responded felt that their children's grandparents would be willing and able to raise their children if something happened to them; however, three-fourths of the grandparents said they would raise their grandchildren if necessary. Sixty-two percent of the grandparents would like to see their grandchildren more often, and almost half said they would babysit anytime they were asked. This is wonderful news for families of multiple birth children!

> Our parents and grandparents and teachers tried very hard to treat each child as an individual, whether single-ton or multiple. It was those "little old ladies" who said, "Oh, look at the twinnies!" who set the babies apart from the rest of the children in our family.
> *1996 NOMOTC Sibling Survey respondent*

If you are fortunate enough to have grandparents or other family members living nearby, make them an integral part of your children's lives. Invite them to babysit (in pairs, at first), help with feedings, entertain older siblings at the park, or help you to take the babies for monthly medical checkups.

As your children grow, you will make many policy decisions regarding what is, or is not, acceptable for your children. Beginning quite soon, in fact by their first birthday, you will know whether you want them dressed alike or not. You will know what types of toys are preferable for multiples, and you will decide whether each child has the same toy, or similar or different toys. You will also grow in knowledge about multiple birth children by reading books such as this one and speaking with other parents of multiples.

Share this information with your extended family members so that they also will have a better understanding of multiple birth children. Let them know that you prefer to have your children called by their names and not referred to as "the twins" or "the triplets." If you prefer to have your children dressed in different clothing, tell extended family members so and return matching outfits when they're given as gifts. You are the guide who sets the limits and dispenses information about your multiples.

CONCLUSION

Multiple birth children add a new dimension to family dynamics. Planning, discussion with other parents of multiples, and sensitivity to each family member's needs will help parents to alleviate stress and avoid some of the common pitfalls which can cause difficulties in family relationships. As many experienced mothers of multiples will admit, taken one day at a time no problem is too great to resolve as long as it's approached with patience, love, and a small measure of humor.

G. JUST FOR DADS

The single largest difference between having one baby and twins (or multiples) is, quite simply, there are two (or more) of them. That's double (or more) the diapers, the bottles, and the fun. These are numerical or logistical differences, which can be dealt with in time. Things WILL take longer to do, there WILL be more laundry, and you WILL end up buying more diapers, formula, clothes, toys, etc. On the flip side, life's joys will be more bountiful; you WILL be loved twice as much (or more); you WILL have twice the fun (or more); you WILL have twice as many fond memories (or more).

For an overview of what's contained here, read the next few bullet points. When you want to read more about a particular idea, skim on down to the relevant section.

- **Whose idea was this, anyway?** deals with taking responsibility and assuming accountability for your actions. Then, once you've stepped up and embraced the idea that you're going to be a new parent, how to get started.
- **But what can I do?** talks about not worrying about getting it ALL right. Don't worry about the little things. Focus on keeping every

one in the family healthy, happy, and prosperous.

- **Establishing parental roles** discusses who does what. This is really hard in a single-parent family when one adult adopts both roles, but it has been done. This section focuses more on the dual-parent situation and provides tips to "manage" caring for the children.
- **When things go wrong** suggests thoughts and ideas to help you overcome life's little speed bumps. If something is seriously wrong, seek professional help. But if you've had a bad day, these tips and ideas can perk you up.
- **What's next?** considers what you do for an encore. This section could also be called "When do I get my life back?"

WHOSE IDEA WAS THIS, ANYWAY?

It's best to start at the beginning. You know how babies happen, right? For most parents, there came a moment in time when a decision was made to have a child. Whether it was by you or with a bit of third party help, events were set in motion. Step up to the plate at the beginning and take responsibility. "She" didn't get pregnant. The two of you are going to have a baby. The sooner you change your perspective on what happened, the easier parenthood will be for both of you.

Having a baby is a life-altering experience; don't let anyone tell you otherwise. And there is no middle ground as to whether you like what is happening to you. Either you do or you don't. No matter how small the irritant, come to peace with the issue and put it behind you. You will need all your patience and stamina once the blessed bundles come into your life.

Logistical difference #1: Mom will be larger, sooner. Don't make fun of her size! Trust me on this one. If she asks you if her clothes make her look fat, answer "Of course not!" no matter what she has on. Vary your answers, though, in case she catches on. Jokes aside, a multiple pregnancy is still considered high-risk. You will face challenges in many areas including mental, physical, and emotional. Be extra attentive and sensitive. Remember, Mom doesn't have a whole lot of control over what's happening inside, and to, her.

BUT WHAT CAN I DO?

Many fathers bring a great deal of frustration on themselves by trying to live up to someone else's expectations of the "ideal father." The media have well chronicled the "super mom" phenomenon but have often overlooked the challenges facing fathers. In many families, the father is still the chief breadwinner. Just as many moms work inside (and yes, outside) the home, many dads have to play multiple roles, such as breadwinner, handyman, coach, etc. Rather than debate the pros and cons of gender-based roles, apply the Nike motto from the '90's: Just do it (to the best of your abilities). If the father is the breadwinner, then so be it. If you've switched stereotypical gender-based roles, then do what you're supposed to do. The objective is not how much money is in the bank, or what kind of car is in the driveway, but how well you're raising your child. Similarly, it doesn't matter how many roles you play in the family, as long as the roles you do play are played earnestly and to the best of your abilities.

Logistical difference #2: Multiple babies often have similar biological clocks. They frequently are hungry, wet, and cranky at the same time. Though you are not equipped for it, helping Mom feed the babies in the wee hours of the morning goes a long way toward maintaining family harmony. Reinforcing the fact that Mom's not in it alone, even if you're holding the second (or third) baby while waiting for the ol' switcheroo, can help.

ESTABLISHING PARENTAL ROLES

Many dads may map out weeks, months, or years in advance the roles they will play for their kids and their families. While consistency is a comfort to everyone involved, good communication with your spouse allows you to take advantage of the opportunities that life presents. Each parent brings into the relationship and the family some skills and abilities that are more developed than the partner's. Whenever possible, go with your strengths. Instead of thinking about which parent should do what, look and listen to what is going on around the home. See what opportunities are brought up for which parent. Very often, the right parent is going to be at the right place at the right time.

There are not very many differences in the role of the parent between singletons or multiple-birth children. Once things get beyond the first few months, and family patterns and cycles — like sleeping and eating times — begin to form, behaviors that are successful get reinforced (for both the child and the parent), and unsuccessful behaviors get modified or dropped from the routine. Parents tend to keep what works and drop things that waste time.

WHEN THINGS GO WRONG

Sooner or later, some of you may experience The Moment Of Doubt. Whether it comes from anger, depression, fatigue, or frustration, the inevitable "Why me?" (or something like it) will be sighed, mumbled, or shouted from your lips. It's OK. There's no telling when it will occur, or why, but here are some of the surrounding symptoms:

1. Some major calamity will happen. It doesn't matter what. You fill in the blank. Whatever major rule you hold sacred, it will be violated.
2. A bunch of little things will pile up until one little thing pushes you over the edge, the classic example of the straw breaking the camel's back.
3. You use emotional transference or overreaction. An obvious example of this is when you've had a horrible day, street traffic has been a mess, and the house is a shambles. Then little Billy tugs on your clothes because he wants to show you something, and you blow up at him. This is different from #2 because little Billy has done nothing wrong himself. You transferred the emotions that you've been bottling up inside yourself all day and released it at an unsuspecting target because he was handy.

As soon as you become aware that you're at the "Why me?" stage, you need to stop and gather yourself. If you've given reasonable thought to the decision to have children and accepted the idea with all that goes with it, then you need an attitude adjustment. If you haven't yet accepted the fact that you are a dad, you need to work on that aspect and work hard at it. Get some help if you need it. Adjusting your attitude is easy to say but hard to do. Can you do it all the time? Maybe. Does it get easier each time you practice it? Absolutely!

There isn't a great deal of logistical difference between singletons and multiple birth children in this area except that having more kids means having to be more disciplined and have greater self-control. The operative thought is that more children offer more opportunities to practice restraint.

WHAT'S NEXT?

     We've covered the basics. We've also looked into how to deal with some of the low points (believing, of course, that the high points will take care of themselves). What's next? Simply put, more of the same. Raising children is a never-ending responsibility. The part that changes is the degree of active participation a parent plays in the life of the child. Some parents have a hard time letting go, while others can't wait to get them out of the house. Whichever camp you fall into, or even if you're somewhere in between, the foundation you build in the early years (diaper age to college age) will pay dividends later.

     As all of your children grow into their own identity, they will each exhibit their particular skills and abilities. The challenge for the parent of multiples is to allow each child to blossom into his or her full potential while understanding that each child's needs may differ, or be totally opposite, from those of the siblings.

Highlights of NOMOTC's 1992 Fathers Survey

- Of the 1,142 responses received, 50 percent were filled out by the mothers and the other half by the fathers.
- Compared with the time spent on baby care with their singletons, fathers with both multiples and singletons spent 14 percent more time doing baby care with their multiples.
- The majority of fathers helped change diapers (92 percent) and gave bottles (89 percent).
- 22 percent shared chores 50/50 with the spouse.
- 42 percent would consider becoming a "stay-at-home" dad if it was financially possible.
- Half felt that having multiples had been a financial burden.
- The biggest surprise about having multiples was the time required for their care.
- When asked if they wanted to have multiples again, 70 percent would not even consider it, while 26 percent said they would enjoy rearing another set.

APPENDIX

APPENDIX A – RESOURCES LIST

1. PREGNANCY – CHAPTER 1
   a. Sidelines, Candace Hurley, Executive Director, 714-497-2265, or Tracy Hoogenboom, 909-563-6199, email: sidelines@sidelines.net. *Non-profit for referral information, support and advocacy for women experiencing complicated pregnancies* <Pregnancy, Bed Rest During Pregnancy>
   b. TTTS foundation and support group: Twin to Twin Transfusion Syndrome Foundation, c/o Mary Slaman-Forsythe, 411 Longbeach Parkway, Bay Village, OH 44140, 216-899-TTTS, info@tttsfoundation.org, www.tttsfoundation.org <Pregnancy, Medical Complications of Multiple Pregnancy, Twin-to-Twin Transfusion Syndrome>
   c. Twin Hope, Inc. (Twin-to-Twin Transfusion Syndrome), c/o Jill Mac-Niven, President, 2592 West 14th Street, Cleveland, OH 44113. 216-731-6940, 216-228-TTTS <Pregnancy, Medical Complications of Multiple Pregnancy, Twin-to-Twin Transfusion Syndrome>

2. SUPERTWINS – CHAPTER 2
   a. Mothers of Supertwins (MOST), c/o Maureen Boyle, PO Box 951, Brentwood, NY 11717. 631-859-1110, maureen@MOSTonline.org, www.mostonline.org. *Support group for parents of triplets, quads, quints, etc.* <Supertwins, By the Numbers>
   b. The Triplet Connection, c/o Janet Bleyl, PO Box 99571, Stockton, CA 95209. 209-474-0885, tc@tripletconnection.org, www.tripletconnection.org. *Support group for parents of triplets.* <Supertwins, By the Numbers>

3. QUESTIONS – CHAPTER 3
   a. PROACTIVE GENETICS, 2 Goodwin's Court, Suite #1, Marblehead, MA 01945. 781-639-5126, info@proactivegenetics.com, www.proactivegenetics.com. *Offers DNA-based zygosity testing that is bloodless and uses PCR technology.* <Questions, Determination of Twin Type (Zygosity), DNA testing>

4. PREPARATIONS – CHAPTER 4
   a. SAFERIDERS, 1100 West 49th Street, Austin, TX 78756-3180. 1-800-252-8255. *Offers advice on carseat safety, owner's manuals, information about carseats that have been recalled.* <Preparations, Carseats>
   b. Kids N Motion, 1-800-890-8960, *Peg Perego Strollers.* <Preparations, Strollers>
   c. Runabout Strollers, 8025 SW 185th, Aloha, OR 97007. 1-800-832-2376. <Preparations, Strollers>
   d. The Baby Jogger Co., PO Box 2189, Yakima, WA 98907. 1-800-241-1848. *Twin and triplet jogging strollers.* <Preparations, Strollers>
   e. Twin and Triplet Stroller Hotline. 1-800-228-TWIN. *Catalog of strollers.* <Preparations, Strollers>
   f. Stroller information: See above for higher birth-order organizations for information about companies that deal in triplet and higher strollers. <Preparations, Strollers>
   g. National S.A.F.E. Home Foundation, Inc., 1333 Strad Avenue, North Tonawanda, NY 14120. 1-800-877-1250 or e-mail at safehome@buffnet.net. *A non-profit charity dedicated to reducing the high number of injuries and deaths from residential fires.* <Preparations, Safety Issues>
   h. The National Organization of Mothers of Twins Clubs, Inc., PO Box 438, Thompson Station, TN 37179-0438. Toll-free referral line: 877-540-2200. 615-595-0936, NOMOTC@aol.com, www.nomotc.org. *Support group for parents of multiples.* <Preparations, Parents-of-Multiples Clubs>

5. INFANCY – CHAPTER 6
   a. Right Start Catalog, Right Start Plaza, 31333 Agoura Road, Westlake Village, CA 91361-4639. 1-800-LITTLE-1. *Baby bottle holder.* <Infancy, Bottle Feeding>
   b. Jancoe Products, Inc., PO Box 606, Gurnee, IL 60031. 1-800-554-9449. *Tend-A-Babe Bottle Prop.* <Infancy, Bottle Feeding>
   c. Podee Hands-Free Baby Bottle, PO Box 502172, San Diego, CA 92150-2172. <Infancy, Bottle feeding>
   d. Double Blessing, 668 Mountain View Rd, El Cajon, CA 92021-3852. 1-800-584-TWIN. *Double nursing pillow.* <Infancy, Breast-feeding>
   e. Four Dee Products, 6014 Lattimer, Houston, TX 77035. 713-728-0389. *Nurse Mate nursing pillow.* <Infancy, Breast-feeding>
   f. Ameda-Egnell Corp. C/o Customer service, Industrial Drive, Cary, IL 60013-1993. 1-800-323-8750. *Breast pump equipment.* <Infancy, Breast-feeding>
   g. Madela, Inc. Breast-feeding Network, PO Box 660, 4610 Prime Pkwy, McHenry, IL 60051. 1-800-TELL-YOU. <Infancy, Breast-feeding>
   h. La Leche League International, 1400 North Meacham Road, Schaum-

burg, IL 60173-4048. 847-519-7730 <Infancy, Breast-feeding>

i. International Board of Lactation Consultant Examiners, 7309 Arlington Blvd., Suite 300, Falls Church, VA 22042-3215. 703-560-7330, www.iblce.org, <Infancy, Breast-feeding>

j. International Lactation Consultants Association, 4101 Lake Boone Trail, Suite 201, Raleigh, NC 27607. 919-787-5181, www.ilca.org <Infancy, Breast-feeding>

6. SCHOOL AGE – CHAPTER 8
   a. National Organization of Mothers of Twins Clubs, Inc.- Placement of Multiple Birth Children in School: A Guide for Educators (2000); Research Report: Multiples in School and Survey of Educators (1989 and 1999); Press Release: "To Divide or Not to Divide" (1998); Publication: Your Multiples and You (2000); Research Questionnaire: Home Schooling (1999); Club TIPS Sheet: Handling of School Issues (1998); Position Paper: Guidelines for the Education of Multiple Birth Children (1998) - PO Box 438, Thompson Station, TN, 37179, 615-595-0936, www.nomotc.org. *NOMOTC publications relating to school issues with multiples.* <School Age>
   b. HSLDA - Home School Legal Defense Association, PO Box 3000, Purcelville, VA 20134. 540-338-5600, www.hslda.org. *Information for home-school families.* <School Age, Home Schooling>
   c. Home School Families of Twins Newsletter, Margie Downey, Founder and Senior Editor, 1112 Eton Drive, Richardson, TX 75080, 972-234-6818, Margie.hsft@juno.com. www.flash.net/~hsft <School Age, Home Schooling>
   d. National Home Education Research Institute, Attn.: Brian D. Ray, Ph.D., President, PO Box 13939, Salem, OR 97309. 503-364-1490. <School Age, Home Schooling>

7. ADOPTION – CHAPTER 12 B
   a. Adoptive Families of America, 3333 Highway 100 North, Minneapolis, MN 55422.612-535-4829.
   b. Adoptees Liberty Movement Associates (ALMA), PO Box 727, Radio City Station, New York, NY 10101-0727. (212) 581-1568.

8. SINGLE PARENTING – CHAPTER 12 C
   a. NOMOTC, Inc., C/o Single Parent Support Services, PO Box 438, Thompson Station, TN 37179. 615-595-0936, www.nomotc.org. *NOMOTC's single parent support coordinator.*
   b. Parents Without Partners, 8807 Colesville Road, Silver Spring, MD 20910. 1-800-637-7974, 301-588-9354. *Support group for single parents.*
   c. North American Conference of Separated and Divorced Catholics, 1100 South Goodman Street, Rochester, NY 14320.

d. Association of Jewish Family and Children's Agencies, PO Box 248, Kendall Park, NJ 08824. 1-800-634-7346.
e. Single Parent Resource Center, 141 West 28th Street, New York, NY 10001. 212-947-0221.

9. SPECIAL NEEDS – CHAPTER 12 D
a. Dr. Elizabeth Pector, PO Box 5845, Naperville, IL 60567. www.onelist.com/subscribe.cgi/specpar. *Can help parents of special needs children find a support group.*

10. LOSS OF A MULTIPLE – CHAPTER 12E
a. NOMOTC, Bereavement Booklet: A guide of support for those who are facing the death of a loved one (1998), PO Box 438, Thompson Station, TN 37179. 615-595-0936, www.nomotc.org. *NOMOTC's booklet on bereavement with emphasis on loss in multiples.*
b. Center for Loss in Multiple Birth (CLIMB, Inc.), c/o Jean Kollantai, PO Box 1064, Palmer, AK 99645. 907-746-6123. climb@pobox.alaska.net. *Support group for parents who have experienced the death of a multiple or multiples during pregnancy, birth, infancy, or childhood.*
c. Twinless Twins Support Group, International, 9311 Poplar Creek Pl., Leo, IN 46765. www.serv1r.fwi.com/twinless/ 219-627-5414. www.serv1r.fwi.com/twinless/. *Serves in support of those who suffer from the loss of companionship of a twin through death, estrangement, or in-utero loss.*
d. Lone Twin Network, PO Box 5653, Birmingham, B29 7JY, United Kingdom.

APPENDIX B — MULTIPLE BIRTH ASSOCIATIONS AND OTHER HELPFUL ORGANIZATIONS

UNITED STATES:

Center for Study of Multiple Birth
Suite 464
333 East Superior St.
Chicago, IL 60611
312-266-9093

International Twins Association, Inc. (ITA),
"A Support Group for Twins"
C/o Lynn Long and Lori Steward
6898 Channel Road N.E.
Minneapolis, MN 55432
612-571-3022

The International Twins Foundation (ITF)
PO Box 6043
Providence, RI 02904-6043
401-729-1000

Louisville Twin Study
c/o Professor Adam J. Matheny, Jr.
Department of Pediatrics
School of Medicine
University of Louisville
Louisville, KY 40292
502-852-5131

Military Parents of Multiples
c/o Sandra Scott
PO Box 302
Henrietta, TX 76365

Mid-Atlantic Twin Studies
The Medical College of Virginia
Virginia Commonwealth University
PO Box 980003
Richmond, VA 23298

Minnesota Center for Twin and Adoption
Research
c/o Thomas Bouchard, PhD
University of Minnesota
Department of Psychology
72 East River Road
Minneapolis, MN 55455
612-625-4067

Mothers of Supertwins (MOST)
c/o Maureen Boyle
PO Box 951
Brentwood, NY 11717-0627
631-859-1110

maureen@mostonline.org
www.mostonline.org

The National Organization of Mothers of
Twins Clubs, Inc.
PO Box 438
Thompson Station, TN 37179-0438
877-540-2200 (referral line)
615-595-0936
nomotc@aol.com
www.nomotc.org

The Triplet Connection
c/o Janet Bleyl
PO Box 99571
Stockton, CA 95209
209-474-0885
tc@tripletconnection.org
www.tripletconnection.org

Twins Days Festival Committee, Inc.
PO Box 29
Twinsburg, OH 44087
www.twinsdays.org

Twin-to-Twin Transfusion Syndrome
Foundation
c/o Mary Slaman-Forsythe
411 Longbeach Parkway
Bay Village, OH 44140
440-899-TTTS
info@tttsfoundation.org
www.tttsfoundation.org

Twin Hope, Inc. (Twin-to-Twin Transfusion
Syndrome)
c/o Jill MacNiven, President
2592 West 14th Street
Cleveland, OH 44113
216-731-6940
216-228-TTTS

INTERNATIONAL:

AUSTRALIA
AMBA - Australian Multiple Birth Assn.
PO Box 105
Coogee, NSW 2034
Australia
www.amba.org.au/

BELGIUM
Assn. Francophone d' Entraide Pour

Naissances Multiples
c/o Madelaine Bouche
1320 Genval
Belgium

BULGARIA
George Tsolov, Ph.D., Chair of the Twins'
Club in Plovdiv & Zlatka Doncheva, Chair
of the Mothers' Section
24 Graf Ignatiev Street
Floor 9, Apt. 34
4000 Plovdiv
Bulgaria

CAMEROON
Cameroon National Club of Twins
c/o TJOMB Daniel Diedonne
PO Box 171
Eseka
Cameroon

CANADA
Multiple Births Canada
P.O. Box 234 Gormley
Ontario, Canada
L0H 1G0
905-888-0725
FAX 905-888-0727
office@multiplebirthscanada.org
www.multiplebirthscanada.org

COMBO
Council of Multiple Birth Organizations -
See ISTS

DENMARK
Trillinge Forzeldreforeningen
Danmark
www.home1.inet.tele.dk/timand/

ETHIOPIA
Ethiopian Gemini Trust
c/o Dr. Carmela Aabate
PO Box 3547
Addis Ababa
Ethiopia

FINLAND
Assn. Of Finnish Triplet Families
www.tripletti.cjb.net

FRANCE
Assn. Nationale d' Entraide des Parents de
Naissances Multiples (ANEPNM)
26 Boulevard Brune
75014 Paris
France

Assn.Provincale des Jumeaux e la Sissilli

(APJS)
Rue Industrielle 22
CH 1820 Montreaux
France
www.jumeaux-infos.com/

GERMANY
ABC Club
c/o Helga Gruetzner
Strohweg 55
D-64297 Darmstadt Germany
www.abc-club.de

INDONESIA
Nakula-Sadewa Indonesia Twins Foundation
c/o Mr. Seto Mulyadi, Chmn.
JI. Taman Cirendue
Permai No. 13
Jakarta 15419
Indonesia

IRELAND
The Irish Multiple Births Assn. (IMBA)
www.homepages.iol.ie/~erogers/imba.htm

ISTS
International Society for Twin Studies
c/o Jaakko Kaprio, Sec. General
Dept. of Public Health
PO Box 41
Mannerheimintie 172
FIN-00014
University of Helsinki
Finland
www.ists.qimr.edu.au

JAPAN
Japanese Assn. Of Twins' Mothers
c/o Yukiko Amau
5-5-20 Minami Aoyama
Minatoku, Tokyo 107
Japan

MEXICO
C.P. Pedro Alfonso Ochoa Ledesma
Asociacion de Nacimientos Multiples
Av. Constituyentes No. 130, Ote.
Col Arquitos, C.P. 76050
Queretaro, Qro Mexico
www.gemelos.org.mx

NETHERLANDS
Nederlands Verniging Van/Tweelingen
2582 NV's Granvenhage
Johan V
Oldernbarneveltlaan 56
Netherlands

Parents of Twins
c/o Mrs.I Patel, President
De Beukems 94
5283 XE Boxtel
Netherlands

NEW ZEALAND
New Zealand Multiple Birth Assn. Inc.
PO Box 1258
Wellington, New Zealand
lizblake@xtra.co.nz

NIGERIA
Worldwide Twins and Multiple Births Assn.
Inc.
Odion and Akhere Eremionkhale
PO Box 8839 Shomolu
Lagos, Nigeria

NORWAY
Tvillingforeldre foreningen
Ingun Ulven Lie
Arvins Gt. 1
0253 Oslo
Norway
www.tvillig.net

POLAND
Parents of Twins Club
Klub Rodzicow Blizniat "Blizniak"
Integracjline Przedskole Miejskie
Number 3
nl. Bema 15
99-300 Kutno
Poland

PUERTO RICO
Elmundo de los Gemelos pr
www.geocities.com/gemelospr/

REPUBLIC OF SOUTH AFRICA
South African Multiple Birth Assn.
(SAMBA)
PO Box 2590
Honeyden 2040
Republic of South Africa

ROMANIA
Asociatia Gemenilor din Romania
Tudor Irimia, President
Str. Paralutelor, nr 11, Bl P45
sc. A etaj 11, ep 6 Sector 6
Bucharest
Romania

RUSSIA
Twins Club "I Am You"
c/o Dr. T.B. Morozova
198052

St. Petersburg
Obvodny Kahal 114
Russia

SPAIN
www.personal1.iddeo.es/olalde/index.html

SWEDEN
Svenska Tvillingklubben AB
Valhallavagen 106, og
S-114 41 Stockholm
Sweden
www.trillingforeningen.a.se/index.html

SWITZERLAND
Association for Parents with Triplets and
More
c/o Claudio Heusser
Dorfstr 16
8175 Windlach
Switzerland

Assn. For Parents with Twins
c/o Barbara Jezler
Grametstr. 18
5272 Gansingen
Switzerland
FAX 062 875 28 64

Swiss Twins Parents Club
c/o Silvia Sinkwitz
44 Avonwood Rd, #318
Avon, CT 06001 USA

Zwillingseltern-Club Aargau
c/o Brigit Brandestini
Schlierenstrasse 87
5400 Ennetbaden
Switzerland

TAIWAN
Taipei Twins Assn.
c/o Chveh Chang, President
No. 1 Jen-Ai Road
Section 1, room 1523
Taipei, Taiwan

UNITED KINGDOM
Multiple Births Foundation
c/o Dr. Elizabeth Bryan
Queen Charlotte's & Chelsea Hospital
Goldhawk Road
London W6 OXG
United Kingdom
mbf@rpms.ac.uk
www.multiplebirths.orguk

Twins and Multiple Births Assn (TAMBA)
Harnott House

309 Chester Road
Little Sutton
Ellesmere Port
CH66 1QQ
United Kingdom
www.orchard.headweb.co.uk/tamba/main.htm

ZIMBABWE
Zimbabwe Multiple Births Association
c/o Mrs. C. Goddard Charleigh
3 Hillmorton Road
Meyrick Park
Marare
Zimbabwe

LOSS/BEREAVEMENT:

American Assn. Of Retired Persons (AARP)
Grief & Loss Programs
601 E Street, NW
Washington, D.C. 20049
202-434-2260
Aiding Mothers (and Fathers) Experiencing Neonatal Death (AMEND)
c/o Maureen J. Connelly, Director
4324 Berrywick Terrace
St. Louis, MO 63128
314-487-7582

Center for Loss in Multiple Birth (CLIMB)
c/o Jean Kollantai
PO Box 91377
Anchorage, AK 99509
907-222-5321
climb@pobox.alaska.net
www.climb-support.org

Centering Corporation
1531 N. Saddle Creek Road
Omaha, NE 68104-5064
402-553-1200

Compassionate Friends, Inc.
c/o Diana Cunningham, Exec. Dir.
PO Box 3696
Oak Brook, IL 60522-3696
630-990-0010
877-969-0010
www.compassionatefriends.org
FAX 630/990-0246

Helping Other Parents in Normal Grieving
(HOPING)
c/o Carolyn Wickham
Sparrow Hospital
1215 East Michigan Avenue
PO Box 30480
Lansing, MI 48090-9986
517-484-3600

Miscarriage, Infant Death, Stillbirth,
Ectopic Pregnancy Support Group (MIDS,
Inc.)
c/o Janet Tischler
16 Crescent Drive
Parsippany, NJ 07054
973-263-6730
mids@nac.net
www.midsinc.org

National Organization of Mothers of Twins
Clubs, Inc. (NOMOTC)
Bereavement Coordinator
PO Box 438
Thompson Station, TN 37179-0438
877-540-2200 (referral line)
615-595-0936
nomotc@aol.com
www.nomotc.org

Pregnancy & Infant Loss Center
c/o Charlene Nelson or Donna Roehl
142 East Wayzata Boulevard, Suite 70
Wayzata, MN 55391
612-473-9372

Bereavement Services
c/o Fran Rybarik, RN, MPH, Dir.
Gundersen/Lutheran Medical Center
1910 South Avenue
LaCrosse, WI 54601
800-362-9567, ext. 4747
608-791-4747
berservs@lhl.gundluth.org
FAX 608/791-5137

SHARE - Pregnancy & Infant Loss Support,
Inc.
St. Joseph Health Center
c/o Catherine Lammert
300 First Capitol Drive
St. Charles, MO 63301
636-947-6164
800-821-6819
share@nationalshareoffice.com
www.nationalshareoffice.com

SIDS Alliance, Inc.
c/o Judith Jacobsen
1314 Bedford Avenue
Suite 210
Baltimore, MD 21208
800-221-7437
410-653-8226
sidshq@charm.net
www.sidsalliance.org

Tender Hearts Group
c/o Triplet Connection

PO Box 99571
Stockton, CA 95209

Twin Hope, Inc.
c/o Jill MacNiven
2592 West 14th Street
Cleveland, OH 44113
216-228-TTTS
twinhope@twinhope.com
www.twinhope.com

THEOS (Loss of a spouse)
1301 Clark Building
717 Liberty Avenue
Pittsburgh, PA 15222-3510
412-471-7779

Twinless Twins Support Group,
International
9311 Poplar Creek Place
Leo, IN 46765
219-627-5414
www.twi.com/twinless/

Unite, Inc. Grief Support After Infant Death,
including Miscarriage and Stillbirth
c/o Jeanes Hospital
7600 Central Avenue
Philadelphia, PA 19111-2499
215-728-3777

SINGLE PARENTS:

Association for Children for the Enforce-
ment of Support (ACES)
723 Phillips Avenue, Suite J
Toledo, OH 43612
419-476-2511

Parents Without Partners
8807 Colesville Road
Silver Springs, MD 20910
800-637-7974
301-588-9354

Single Moms of Triplets
c/o Linda Willis
308 Rena Drive
Lafayette, LA 70503
318-981-7167

Single Mother, bi-monthly newsletter of
the National Organization of Single Mothers, Inc. (NOSM)
PO Box 68
Midland, NC 28107-0068
704-888-2337
Single Parent Resource Center - network of

single parent self-help groups
141 West 28th Street, #302
New York, NY 10001
212-947-0221

Single Mothers By Choice
c/o Jane Mattes
PO Box 1642
Gracie Square Station
New York, NY 10028
212-988-0993

MISCELLANEOUS:

Big Brothers/Big Sisters of America
230 North 13th Street
Philadelphia, PA 19107-1510
215-567-7000

Displaced Homemakers Network
755 8th Street NW
Washington, DC 20001

Mid-Atlantic Twin Studies
Medical College of VA Commonwealth
University
PO Box 980003
Richmond, VA 23298

Military Parents of Multiples
c/o Sandra Scott
PO Box 302
Henrietta, TX 76365

Multiple Births Foundation of No. America
PO Box 146
Wake Forest, NC 27588

National Committee for Prevention of
Child Abuse
322 South Michigan Avenue
Suite 950
Chicago, IL 60604-4357
312-663-3520

National Salvation Army Headquarters
615 Slater Lane
PO Box 269
Alexandria, VA 22313

Tough Love (troubled families)
Box 1069
Doylestown, PA 18901
1-800-333-1069 or 215-348-7090

United Way of America
First Call for Help
Community Resource Division

701 North Fairfax Street
Alexandria, VA 22314-2045

World Multiple Organization
1120 Linden Drive
Aurora, IL 60507

Young Men's Christian Association of USA
(YMCA)
101 North Wacker Drive
Chicago, IL 60606
1-800-872-9622

Young Women's Christian Association
(YWCA)
726 Broadway
New York, NY 10003
212-614-2700

GOVERNMENT SERVICES

Federal Information Center
1-800-366-2998

Head Start Bureau
U.S. Dept. Of Health & Human Services
PO Box 1182
Washington, D.C. 20013

Internal Revenue Service
1-800-829-1040

Women's Infants and Children Food
Program (WIC)
1-800-525-2521

APPENDIX C — ONLINE RESOURCES

MULTIPLES

www.ghgcorp.com/4dee/html   *Twin Net - list of manufacturer freebies.*

www.katsden.com/webster/twins.html   *Twins on the net.*

www.mostonline.org   *Website for Mothers of Supertwins, a support group for parents of triplets, quads, quints, etc.*

www.nomotc.org   *Website for the National Organization of Mothers of Twins Clubs, Inc.*

www.parentsplace.com   *Twin Services.*

www.proactivegenetics.com   *DNA testing for zygosity.*

www.pubweb.acns.nwu.edu/~lgk395/csmb.html   *The Center for Study of Multiple Births.*

www.tttsfoundation.org   *Information and support for parents dealing with Twin-to-Twin Transfusion Syndrome.*

www.tripletconnection.org   *Support group for parents of triplets.*

www.TWINSmagazine.com   *Twins Magazine.*

www.twinz.com   *The lighter side of multiple information.*

CHAT BOX:

The Triplet List - Majordomo@Tripcom.com (type: subscribe triplets)
Triplets Internet List - triplets-request@tripcom.com (type: subscribe)
Twins Digest - twins-Request@cup.hp.com (type: subscribe twins-digest)

PREGNANCY, INFANCY, CHILDCARE

www.thebabynet.com   *Includes information on pregnancy and delivery, parenting, and additional resources for pregnant and new mothers.*

www.babynews.com   *Newborn and infant pictures put online.*

www.childadvocacy.org   *Nationwide network of nonprofit, multi-issue, nonpartisan state and local child advocacy organizations working to ensure children's safety, security, health, and education.*

www.lalecheleague.org *For expectant and new moms who want to breast-feed. Contains information, frequently asked questions, information on upcoming seminars and workshops, as well as links to related sites.*

www.medsch.wisc.edu/childrenshopsp/parents_of_preemies/indes.html *Center for perinatal care.*

www.mommytimes.com *Good for moms of preschool children. Monthly editions include articles such as : "Super Software Selections: Jumpstart Spanish," "Feed Me," "Getting Ready for Back to School," "Household Humor," etc.*

www.momsonline.com *A current site that offers information on latchkey kids, busy school days, stepfamilies, finding friends for moms home alone, message boards, chat rooms, etc.*

www.parentsoup.com *Parenting advice and networking.*

www.pedianet.com *Good source for online information about children's medical and safety issues.*

www.storksite.com *Online library, parenting tips, chat box, name database, e-mail to childbirth educators.*

DISABILITIES/SPECIAL NEEDS

www.pcnet.com/~orphan *National Organization of Rare Disorders.*

www.onelist.com/subscribe.cgi/specpar Can help parents of special needs children find a support group.

CHAT BOX:

Behavioral Problems - listserv@asuvm.inre.asu.edu
Developmental Delays - majordomo@tbag.osc.edu
Disabilities - listserv@gitvm1.bitnet
Fathers of disabled children - listserv@ukcc.uky.edu
Special Health Needs - listserv@nervm.nerdc.ufl.edu

E-MAIL:

Nat'l Organization of Rare Disorders - orphan@nord-rdb.com
Special Children - spclchdrn@aol.com
Twin Studies - apmath01@ulkyvm.louisville.edu

EDUCATIONAL ISSUES

www.trioprograms.org *Strives to increase access to high-quality resources for individuals, parents, and organizations interested in ways and means to enable low-income, first-generation, and disabled students to attend.*

www.nea.org *Website for the National Education Association.*

www.ncea.org *Website for National Catholic Education Association.*

www.pta.org *Good site for parents of school age children. In addition to organization information, it contains helpful information on a variety of child-rearing topics such as raising alcohol- and drug-free children.*

HOMESCHOOLING

www.home-ed-press.com *Home Education Magazine presents free online newsletters, discussion boards, a networking list, and selections from the magazine.*

www.home-school.com *The latest homeschooling news, articles, organizations, events, Homeschool Mall, and much more.*

www.hslda.org *Home School Legal Defense Association, for home-school families.*

STAY-AT-HOME MOMS

www.femalehome.org *This is a non-profit organization supporting mothers who have altered their career paths in order to care for their children at home.*

www.hearts-at-home.org *A site for stay-at-home (SAH) moms, it includes information about annual conferences, a monthly magazine, and a moms referral network.*

www.hbwm.com *Address for Home Based Working Moms, a site for SAH Moms. Includes a variety of information including tips from home based working moms, prizes/contests, web page links, message boards, etc.*

www.momsrefuge.com *Provides SAH moms with a variety of information including family issues, career, single moms articles, a bookshelf of related reading materials, current news issues, recipes, and additional resources.*

MOMS EMPLOYED OUTSIDE THE HOME

www.advancingwomen.com *Good for SAH and working moms. A resource destination for business and career women, but also has information on networking with business women, recruiting opportunities, as well as information on national and international women's business organizations.*

www.en-parent.com *For the entrepreneurial parent, this site includes information on career counseling, a resource center, how to raise a family and have a career, and listings of books and articles about home businesses.*

www.wahm.com *Work at home moms; gives SAH moms an opportunity to register with services which will find them a work-at-home job opportunity, chat rooms, at-home business promotions, plus other at-home services such as grocery delivery.*

APPENDIX D — BIBLIOGRAPHY

Boklage C., *Frequency and Survival of Natural Twin Conceptions*, Department of Pediatrics, East Carolina University School of Medicine (Greenville, N.C.), presented at 8th International Congress on Twin Studies, May 1995.

Curtin S.C., Martin, J.A., *Births: Preliminary data for 1999*, national vital statistics reports, vol. 48, no. 14 (Hyattsville, Md.: National Center for Health Statistics, 2000).

Duncan, B.; Ey, J.; Holberg, C.J.; et al., *Exclusive breast-feeding for at least 4 months protects against otitis media*, Pediatrics 1993, vol. 91, pp. 867-872.

Downham, M.; Scott, R.; Sims, D.G.; et al., *Breast-feeding protects against respiratory syncytial virus infections*, British Medical Journal 1976, vol. 2, pp. 274-276.

Hall, D., *Analysis of identical twins, same-sex fraternal twins and same-sex siblings close in age relationships using structural analysis*, NOMOTC Research Reports, 1988; reports 22 and 22A.

Howie, P.W.; Forsyth, J.S.; Ogston, S.A.; et al., *Protective effect of breast-feeding against infection.* BMJ 1990, vol. 300, pp.11-16.

Kardel, K.R.; Kase, T., *Training in pregnant women: effects on fetal development and birth.* American Journal of Obstetrics and Gynecology 1998, vol. 178(2), pp. 280-286.

Kjos, S.L.; Henry, O.; Lee, R.M.; et al., *The effect of lactation on glucose and lipid metabolism in women with recent gestational diabetes.* Obstetrics and Gynecology 1993, vol. 82, pp. 451-455.

Lawrence, R., *Breastfeeding: A guide for the medical profession*, 4th edition (revised), C.V. Mosby (St. Louis, 1994).

Lucas, A.; Brooke, O.G.; Morley, R.; et al., *Early diet of preterm infants and development of of allergic or atopic disease: randomised (sic) prospective study*, BMJ 1990; vol. 300, pp. 840-844.

Luke, B., *The Changing Pattern of Multiple Births in the United States: Maternal and Infant Characteristics, 1973 and 1990*, Obstetrics and Gynecology 1994, vol. 84, pp. 101-6.

Material for Kegel Exercises adapted from Katherine Jeter, Ed.D., E.T., director of Help for Incontinent People.

Mayer, E.J.; Hamman, R.F.; Gay, E.C.; et al., *Reduced risk of IDDM among breast-fed children*, Diabetes 1988, vol. 37, pp.1625-1632.

Moore, K.L., *The Developing Human: Clinically Oriented Embryology*, 2nd ed., W.B. Saunders (Philadelphia, Pa.,1977).

Newcomb, P.A.; Storer, B.E.; Longnecker, M.P.; et al., *Lactation and a reduced risk of premenopausal breast cancer*, New England Journal of Medicine 1994, vol. 330, pp.81-87.

Nichols, F., and Smith Humenick, S., *Childbirth Education: Practice, Research and Theory*, W. B. Saunders Company (Philadelphia, Pa., 1988).

Olds, S.; London, M.; Ladewig, P.; et al., Obstetric Nursing. 1980 ed., Addison-Wesley Publishing (Menlo Park, Ca. 1980).

Segal, N., *Entwined Lives: Twins and what they tell us about human behavior*, Penguin Putnam Inc. (New York, 1999).

Shnider, S.M., and Levinson, G., *Anesthesia for Obstetrics*, 2nd ed., Williams and Wilkins (Baltimore, Md. 1987).

Stover, A., and Marnejon, J., *Postpartum care*, American Family Physician 1995, vol. 52, pp.1466-1471.

Willinger, M.; Hoffman, H.J.; Hartford, R.B., *Infant sleep position and risk for Sudden Infant Death Syndrome: Report of meeting held January 13 and 14, 1994, NIH, Bethesda, MD.* Pediatrics 1994, vol. 93, p. 5.

Wright, A.L.; Holberg, C.J.; Martinez, F.D.; et al., *Breast-feeding and lower respiratory tract illness in the first year of life*, BMJ 1989, vol. 299, pp. 946-949.

APPENDIX E — READING LIST

FURTHER READING:

OTHER NOMOTC PUBLICATIONS/PRODUCTS

Bereavement Booklet: *A Guide of Support for Those Who Are Facing the Death of a Loved One.* Albuquerque, N.M.: NOMOTC, 1998.

"Guidelines for the Education of Multiple Birth Children." Albuquerque, N.M.: NOMOTC position paper, 1998.

How To Organize A Parents Of Multiples Club. Thompson Station, Tenn.: NOMOTC, 1999.

National Organization of Mothers of Twins Clubs, Inc.(NOMOTC). Research Reports "Partners In Education" school placement packet. Thompson Station, Tenn.: NOMOTC, 2000.

*Placement of Multiple Birth Children in School: A Guide for Educators.*Thompson Station, Tenn.: NOMOTC, 1991, revised 2000.

Your Multiples and You (pamphlet). Thompson Station, Tenn.: NOMOTC, 2000.

Your Multiples and You: Conception to Six Months (videotape). Albuquerque, N.M.: NOMOTC, 1995.

Your Multiples and You: Toddlers and Preschoolers (videotape). Albuquerque, N.M.: NOMOTC, 1998.

BOOKS WITH USEFUL INFORMATION FOR A MULTIPLE PREGNANCY

Agnew, C.L.; Klein, H.; Ganon, J.A., *TWINS! Expert Advice From Two Practicing Physicians on Pregnancy, Birth, and the First Year of Life*, Harper Collins (New York, 1997).

Birch, K., and Bleyl, J., *Exceptional Pregnancies: A Survival Guide to Parents Expecting Triplets or More, The Triplet Connection* (Stockton, Calif., 2000).

Eisenberg, A.; Murkoff, H.E.; Hathaway, S.E., *What to Expect When You're Expecting*, Workman Publishing Co. (New York, 1984; 2nd ed., 1991; hardcover, 1996).

Johnston, S.H., and Kraut, D.A., *Pregnancy Bedrest: A Guide for the Pregnant Woman and Her Family,* Henry Holt and Co. (New York, 1990).

Luke, B., and Eberlein, T., *When You're Expecting Twins, Triplets, or Quads*, Harper Collins (New York, 1999).

Noble, E., *Having Twins: A Parent's Guide to Pregnancy, Birth, and Early Childhood*, Houghton Mifflin (Boston 1980, 2nd ed. 1991).

Rich, L.A., *When Pregnancy Isn't Perfect: A Layperson's Guide to Complications in Pregnancy*, Larata Press (New York, 1991, 2nd ed. 1993).

BOOKS ABOUT PREMATURITY

Klein, A.H., and Ganon, J.A., *Caring for Your Premature Baby: A Complete Resource For Parents*, Harper Collins (New York,1998).

Manginello, F., and DiGeronimo, T.F., *Your Premature Baby: Everything You Need to Know about Childbirth, Treatment, and Parenting*, John Wiley & Sons (New York, 1991, rev. 1998).

Tracy, A., and Maroney, D., *Your Premature Baby and Child*, Berkley Publishing Group (New York, 1999).

BOOKS ABOUT PARENTING MULTIPLES

Bryan, E.M., *Twins, Triplets and More: From Pre-Birth Through High School – What Every Parent Needs to Know When Raising Two or More*, St. Martin's Press (New York,1992, rev. 1999).

Gromada, K.K., *Mothering Multiples: Breastfeeding & Caring for Twins or More*, La Leche League International (Schaumburg, Ill., 1985, rev. 1999).

Laut, W.S., *Raising Multiple Birth Children: A Parents' Survival Guide*, Chandler House Press (Worcester, Mass., 1999).

Malmstrom, P.M., and Poland, J., *The Art of Parenting Twins: The Unique Joys and Challenges of Raising Twins and Other Multiples,* Ballantine Books Trade Paperback (New York, 1999).

Novotny, P.P., *The Joy of Twins and Other Multiple Births: Having, Raising, and Loving Babies Who Arrive in Groups*, Crown Publishers (New York, 1988, rev. 1994).

Pearlman, E.M., and Ganon, J.A., *Raising Twins: What Parents Want to Know (and What Twins Want to Tell Them)*, Harper Collins (New York, 2000).

Rothbart, B., *Multiple Blessings: From Pregnancy Through Childhood, A Guide for Parents of Twins, Triplets, or More*, Hearst Books (New York, 1994).

BOOKS ABOUT GENERAL PARENTING CONCERNS

Burns, M.S.; Griffin, P.; Snow, C.E., *Starting Out Right: A Guide to Promoting Children's Reading Success*, National Academy Press (Washington, D.C.: National Research Council, 1999).

Ferber, R., *Solve Your Child's Sleep Problems*, Simon & Schuster (New York, 1985).

Woessner, C; Lauwers, J.; Bernard, B., *Breastfeeding Today: A Mother's Companion*, Avery Publishing Group (Garden City Park, N.Y., 1996).

BOOKS ON TWINSHIP

Ainslie, R., *The Psychology of Twinship,* Jason Aronson, Inc. (Northvale, N.J., 1985, rev. 1997).

Case, B.J., *We Are Twins, But Who Am I?* Tibbutt Publishing Company (Portland, Ore., 1991).

Cassill, K., *Twins: Nature's Amazing Mystery*, Atheneum (New York, 1982).

Collier, H.L., *The Psychology of Twins: A Practical Handbook for Parents of Multiples, The Business Word* (Englewood, Colo., 1974, rev. 1996).

Hagedorn, J.W., and Kizziar, J.W., Gemini: *The Psychology and Phenomena of Twins, The Center for Study of Multiple Birth* (Chicago, Ill., 1974, 2nd ed. 1977, reprinted 1983).

Segal, N.L., *Entwined Lives: Twins and What They Tell Us about Human Behavior*, Dutton (New York, 1999).

BOOKS FOR CHILDREN

Abolafia, Y., *My Three Uncles,* Greenwillow Books (New York, 1984).

Adalpe, V.T., *David, Donny, and Darren: A Book about Identical Triplets,* Lerner Publishing (Minneapolis, Minn., 1997).

Aliki, *Jack and Jake*, William Morrow (New York, 1990).

Cleary, B., *The Real Hole*, William Morrow (New York, 1960, 1986, 1996).

De Paola, T., *Too Many Hopkins*, Putnam (New York, 1989).

Fuchshuber, A., *Two Peas in a Pod*, Millbrook Press (Brookfield, Conn., 1998).

Hutchins, P., *Which Witch Is Which?* Greenwillow Books (New York, 1989).

Lacoe, A., *Just Not the Same*, Houghton Mifflin (Boston, Mass., 1992).

Lerner, M.R., *Twins: The Story of Twins*, Lerner Publications (Minneapolis, Minn., 1961).

Lindman, M., *Flicka, Ricka, Dicka and the New Dotted Dresses*, Albert Whitman (Chicago, Ill., 1939, reprint 1994).

Murphy-Melas, E., *Watching Bradley Grow: A Story about Premature Birth*, Longstreet Press (Atlanta, Ga., 1996).

Pallas, J., *Twins Together*, Good Growing Books (Grosse Pointe, Mich., 1995).

Pirani, F., *Triplets*, Viking (New York, 1991).

Rogers, F., *The New Baby*, Putnam (New York, 1985).

Rotner, S., *About Twins*, DK Publishing (New York, 1999).

Scott, E., *TWINS!* Simon & Schuster (New York, 1998).

Seuling, B., *The Triplets*, Houghton Mifflin (New York, 1980).

Seymour, J., *Boing! No Bouncing on the Bed*, Putnam (New York, 1999).

Wisniewski, D., *The Warrior and the Wise Man*, Lothrop, Lee & Shepard (New York, 1989).

BOOKS FOR OLDER CHILDREN

Bradley, K., *One-of-a-Kind Mallie*, Delacorte Press (New York, 1999).

Boyd, C., *Circle of Gold*, Scholastic (New York, 1984, rev. 1994).

Cleary, B., *Mitch and Amy*, William Morrow (New York, 1967, 1991).

Hamilton, V., *Justice and Her Brothers*, Greenwillow Books (New York, 1978. Reissued: Harcourt Brace, New York, 1989, 1998).

Hurwitz, J., *Class Clown*, William Morrow (New York, 1987).

L'Engle, M., *Many Waters*, William Morrow (New York, 1987).

Paterson, K., *Jacob Have I Loved*, Harper Collins (New York, 1980; 1990).

Pevsner, S., *I'm Emma: I'm a Quint*, Houghton Mifflin (New York, 1993).

Reiss, K., *Paperquake: A Puzzle*, Harcourt Brace (New York, 1998).

Sachs, M., *Thirteen Going on Seven*, Dutton (New York, 1993).

BOOKS FOR SINGLE PARENTS

Atlas, S., *The Parents Without Partners Handbook*, Running Press (Philadelphia, Pa., 1984).

Dodson, F., *How to Single Parent,* Harper and Row (New York, 1986).

Gathy, R.H., and Kouloch, D., *Single Father's Handbook*, Doubleday (Garden City, N.Y., 1979).

Goldstein, S., and Solnit, A.J., *Divorce and Your Child*, Yale University Press (New Haven, 1985).

Jewett, C., *Helping Children Cope with Separation and Loss*, Harvard Common Press (Cambridge, Mass., 1982).

Krementz, J., *How it Feels When a Parent Dies*, Knopf (New York, 1983).

Le Shan, E., *When a Parent is Very Sick,* Atlantic Monthly Press (New York, 1986).

Wallerstein, J.S., and Kelly, J.B., *Surviving the Breakup*, Basic Books (New York, 1980).

INDEX

Acetaminophen 8, 15
Adoption 233-38
ADD (attention deficit disorder) 164-65
ADHD (attention deficit hyperactivity disorder) 164-65
Adolescence 174-76
AFP (alpha-fetoprotein) 1,16
Afterbirth 90
After-pains 95
Alcohol 16
Amniocentesis 17, 21
Amnion 21, 22, 58
Amniotic fluid excess 20, 21
Anemia 5, 7, 12
Anesthesia 92-4
  epidural block 93, 94
  general 93
  narcotics 93
  regional 93-4
  spinal block 94
Anorexia nervosa 170-71
Antacids 8, 15
Antibiotics 15, 86
APGAR score 19, 94
Apnea monitor 27, 34
Aspirin 8

Baby books 70
Baby wipes 72
Backache 7
Backpack 77
Bathing 122
Bed rest 15, 29-30, 31
Beds 141
Bed-wetting 144
Bereavement 251-57
Betamehasone 87
Biophysical profile (BPP) 18, 19, 31, 87
Birthday cakes 173
Biting 87
Bladder infection 6
Blood Pressure 19, 20
Bloody show 84
Bond with co-multiple 180,185,232-33, 255
Bottle feeding 41-2, 115-16
  formulas 41, 75

preparing formula 116
propping 42,116
sterilizing 42,116
warming 42, 116
Breast-feeding 103-15
  amount 105
  benefits 104
  in C-Section 92
  classes 114
  electric breast pump 39, 111, 112
  engorgement 39
  expressing milk 41
  father's role 106-7
  higher order 38-41
  inverted nipples 6, 111
  lactation consultant or nurse 112, 115
  leaking milk 106, 109
  let-down 39, 105, 108, 109, 112
  mastitis 39
  nursing bra 39, 106
  one-on-one 108
  poor weight gain 112
  positions 107
  preemies 110, 111
  products 105-6
  pumping 39-40, 107, 109, 110, 111
  returning to work 110
  scheduling 40, 111
  sleepiness 113
  SNS system 110-11
  soreness 106
  supplements 109, 112
  tandem 108, 108h6
Breath-holding 137
Breech presentation 91
Brewer diet 29
Buccal smear 59
Butorphanol 93

Caesarean section 26, 32-33, 40, 84, 90, 91-2, 93
Calcium 8, 12, 13
California department of Health Services Daily Food Guide 12, 29
Calories 9
Cameras 70
Car 37-8

Handicapped parking sticker 30, 44
Headache 8, 20, 94
Health care provider
  appointments 148
  choosing a doctor 3, 25-6
Health insurance 79
Heat 14
Heartburn 6, 8, 20
Heimlich Maneuver 133
HELLP syndrome (Hemolysis, Elevated
  Liver enzymes, and Low Platelets) 20, 31
Hemorrhoids 6, 8, 95
High blood pressure 19, 20
Highchair 69, 117
Higher order multiples 24-47
  bottle feeding 41-2
  breast-feeding 38-41
  complications 31-2
  diet 29
  exercise 13
  identical triplets 25, 51
  incidence 25, 54
  labor and delivery 32-4
  medical team 25-6
  monitors 31
  NICU 26, 34
  outings 44-5
  preterm labor 29-30
  quadruplets 24, 25, 50, 51
  quintuplets 24, 25, 50
  rate or incidence of 25
  selective reduction 27-8
  septuplets 24, 50
  sextuplets 24, 50
  siblings 35
  survey 47
  triplets 24, 25, 50-1
HLA typing 59
hMG (human menopausal gonadotropin)
  60
Home School Legal Defense Association
  (HSLDA) 167
Home schooling 166-67, 194
Home uterine monitoring 15
Hospitalization 149

Identical twins 50, 51
  causes of 57
  complications of 57
Individuality 229-32
Individuals with Disabilities Education Act
  (IDEA) 165
Idiolalia 131, 193
Illness 146-50, 222
Incidence of multiples 53
  by age 55
  by diet 56
  by geography 53, 56

by race 55
by seasons 56
by social habits 56
by twin-type 54
due to fertility treatments 55
factors affecting 54-6
of triplets and higher 54
Indomethacin 87
Injuries 139
International Board of Lactation Consul-
  tant Examiners 114
International Lactation Consultants Associ-
  ation 114
Interval birth 21, 53
Inverted nipples 6, 111
In-vitro fertilization 54, 61-2
IQ scores 3
Iron 7, 12-13
Isolette 102
Itching 9
IVF-ET (In vitro Fertilization and Embryo
  Transfer) 61

Jobs / Careers 182, 214-15, 217
Job sharing 215

Kangaroo care 101-2
Kegel exercises 13-14, 98
Kidney infections 6

La Leche League 113
Labor 83-96 (see also "Preterm birth,"
  "Preterm labor")
  active phase 88
  after-pains 95
  contractions 84, 88
  false 85
  first stage 88
  fourth stage 90
  infections 86
  natural childbirth 92
  nesting syndrome 83
  onset 83-4
  pitocin 89, 90
  pushing 89
  rupture of membranes 84
  second stage 89
  signs 84
  signs of preterm labor 85
  third stage 90
  treatment of preterm labor 86-7
  transition stage 89
  true 85
Lactation consultant or nurse 114
Lamaze classes 4, 92
Laser coagulation in TTTS 22
Laxatives 7, 8
Layette 65-7

Umbilical cord 94, 122
Uric acid 31
Urinary tract infection 6, 10, 86
Urination 5, 9

Vacuum extractor 90
Vanishing twin 2, 62-63
Varicose veins 9
Ventilator 100
Vitamins (see also, "Nutrition")
   vitamin, A 11, 12
   vitamin, B6 9, 11
   vitamin, B12 11
   vitamin, C 11-12
   vitamin, D 11, 12
   vitamin, E 11, 12
   vitamin, K 95
Volunteering 196

Walking 130
Water breakage (rupture of membranes)
   84, 20

Water consumption 10
Weaning from pacifier 138
Weight gain 4, 10-11, 12, 28
WIC (Women, Infants and Children) 36,
   79, 241
Working at home 214-15
Work-site day care 223
Yam (Dioscorea rotundata) 55

Yoruba tribe 56

ZIFT (Zygote Intrafallopian Transfer) 61
Zona pellucida 62
Zygosity determination 57-59
   blood testing 59
   DNA testing 59
   placenta method 58
   similarity method 58

ABOUT THE EDITOR

Rebecca Moskwinski received her B.S. degree in Biology from Purdue University, then earned her medical degree from Indiana University School of Medicine. Dr. Moskwinski specializes in Family Practice and Sports Medicine at the University of Notre Dame. She serves as a team physician for Notre Dame's women's National Championship basketball team, and the volleyball and softball teams.

Dr. Moskwinski experienced a life-changing event when she delivered her identical twins, Bridget and Lindsay, during the second year of her Family Practice Residency. She immediately became involved in her local parents-of-multiples club and the National Organization of Mothers of Twins Clubs, Inc., where she has served on the Board of Directors since 1992. She feels this helped greatly in dealing with her surprise situation. A firm believer in the statistics stating that identical twins are a chance phenomenon and don't often happen twice, Dr. Moskwinski then had four singleton children. She resides with her six children and her husband, Jerry, in Granger, Indiana, along with six cats, a dog, a turtle and a snake.

ABOUT NOMOTC

The National Organization of Mothers of Twins Clubs, Inc. is a support group for parents of twins and higher order multiples established to cooperate with medical and educational professionals engaged in multiple birth research, increase the understanding of child development, and rearing especially relating to multiple births, and to increase awareness of the individuality of each child.

FOOD FIGHT INC.

Napkin Sketches to Retail Shelves:
An Entrepreneur's Odyssey
of Triumphs and Lemons

MIROLAND IMPRINT 11

Canada Council **Conseil des Arts**
for the Arts **du Canada**

ONTARIO ARTS COUNCIL
CONSEIL DES ARTS DE L'ONTARIO
an Ontario government agency
un organisme du gouvernement de l'Ontario

Guernica Editions Inc. acknowledges the support of the Canada Council
for the Arts and the Ontario Arts Council. The Ontario Arts Council
is an agency of the Government of Ontario.

We acknowledge the financial support of the Government of Canada.

FOOD FIGHT INC.

Napkin Sketches to Retail Shelves:
An Entrepreneur's Odyssey
of Triumphs and Lemons

Bruno J. Codispoti

www.foodfightinc.ca

MiroLand
publishers

MIROLAND (GUERNICA)
TORONTO • BUFFALO • LANCASTER (U.K.)
2017

Connie McParland, series editor
Michael Mirolla, editor
David Moratto, cover and interior book design
Chapter icons from www.flaticon.com
Guernica Editions Inc.
1569 Heritage Way, Oakville, ON L6M 2Z7
2250 Military Road, Tonawanda, N.Y. 14150-6000 U.S.A.
www.guernicaeditions.com

Distributors:
University of Toronto Press Distribution,
5201 Dufferin Street, Toronto (ON), Canada M3H 5T8
Gazelle Book Services, White Cross Mills
High Town, Lancaster LA1 4XS U.K.

First edition.
Printed in Canada.

Legal Deposit—First Quarter
Library of Congress Catalog Card Number: 2016952736
Library and Archives Canada Cataloguing in Publication
Codispoti, Bruno, author
Food Fight Inc. : an entrepreneur's journey and subsequent
lessons on trying to make money in the grocery business / Bruno
Codispoti. -- First edition.

(MiroLand imprint ; 11)
Issued in print and electronic formats.
ISBN 978-1-77183-224-3 (paperback).--ISBN 978-1-77183-225-0
(epub).--ISBN 978-1-77183-226-7 (mobi)

1. Grocery trade--Canada. 2. Food--Canada--Marketing.
3. New business enterprises--Canada. 4. Entrepreneurship--Canada.
I. Title. II. Series: MiroLand imprint ; 11

HD9320.C32C63 2017   381'.4564130971   C2016-905972-3   C2016-905973-1

Contents

Preface

On a late afternoon in fall, escape from the office often leads to a quiet patio table at the closest Starbucks where the sight of people 'brown bagging it' is of no consequence. The surprise interruption of my solitude with one said brown bagger would demand my time and attention. The man sidling up to my table has obviously other intentions than to take delight in his homemade lunch and his introduction to me is a fully confident one: *"The lady in your office said I would find you out here. I understand you take popular restaurant recipes and food ideas and introduce them into grocery stores across the country."* The awkward pause that follows does not deter him. *"You have to try one of my wife's famous* dulce de leche *infused mini scones; she tops them with chunks of crunchy real Canadian bacon dunked in dark chocolate! Go on, try one."* He leans in closer and whispers in my ear: *"We'll make millions together."*

Now, aside from the fact that reaching my hand into a stranger's brown bag, however deliciously described, is beyond unappealing, I am now faced with the dilemma of the short or long answer as to how financially risky and utterly nervy his assumption really is. Where do I start? Do I tell him to take his head out of the bacon and chocolate covered clouds and send him and his brown bag on their way? Or, do I take the more responsible and onerous road, as I want to do, and begin to sketch out the fundamental blueprints for the epic, and frequently fruitless journey. I often begin by saying: *"You learn more about what not to do when you lose money doing the wrong thing. I can tell you how I've*

1

lost a boat-load of it over the past 20 years playing this game of delusional buffet-sized profits."

This book is a hard-earned collection of stories that have to do with being fanatical about finding the next big food and drink thing, that next sliced-bread or Coca-Cola idea. It's about surprising, and sometimes unplanned, successes and carefully planned product launches ending in agonizing failure. Generously filled with themes of persistence and perseverance, and spiked with a pinch of humility, *Food Fight Inc.* is a spoonful of reality mixed with sugar to make the medicine go down. In the same breath, it's a testimony baked with fundamental lessons and practical guidance that can be applied to any aspiring entrepreneur's crusade, particularly those with only modest means, looking to unchain a product idea so that they can share it with the world. Regardless of the industry you're trying to break into, I hope that my adventures, particularly the brutal failures, the really sour lemons, will cause you to take a big step back to rethink your path.

From crafting tequila cocktails for former Van Halen front-man, Sammy Hagar, to popping too much popcorn for Pope Saint John Paul II, there's a little somethin' somethin' for even the pickiest of eaters. At times, the lessons and guidance may be a little difficult to taste because they'll be soaked in tales of booze and butter. But trust me, they're in there, sticking to the sides of the bowl. Learn, respect and practice the basics in this book, and you'll be able to make your product launch mission tastier and much more financially digestible should the soufflé sink when it's pulled from the oven.

As with any maiden journey, the first attempt is generally the hardest one. More often than not, it's also the most painful one. And like with most journeys, you'll begin to move faster and more freely with a knowledge of avoiding danger zones the more the road is travelled. It's nothing short of exhilarating and liberating to dream up your own product idea, sketch it out on a cocktail napkin and then gaze up at the outcome on a retail shelf a year or so later. When you get the launch formula right, it's a beautiful thing. When you get it wrong, and chances are that you will, more than once, chalk it up as a valuable lesson learned, wipe the counter clean and then start over again. Making mistakes is not only acceptable gameplay, it's a secret ingredient. Remember, it takes repetition to build muscle. To that end, if I can save one person from betting the farm on their Grandmother's secret Saskatoon Berry Jam, or help them in successfully selling a truckload of the silky organic sesame miso marinade they discovered in Osaka Japan— then my food fight will have been worth it.

CHAPTER 1

Gathering Substance

It's Always Been About Food

My brother Dave and I have always had our own personal strengths, his being academia and mine, despite my body type being reminiscent of Shaggy from Scooby Doo, was being able to eat a lot. Perhaps not the typical strength to brag about, but it has served me well now in my pursuit of delicious food and has been a source of amusement for my family and friends for as long as I can remember. My Uncle Lou loved to watch me devour a thick stack of fried veal cutlets during Sunday lunch, and then jog the block to digest just enough to put down another plate. The staff at Chinese Food Buffets were warned that "all you can eat" was a dangerous proposition when I walked through the door. My friends cheered me on to tackle a third soft serve cone, or the Flintstone-sized steak.

It is only fitting then that my first job was as a stock boy at the local Red & White grocery store. There I was, a thirteen-year-old budding foodie making $3.81 an hour facing-up canned goods and carrying out paper grocery bags for nice old ladies for a 25-cent tip. Ten years, and many more veal cutlets later, I would find myself working for my Uncle El in his boutique design and print firm, Rockprint (now Creative Rock / creative rock.net). His main gig was, and still is, designing and printing food packaging for a large (and now monster large) food company called Johnvince Foods (johnvincefoods.com). This is an over-40-year-old family owned establishment that both repacks (other companies' bulk products) and manufactures a colourful multitude of both commodity-driven and unique food products, selling to nearly every retailer in Canada—and more recently in the US—that vends food.

Looking back to the mid '70s, Johnvince was fundamental in kick-starting and then shaping the concept of ditching expensive packaging to sell food in bulk to save consumers money. My Uncle introduced me to Joe Pulla, the company's owner and opportunity-finding savant, who instantly became a welcome mentor. Joe was, and remains, the most alarmingly clever and convincing entrepreneurial warrior with whom I've crossed paths. The words *impossible* and *surrender* are not in the man's dictionary. If he should ever decide to write his memoir, buy it. Trust me. Following him into his warren of food glory changed my life's trajectory for the better.

In the late '90s, J.P. (as Joe is affectionately called by his close peers; or the BrandFusion-staff exclusive nickname, 'Jeepers') scooped up both Planters Peanuts® and Lifesavers® from Nabisco, which immediately injected a level of admiration and notoriety into his already thriving food empire. The acquisition of the lovable, monocle sporting Mr. Peanut® gave him one of the most identifiable brand icons in the world. Lifesavers was enlisted into another of his growing subsidiary companies called Beta Brands.

In an effort to score myself a more permanent spot on JP's stacked bench of regular players, I took a long shot by offering up a very simple 5-page marketing plan detailing some ideas I had on rebuilding the dangerously out-of-date Lifesavers brand. If truth be told, it was my first attempt at penning a marketing plan, and although it was admittedly the absolute worst plan that I had ever produced, it proved to also be the most profoundly life-changing. The very next week I was given a job and a small desk located right outside JP's office door. I like to think that it was because he was able to see past my cryptic ideas and found a hungry and trustworthy student to mould. The position paid very little in salary, but paid off in spades in terms of providing a driver's seat vantage point, and to opening my sheltered eyes to a fun new world where anything seemed possible.

Beta Brands operated out of the timeworn, but very charming McCormicks Candy® manufacturing facility in London, Ontario. Eager to learn the food business, I packed my bags and moved into a small townhouse that the company had rented for management relocating from Toronto during the weekdays. Although unseasoned, I was an energetic player in a crowd of accomplished and driven food-athletes. The early mornings were launched with a couple of short espressos in order to reach the office by 6:30 a.m. and work straight through until 8 p.m. We grocery shopped, cooked and ate dinner together, caught up on the local evening news and would all then beat a hasty retreat to our rooms.

It should be noted that there weren't enough bedrooms so I was delegated to crash on a mattress placed on the floor in the living room with musty and ancient brown office dividers for a little privacy. For me, this unusual frat house served as a CPG (consumer packaged goods) Food Industry University, but instead of spending time with beer guzzling frat brothers, much of my precious waking time was spent with the CEO, COO, CFO, CIO and specialized consultants. Being in their proximity made it inevitable that I would pick up a few golden food-biz nuggets.

In the candy factory I spent the next few years happily tucked away on the vast and nearly abandoned top floor with a fellow recruited from the Willy Wonka candy company. Unlike the Oompa-Loompas in Charlie's Chocolate Factory, the sprightly Mr. Blair Neuss was a buttoned-down and veteran marketer with an infectious laugh that echoed down the lonely fifth floor halls like rolling thunder. The 432,000 sq.-ft factory was our candy-playground to experiment with. On shoe-string budgets we developed and helped launch over a hundred delightful and funky confectionary creations. Some were instant hits, like sour green apple alien head gummies, and others, like the Dr. Suess inspired green 'chocolate-y' eggs with multi-coloured marshmallow centres, were blockbuster sugar-bombs.

Unlike working in an overly structured, cubicle-freckled corporate environment, we had complete free rein to self-indulge in any crazy idea our hungry hearts desired. This was a fortunate opportunity and effective method to learn what worked and what didn't on someone else's dime. It also didn't hurt to have a 10kg shipping carton of peanut butter cups hidden under my desk at all times. Purely for inspiration, of course.

On an early morning bike ride during a weekend getaway at JP's cottage, he and I chatted openly and intensely about my next career move. I explained that it might be a suitable time for me to take leave of the cozy rabbit-hole in search of a more corporate company chapter with whom to continue my food journey, with the promise to return one day with more to offer both him and myself. With a charming and heavy grin, he gave me his official blessing. Three weeks later I received my first offer from The Quaker Oats Company in Peterborough, Ontario and I swiftly accepted it. Little did I know that, over the course of the next ten years, all of my major career decisions would be thoughtfully discussed and forged during early morning bike rides at JP's cottage. Always over a hot Tim's coffee and a freshly buttered 'everything' bagel while dangling my feet from the same public picnic table overlooking the lake.

Quaker was a barn-sized culture shock for me, as my vast fifth floor playground was replaced with a closet-sized cubicle. Where I once had the freedom to exercise my impulsive ideas and get involved with all things marketing, sales, operational, and legal, I was now boxed in by a very restricted set of marketing responsibilities and measured deliverables. Everyone spoke in a strange foreign tongue filled with acronyms and buzzwords I didn't understand. I felt like an Italian immigrant getting off the boat at Pier 21 into Halifax trying to settle into my strange new surroundings. As with all new adventures, there was an adjustment period and things did eventually click and I found a voice and my groove. The majority of my fellow Quakers proved to be fabulously sharp and highly motivated companions.

I learned how to dig deep into the countless dollars spent on consumer research to decode the food business at a different level. I learned how to structure, deliver and execute a proper product launch. I enjoyed exercising my multi-million marketing budget and I picked up a little corporate-poise along the way. Thank the food Gods for my brief stint at Quaker, as without it, the recipe that ended up becoming my career would have been dangerously void of salt and pepper. I like to think I made an impression on my new family at Quaker: the Marketing Director told me the prudent and well-respected then CEO blurted out a 'Fuck No' when he heard of my departure.

With my feet dangling once again from the lakeside picnic table, JP took a bite of his buttered 'everything' bagel, looked over the water and made me a casual and hefty offer. '*I have an opportunity. It won't pay anything for at least a year, but it could turn into something.*' I was still unmarried, with no brood of my own to watch over. The timing felt right in the pocket as the corporate life, although stable and promising, just didn't feel like me. With a few exchanges and high-fives, it was done. (Seriously, there were, and usually still are, solid old school high-fives to consummate such decisions.) JP and I were now business partners in a company that I would operate and he would watch over with a helpful hand and a keen eye.

Settling into my entrepreneurial life at the newly formed Brand-Fusion Ltd. (brandfusion.ca), I could faintly sense the value and strength that my experience up until this point had given me. I was able to meld together the youthful spirit and take-no-prisoners approach of working in a private and flat-structured organization with the discipline and methodology of working in a large public corporate setting—I've tried to uphold the right balance between these contrasting worlds ever since. Over the next 17 years, with a growing band of fanatical foodies, I would be devoted to trying to unearth the next food product sensation. And I'm still at it.

CHAPTER 2

Grocery Math

What to Expect

For those of you wanting to get into the grocery game, or into any product launch game for that matter, here are the Coles Notes; for a small start-up enterprise it's all in the cold math. How many store shelves can I squeeze my product onto? What will it cost me to get there? How many units per week, per year, can I conservatively move? Do I have the mandatory cash flow and the patience to wait until my return on investment clears the breakeven hurdle? If my product doesn't move can I finance the messy aftermath cleanup? Therein lies the rub. And unless you're cutting a deal in some quaint Farmer's Market where a transaction is consummated with a firm handshake, things can get costly and complicated quickly.

Let's start from the ground up. To get the ball rolling, you have to find a reputable and accessible contract packer (also known as co-packers or private label manufacturers) that will translate your small-batch kitchen recipe into one that can be commercialized and cost effectively mass-produced. Essentially, contract packers are manufacturing companies that you can commission to produce and pack your product. They can also be positioned to appear as if the product were manufactured directly by you. This is the stage where your virgin recipe usually ends up somewhat manhandled and transforms into a slightly adulterated version of its former self. It's important to stick to your guns. Do not compromise your recipe concept and vision in an act of desperation. A contract packer will always reach for the big red easy button and opt for what's economical and most closely aligned to his existing production capabilities. Unless you have a proven track record, or can demonstrate that your innovation will make big money in short order, or you are able to create an alliance with a rare and benevolent contract packer, you'll be charged a nominal lab fee—your first donation into your contract packer's notorious food bank, a bank that witnesses far more deposits than withdrawals. If your product calls for unique ingredients or components that the contract packer must procure and store exclusively for you, you'll be on the financial hook for their entire minimum commitment should your product eventually see daylight.

Before you get ahead of yourself and start spending money on whimsical packaging designs, understanding the contract packer's requirements, production limitations and flexibilities is vital. Granted, it is feasible to start fishing around for prospective retailers without investing upfront time with a contract packer. However, what's your end game if you miraculously convince a smaller mini-chain store to take a chance on you without knowing your true cost of goods (COGS), your minimum production run size commitment and lead times, packaging format capabilities, the product's shelf life or chemical reactions over time, etc.? Selling 100 cases of an authentic spicy Greek taramosalata when you have to pay your contract packer for a run of 500 cases will eventually leave you having to sell 400 cases to a shifty clear-out artist for the cost of a dinner at one of Mario Batali's New York City restaurants.

Armed with your mass-production recipe requirements and a reasonable grasp of how to navigate through the contract packer's requests and limitations, you would then move to honing your brand vision and crafting a packaging design. For a start-up mission this is a critical stage because the packaging design must perform the lion's share of heavy lifting with respect to drawing consumer attention. It's very possible to create a contagious brand buzz without having a consumer-marketing budget (i.e. print, television, radio, social media, PR, couponing, sampling, etc.) but it doesn't happen all too often. When it does, it is because someone has found the elusive and magical combination of introducing the right product with a design that speaks the perfect message, at just the right point in time, merchandised in a perfectly precise place in the store.

The design phase is also a liberating stage as your personal vision and aspirations become a more tangible reality. The process is very personal but also demands a fluid and open mind for constructive criticism. God knows that every friend, family member and the mailman will have a spirited opinion. Be sure to smile politely, nod acceptingly and process the suggestions and criticism internally. Only you can sort the treasure from the trash. The design phase is also the first potential financially hazardous stage because it's where the second and considerably larger contribution is made to fund your mission.

There are many echelons of design firms in both Canada and the US. A fresh and new-fangled design can run anywhere from $2,500 to $25,000 per sku. If you're taking a chance on your first food venture with a modest to medium tolerance for pain, I advise sticking to the former. The downside is that the risk is heavily weighted on your natural ability to recognize a brand design and narrative that will look suitable, will have both a memorable and proprietary feel to it, and will communicate the right message to your target audience in a meaningful way. The upside is that saving $20,000 in design suggests that you'll be 20,000 units closer to a breakeven scenario based on a food product that puts $1 per sale back into your pocket.

I imagine this will be a controversial point because someone (most likely, and rightfully so, a marketing agency or pricey design firm resident) will argue that an out-of-the-park design and brand message conjured up by a seasoned pro will help sell truckloads more product. I completely agree. Maybe. Sometimes. However, I've had the privilege to peruse the balance sheet of quite a few food start-up failures who were badly in need of a shot of capital to keep them alive. Spending beyond their financial means too quickly in the game for brand development, packaging design and website development is usually the first menacing number that jumps off the page like a signal fire. It's a tough call as I've had the pleasure of introducing both successful brands and products built using minimal outside aid, and the pain of unleashing stink bombs built with small fortunes and over countless pricey strategy dinner meetings; why do consultants always seem to choose the overpriced Brunellos? Once again, it depends on your risk tolerance against the size of the opportunity and how strongly you believe that your drilling for the ultimate packaging design will help tap into a sales-gusher.

I can stare at the first mocked-up product for hours on end. It feels so damn good. It's like staring at your baby wondering what it will grow up to be. Will she be strong and admired or awkward and reclusive? With a decent mock-up and reliable COGS in hand, it's finally show time. Do not spend another red cent until you have a decent sized fish hit the bait hard enough. You could, I suppose, invest in a small packaging run and convince your still somewhat sceptical contract packer to run the absolute minimum number of cases so that you have an actual finished product to flaunt. At that point, however, consider that you're now fully invested to make things fly. A little pressure and a sense of urgency is undoubtedly useful, but it also means that if you can't get a retailer interested you may also start to panic because of the skin you now have in the game. If your concept is in fact worthy, and the buyer knows and does his job properly, they'll be able to see past the scotch tape and fugitive glue dots. The leading advantage of clenching your purse strings tightly at this stage is that you'll safeguard the ability to tweak and improve your product by incorporating the buyer's requests and recommendations—that little dash of retailer ownership is usually worth its weight in gold. What's more, if the sales performance begins to falter, you might just get that indispensable helping and forgiving hand you wouldn't have otherwise experienced.

Boom baby! After a sack full of email requests and countless phone calls into a seemingly always-full voicemail box, you get a rare chance to deliver your sales pitch. And you pretty much nail it. That once unbelievably impossible to reach buyer has bought into your vision, and better yet, your precious creation. This is it; your chance in the big leagues to make an honest buck after probably a year of dispensing cash like a human ATM. Ah, wait a minute. How did we go from a snazzy scotch-tapped sample to a profitable product on the shelf, you ask? Well, it's quite simple. It's all about the 3 P's, baby—you'll need the persistence of Rocky Balboa coupled with the presentation skills and passion of Steve Jobs. Did I overkill my point? Of course I did, but this is the mother of all junctures in your napkin-sketch-inspired quest. If you do nail it, it's the one moment that you'll most likely take the time to truly celebrate because it's now legitimately game-on. Once you're in the pool using both your hands to tread water, there's no opportunity for high-fives. Your presentation handout must be succinct and compelling, and your delivery must be confident and convincing. The squinty-eyed and usually intense personality sitting on the other side of the negotiation table is waiting to jet back to their desk to respond to 500 new emails, most of them peppered with fires needing to be extinguished.

Let It Simmer ~

1. *Does your product concept adequately fill a meaningful consumer void and opportunity gap within the category it will be sold in?*
2. *Are the driving benefits of your concept truly valuable and unique, or have you simply created sexier packaging for a me-too product? Remember, you can put lipstick on a pig, but it's still a pig.*
3. *Have you personally scoured every store shelf to ensure that your product concept will help to enhance their existing assortment offering?*
4. *Have you cut (i.e. taste tested) your product against the competition's to ensure that it meets or exceeds your pledge to the consumer?*
5. *Is your product concept priced realistically and fairly when compared to similar offerings in the marketplace?*
6. *If shelf space is limited, what is your recommendation to the retailer for possible placement? Which competitive products should get the cold boot to clear space for your undertaking and why?*
7. *Try to snap a picture of your mocked-up product set up on a retailer's shelf to see how it looks in action (note—always ask the store manager for permission, or a smock-sporting bouncer may ask you to kindly leave).*
8. *How will you support and nurture your product concept once it's impatiently sitting on the shelf?*
9. *How much money can you stomach parting with to help mop up the aging inventory should the product not meet with the retailer's expectations?*

CHAPTER 3

Show Me The Cheddar

Rules of Engagement

S how me the golden cheddar! That first cheque stub deserves to be proudly framed and displayed on the fireplace mantel beside your kid's first picture with creepy mall Santa. So be prepared, and avoid personal devastation when that cheque finally arrives in the mail with a figure that's only a mere fraction of what you expected to receive. Build your pricing model with great care. Retailers will want to keep you fed and alive, but do not want to fatten you up. How much they believe you take home versus how much you actually end up banking are two very different stories. Don't be greedy, or if you're lucky enough to get through the door and onto the shelf, your retails may end up hopelessly high. Don't price your product too low just to get through the door, or you won't have the necessary funds and fuel to travel far enough on your journey.

Striking the ultimate balance between achieving a realistic retail while giving the retailer the top end of their desired gross profit margin, and still managing to keep enough bread for your table, isn't always easy. Before you slide a piece of paper with a penciled price across the buyer's table, you have to know the retailer's pricing program expectations. Except for a select few, each retail chain has a custom mélange of financial contribution requirements; no doubt spurred on by crafty accountants. And unless you build in a reserve for a 5% Co-op fee, 2% Volume Rebate, 2% Damage Allowance, 1.5% Business Development Fee, 1% Cash Terms and a .025% Clean Underwear Fee, you'll squeeze yourself out of the financial picture.

Like most business ventures, planning for the worst-case scenario while secretly hoping for the best outcome is always a prudent approach. Crunch and munch the numbers to ensure that you can store enough acorns away should the retailer turn the tables and want restitution for poor performance.

In addition to the retailer's obligatory programs, build in some monies to protect your precious new real estate by supporting the marketing efforts needed to draw in attention to your tasty vittles so that they don't collect dust sitting on the shelf. When operating with a restricted budget, temporarily reducing your sell price to help fund in-store feature deal activity (e.g. 2 for $5.00 vs. a regular price point of $2.99 each) is a safe wager among the many more futile and fruitless retailer managed marketing options. Its effectiveness is highly measureable and, for the most part, it can still be profitable if your COGs (Cost of Goods) are intact and the retailer chips in on the deal. Unless you can piece together a consistently effective social media campaign, most other aggressive out-of-store consumer marketing activities are ordinarily beyond financial reach at the start line.

Confused? Don't be. I'll compare and contrast the paybacks and pitfalls of **out-of-store advertising** vs. **in-store promotional** marketing in *Chapter 31: Milk Money*. For now, let's make a note to play it safe by building in a set amount of money for marketing activity contribution into your pricing model. For example, for a product that retails for $3 up to $5, try to work in 50¢ per unit. Better yet, if you can afford to assign 75¢ to $1.00 per unit, you're groovin'. If not, allocate what you can comfortably afford until your volumes and production efficiencies eventually increase, thus causing your COGs to decrease, at which point you should be able to start setting aside more marketing monies. Take heed. In the early going you'll find that production and order fulfilment efficiencies are thrown out the window in an effort to stay afloat. Until you fall into a steady supply and demand rhythm, plan for your COGs to be a conservative fifteen percent north of your initial calculations.

Aside from the more conventional marketing expenses, there's a handful of supporting role services that will serve to raise your tab. For example, hiring a third-party merchandising team to visit high traffic stores to ensure that your product is in stock as well as properly placed and represented on shelf will become an eventual rule of engagement. However, at $20 to $30 per store for a one-hour call, you'll have to put this one on ice until you can build your empire a little. More often than not, we'll price out a product putting every minuscule drop of profit we pocket within the first two years straight back into the campaign to ensure that we have a fighting chance. As long as you can afford to wait it out, breaking even in the short term is not only customary, it's prudent if you know that you'll gain efficiencies and pick up more margin down the road.

Take into account that buying a truckload of butter, or sugar or black mission figs will be much cheaper than buying only a couple of pallets at the onset. Ordering 50,000 cartons or impressions of packaging film will be significantly cheaper than ordering the minimum amount—which is customarily plus or minus 10,000 units or so. Let's say that you save 20 cents per unit as a result—on a master shipping case of 12 units that's an additional $2.40 in your piggy bank. Having said this, it's tempting to bite the bullet and fork out the cash required for the larger run in order to start your race with lower COGs and a more comforting profit. Personally, unless the overall cash outlay is close, I'd rather order fewer materials and take the temporary margin hit upfront associated with ordering a more controlled 10%-15% over what's truly required. Otherwise you'll be gratuitously chewing up your bank account, increasing your cash burn rate, and may run the risk of indeterminately storing unused packaging and wasting warehouse space (or worse yet, valuable garage space). Don't fret. We'll delve deeper into the numbers and the corresponding success metrics a little later in the book.

Seeing the first Purchase Order (PO) appear in your otherwise empty inbox, or patiently resting in the fax tray, is a wonderfully euphoric, yet anxious moment. Feelings of jubilation and fist pumps are closely followed by pensive thoughts of: *'Can I pull this off in time? Have I covered all my bases with respect to the other players involved that will need to do their part in order for me to pull this off?'* The irony is usually that it will take a dog's age to squeeze the first order out of the retailer, yet they'll want you to deliver it yesterday. And, by the way, if you don't deliver the goods on time you'll be fined, tarred and feathered. This is when you need to exercise your basic management skills. Triple check absolutely everything. Walk through every step with everyone involved in the game—your team, the packaging company, the contract packer, the guy on the line attaching the doohickey to the whatchacallit, the freight company, etc.

Murphy's Law: the one single and seemingly inconsequential step or piece or person that you don't check will bring down your house of cards. It's remarkable how many folks in business, irrespective of the industry they work in, don't practice this attention to detail methodology. After my first year in business, the president and founder of Kernels Extraordinary Popcorn®, Scott Staiman, expressed this notion to me: *'It's surprising how many people don't have "it" when "it" is the most important quality to have.'* I never forgot that.

You park in the tic-tac-toe of cars and abandoned grocery carts. Walking through the sliding doors, you feel giddy and your stomach is in knots. Did my product make it into this store or is it helplessly trapped in the retailer's distribution centre, or lost here somewhere in their box-city of a backroom? Walking down aisle 5 you catch a glimpse of a red box on the shelf at the other end of the store. Is that my little red box? Tears of joy and pride christen your cheeks as you realize it is your glorious, most perfect crimson little red box of promise smiling back at you on the very top shelf. You wish it wasn't on the top shelf because you can't reach it and worry about who actually can. But, that's a problem for another day. For today is your first official day in business.

CHAPTER 4

Breaking Bread

Compatibility

Many of our business escapades have dealt with licensing and leveraging a well-known restaurant or an established food brand. In the beginning, we were super-green and super-eager, so we ended up saying '*Hell YEAH*' to 95% of the opportunities that crossed our vacant desks. Today, we have double the opportunities and say '*Hell NO*' to 95%. Most often it's because we don't get the right vibe from the prospective business partner. The business idea could feel rock solid. The strategic fit with our business, existing relationships and capabilities may make perfect sense, but something will just seem uncomfortably ... alien. At first, we fooled ourselves by thinking that the awkwardness would eventually wane the closer we worked and grew with a person or another company.

After a dozen or so such partnerships we eventually realized that there was a strong and undeniable correlation between people that we felt naturally comfortable with and a product's ultimate trajectory. Similarly, we noticed that the partners we couldn't relax with would eventually cost us the most time, money and aggravation. Perhaps it's a self-fulfilling prophecy to evaluate people and opportunities with this jaded lens? I don't think so. Having fun and gelling with those involved in your mission is an absolute must. These days, our standard issue acid test is what we call the breaking bread factor. Can we sit down at a table with a prospective partner and really enjoy a meal together? Does it feel forced or is there a natural spark (without the assistance of a bottle of

Brunello)? Do you wince when their call comes through or perk up in your chair with enthusiasm to pick up the phone?

For all intents and purposes, a healthy partnership isn't any different than a healthy marriage—if you can't sit across the dinner table and break bread with your potential spouse, would you want to get married? Dave and I have developed such trepidation for toxic relationships that we pull out the break-up card at the first sign of foreboding. Remember, the deeper you dive, and the more time you spend with one another, the tougher it is to pull the plug so you might as well be honest with yourself and them. As you read through the compilation of case studies that follow, many of which involve both fruitful and fruitless partnerships, you'll begin to see a pattern: the healthy relationships most often ended in making money. And the bad ones, well, save for the hard lessons learned, were bad ones all around.

CHAPTER 5

Eat Well, Sleep Well

Do What's Right

Nice guys finish last, do they? This may hold true in stories and myth, and occasionally in the real world, but we pride ourselves on running our business with integrity and respect. Perhaps we would be further ahead in the profit game if we played dirty, but empty victories won't sustain you. For every morally decent person out there, there are double the number of jerks without a conscience hacking away to get what they want despite any collateral damage they create. I'm not trying to sound self-righteous or ostentatious, it's just the mould in which I was cast. As a result, many of you might read a thing or two and disagree with how we ultimately handled a situation. *'You should've gone legal.'* Or: *'Come on, man, fight back!'* are a couple of choice phrases that you might want to mutter under your breath as you continue to read on. That's fine, I can respect that, but I need my sleep and can only get it when my head hits the pillow without preventable conflict or sobering regret. Lose money on a bad assessment or poor decision, so be it, you'll recover. Unethically torch an otherwise good relationship over anything other than an unrecoverable loss, particularly when a close friend or family members are involved, no thanks, I'll pass. I prefer to take in only what I know I can digest without heartburn.

CHAPTER 6

Eat In Moderation, Not Deprivation

Love What You Do

When the Toronto Blue Jays were battling it out in the 2015 MLB postseason, the fellas in the office and I took a minimum five-minute break to play catch in the parking lot at least once every 2 or 3 hours. Outside the postseason, we like to keep parking-lot-catch down to a more respectable once a day. Now, guitar playing in the office is a much more frequent and religious practice. My office-acoustic guitar (once owned by Glass Tiger's Alan Frew) is never more than ten feet away from my enthusiastic reach. Some people chain-smoke to calm their shot nerves. I enjoy bending and sliding out a few choice riffs to help regulate my blood pressure after either wrapping up a jittery customer call or to celebrate after intercepting a much anticipated purchase order.

Most of the time I sit on the cushy couch by the fireplace in my office and play softly so that I don't disturb the others. However, on Friday afternoons during our 'Gentlemen's weekly' toast, I get a kick out of strumming a few fresh new licks for the fellas while we leisurely sip our single malt scotch and passionately chat about the upcoming week's ambitions. If Dave has cooked a little extra fare earlier that afternoon in our test kitchen, it's also a good opportunity to double back and clear out the fridge. If we've hosted a tailgate barbeque party in the parking lot earlier that week for our sales team, or as neighbourly thanks to our local Starbucks barista gang, chances are there's a giant foil-tray loaded with spicy Italian sausages. Which incidentally, goes perfect on a fresh bun with my Grandmother's homemade Sicilian caponata (chopped fried eggplant, olives, capers and sweet sautéed onions)—we always have a jar or two on hand.

During school holidays, a couple of jumbo ice cream sandwiches for dessert is also in the cards as my eleven-year-old son, Gabe, runs his beach-themed popsicle bar (*Gabo Wabo's*) from the sidewalk outside our office during lunch hour. On Thursdays during the late fall through to early spring (indoor pizza oven season) and sometimes during mid summer (outdoor pizza oven season), we try to schedule our meetings around making fresh batches of Neapolitan pizza dough, using a 'poolish' bread starter, before the long weekends. Before you judge me, let me explain, it's completely necessary because the *KicthenAid®* stand mixer at the office has a much larger bowl and is more capable than the ancient one I have at home. Plus, making pizza dough forty-eight hours before you actually need it, and then storing it in the fridge, allows it to gradually rise, giving your crust a bolder taste and airier texture—bada bing!

Throughout the day, it's customary for the gang to breakout into ridiculous wisecracker songs about Archie (our beloved veteran new product developer) and his interesting 80s-themed colourful fashion choices or his peculiar bird-like eating habits. Rest assured, it's only because we admire the ol' boy. Integrating silly humour and chanting foolish songs about coworkers and supply partners (i.e. contract packers and suppliers of raw material ingredients and packaging) plays an immense role in our work life. It lies deep at the core of our office culture. Without humour, and without lively song, the day somehow feels painfully long and the office vibe much too sombre—which also explains why everyone in the office loves to play Boom 97.3's *'Just a Sec'* daily name that tune challenge. (By the way, Arch is also our resident champion.)

I didn't realize how strange and outrageous our work philosophy was until we had our accountant spend a full day in the office with us. At first glance, I'm more than certain that we all seem shockingly childish and unfocused at best. Or at least, I hope we do. But listen up, don't assume that our light-hearted conduct means that we're unproductive or disinterested. Conversely, you'll find us problem solving until late in the evening and on the weekends long after the regular work folk have eagerly punched out. My best ideas, strongest inspiration and the courage to provoke big change, come to me when I step away from my desk.

The key, however, is knowing when it's time to hunker down. When the bough breaks, turning off the music and stepping up to quickly lick an impending issue should be automatic. Firmly taking hold of a slippery opportunity has to materialize instinctively and effortlessly. I do believe, and have experienced, that work cultures fabricated on enforced structure, management intimidation, and most notably, without simple amusement, are both stifling and downright depressing. It's a terrifying approach and scene that scares me to the point of constant paranoia of losing what we've built.

Over the years, success has become less about strictly financial reward, and more about being able to preserve the unique and quirky culture I've come to love. To boot, I know that our small seasoned and spicy team of loyal food warriors is more productive and determined than a room full of uninspired workers. When you have the right crew, they'll recognize when the line slips out of hand and needs to be reeled back in. If you have the best players on board, they'll be self-motivated and self-driven. Making sure that they're inspired, stimulated and unencumbered is where I focus my energy. (Speaking of comfortable, you can't beat the custom BrandFusion slippers we like to sport in the office during frosty Canadian winter days.)

I'm also too distracted being in constant awe over how quickly we can dream up, develop and bring a new food product to market compared to larger and more regulated companies. We may not always achieve the same level of case volume sales or consumer awareness that a larger and more financially equipped company can reach; however, our cost to operate the business, and the number of mouths we need to feed are both drastically fewer. If my memory serves me correctly, we've boldly pedalled through the entire launch process in 20 weeks. Granted, the path to market was considerably unorthodox and freckled with luck but we pulled it off just the same.

I don't sanction this loose approach or relaxed attitude on a regular basis by any means, but once in a blue moon it's healthy to throw caution to the wind. Don't try this at home without adult supervision, but the 20 weeks looked a little something like this:

- **week 1**—product concept ideation—*'Hey guys I have an interesting idea'*
- **week 2**—identified a popular brand licensor to partner with —*'I bet if we could market this product under that popular restaurant name, we'd sell truckloads more than any brand we develop ourselves'*
- **week 3**—designed preliminary packaging design and mocked-up a credible sales sample—*'Whoa! This actually looks credible! Well worth the $500 investment. Let's flaunt it around to a few choice retailers to see if we can get a decent bite before we're in too deep and spend too much time and money on fine-tuning things'*
- **week 6**—locked-up a retailer and an opening order commitment before we actually knew who would build the product for us, or if the brand licensor was even interested —*'Glad to hear you like the product. We'll fill out the new item forms and get back to you in a few weeks with a confirmed lead-time for shipment of the first order'*
- **week 9**—approached and locked-up the brand licensor partner based on the retailer's commitment to purchase
- **week 12**—sourced and secured a manufacturing contract
- **week 19**—completed recipe development, product testing, regulatory requirements, polished up packaging design, ordered raw materials and production; week 20—ran product and fulfilled opening order
- **week 21**—take an extra long weekend

In order to pull off this hocus-pocus of a product launch, you'll need a very fluid project management approach, a giant pot full of luck and a big love for what you do. Trust me, without a genuine affinity for the game, you'll want to tap-out long before the PO appears in your inbox. I'm constantly amazed at the sheer volume of projects we can comfort-ably balance efficiently at once and how each member of the team can easily slip in and out of wearing multiple hats-of-responsibility on any given day; from researcher, to data analyst, to designer, to lawyer, to sales person, to production manager. I'll spare you from citing the old cliché that says: '*Do what you love and you'll never work a day in your life.*' So let me just say this and be done with it: '*Do what you love and you'll never work a day in your life.*'

Let it Simmer ~

1. *Do you truly love your product concept, its ultimate purpose and the impact that it will have in the marketplace? Bear in mind that at some point, or more accurately, at multiple points in the process, your affinity for your product and the mission will be your solitary touchstone.*

2. *Are you building a team and company culture that will keep both you and them interested in the long run, and that will attract and preserve the calibre of players you need to succeed?*

3. *How quickly and competently can you launch your product when your back is against the wall with a do-or-die opportunity? What factors would be holding you back from racing through a hurried product launch? Can you deal with and improve those factors now so that you're ready if and when the opportunity presents itself?*

4. *Are there amusing rituals and activities related to your industry that you can incorporate into your day to help create an inspiring and creative environment? Making Neapolitan Pizza dough, playing guitar and scarfing down jumbo ice cream sandwiches are my vice, what's yours?*

CHAPTER 7

Pop Goes The World

First-Mover Advantage

I love hot, buttery popcorn—the childlike anticipation of waiting for the first kernel to reach 450°F, where moisture turns into steam and creates a transformational and magical 'pop'. Be that as it may, I never would have guessed I'd spend my first two years at BrandFusion convincing retail chains and Canadians alike that they ought to eat the beloved snack generously sprinkled with Kernels Extraordinary Popcorn® seasonings (kernelspopcorn.com / kernelsfun.ca). Long live *Mmmm ... White Cheddar* and *Dill-irous*! It took well over a year's time and the patience of Job, but soon Blockbuster Video and Walmart and then Loblaws jumped on board our flavour-train. Had I not started the company with this seemingly cute and impulse-driven snack food product, I might not have had the privilege to share the many adventures that follow this lucky one.

This product launch effort is chockful of fundamentals with respect to introducing the right product, at the right point in time and in all the right places. I also have to take this opportunity to offer a solid chunk of credit to the strategy and instinct of a lay-it-on-the-line food sales warrior named Don Lock. Before I strolled into the Kernels Popcorn picture, he was the guy who insisted that Kernels (a 30-plus-year-old Canadian franchise with over 70 kiosks popping perfect popcorn flavours) shouldn't make its entrance into the grocery game with yet another bag of popped popcorn. Why fight for a share of the consumer's stomach and the retailer's self-space with the brash titans of the potato chip world? Why not invent a new sub category by giving consumers a choice to dial up the flavour and customize their microwave popcorn—a potentially much smaller segment, but one wide open for innovation?

The timing was textbook for me as I had just spent the past two years at The Quaker Oats Company delving deep into the salty snack world with *Crispy Minis*® Rice Chips. The core idea was essentially the same as Kernels Popcorn Shakers. They both are rooted in offering consumers a healthier alternative to potato chips without sacrificing the crunchy texture and the funky and intense chip flavours.

So, what were the big lessons jammed into that little clear plastic jar? Unlike many of the other popcorn-related products that we developed in subsequent years, our seasoning shaker concept had enough profit seared in to allow us to finish the lengthy and exhausting race with a little gas left in the tank to spare. Remember, no margin, no ticket to ride. If you latch onto an opportunity that doesn't pay you back a useful amount of margin after all of the pipers are paid, and ugly messes are cleaned up, you won't travel too far down the road. We all know that it takes money to make money. In the case of the game of grocery, paying yourself back is a luxury if it should miraculously happen within the first year or so.

We were first to market in grocery stores with our popcorn shakers. Granted, there were a handful of lesser known and more regional popcorn shaker products in the market at the time of our incursion, but their presence and approach was small-scale in comparison. To boot, many Canadians already had a sweet love affair going on with Kernels Extraordinary Popcorn so our duty was more about accurately representing and respecting the consumer's great expectations of the brand rather than disappoint them. As an entrepreneur, if you're smart and fortunate enough to invent and then successfully introduce a truly new concept platform, respect that it's a rare opportunity and give it all you've bloody got. Always manoeuvre as if your competition is close behind nipping at your heels and trying to lift your idea—because they are.

If you can reach solid ground and penetrate the market quickly and then protect what's yours by doing right by your product and brand (i.e.

avoid cutting corners on quality, service and customer satisfaction), you'll have a chance to drive from the pole position for a while. When the big boys come knocking (and they eventually will if the prize is worth it), you'd better have pulled so far up in front of the race that they have to sweat hard to catch up with you. The paranoid survive. On the flip side, if you're trying to break into a category that has an established player driving in the pole position, irrespective of their size, you'd better have a meaningful and enduring product advantage — something much much sexier than merely a slight price or packaging design and/or format improvement.

One of the most undervalued advantages we had going into the game was that the ritual of shaking chip-inspired seasoning flavours onto popcorn was already well established with consumers. Folks were already conditioned to dress their hot and fresh popcorn with White Cheddar, Dill Pickle, Ketchup, BBQ, Salt & Vinegar and Sour Cream & Onion seasonings at movie theatres and concession stands in sporting areas, etc. We didn't appreciate how valuable this well-established ritual was until we tried to follow up our Kernels Popcorn Shakers success with similar seasoning concepts in various other food categories using various other quick service restaurant brands — among others, New York Fries® French fry seasonings, Teriyaki Experience® Pan Asian seasonings, Golden Griddle® egg seasonings, Schwartz's deli seasonings, Mr. Greek® Mediterranean seasoning and Sbarro® pizza seasoning.

While each of these follow-up seasoning products were supported and validated by well-known quick-service restaurant brands, they eventually flopped. Granted, the absence of a deep-rooted consumer eating ritual wasn't the sole missing ingredient in each of these failed attempts, but I believe it was the driving factor. Had we needed to invest adequate marketing funds and our time to educate consumers on why they must have the Kernels product, our journey would've been radically more expensive and a lot trickier. The usefulness of the product was already more or less proven so it also made for an easier sale with retailers. And because the product added new, impulsive and incremental sales to the microwave category, negotiating a more digestible cost of entry (i.e. listing / slotting fees) was often the case. Had we tried to push our way into the popcorn category with yet another copy-cat ready-to-eat or microwave popcorn product, I believe the reverse would've been true and we'd have to have paid a higher than average ticket to ride. Put differently, the more innovative your concept is, the more you'll be able to fly under the radar with respect to the retailer's arbitrary costs of entry and successive account maintenance charges.

Product placement within the store was a massive game changer. Would you buy as much salsa if it wasn't sitting next to the tortilla chips? Had we been relegated to the spice section alongside black pepper and cumin, Kernels Popcorn Shakers might've eventually gone stale. Granted, being awarded prominent shelf space within the colourfully crowded snack section was also a rare and real coup for an unassuming jar of seasoning. But then again, we were packing a well-established snack brand with plenty of popcorn prestige.

The physical size of our product also gave us an unexpected leg up on the economics of our mission. Despite the similar retail price points, our popcorn shaker jars are quite small in comparison to the cartons of microwave popcorn and pillowy bags of ready-to-eat popcorn that they sit beside. On the other hand, despite taking up a fraction of the shelf space, their profit contribution per unit of sale for the retailer is nearly equal to the other products in the category. As a result, we're able to occupy much less real estate and still deliver a higher profit per square inch. Given that shelf space comes at a stiff premium, I guess size does matter. What's more, from a freight cost perspective, shipping a small and dense product from coast to coast is also much more cost-effective than shipping a larger and airy one. For example, there are 3,168 shakers on a pallet compared to 456 cartons of microwave popcorn. Considering that it costs about $350 to ship one pallet of goods from Toronto to Vancouver, freight would eat up a digestible 11¢ per shaker vs. a more indigestible 77¢ per microwave popcorn carton. Remember, when it comes to shipping product, good things do come in small packages.

Admittedly, there were a few contributing factors to our success which were less about strategy, and perhaps more about good fortune. The core competency of Johnvince Foods, our distribution partner and a terrifically close ally, is the sale and distribution of snack foods into grocery stores. Their flagship brand is Planters® Peanuts which conveniently is sold through the same salty snacks category buyer, and sits right next to the popcorn section within the store. Ergo, building the Kernels brand with Johnvince at our side was mutually beneficial rather than a stretch and a strain on both their business and on the relationship with its owner and my business partner, JP.

The other Godsend was our rare relationship and the mutual respect that we shared with our licensor partners at Kernels Extraordinary Popcorn. Going back to *Chapter 4: Breaking Bread*, we naturally gelled with our popcorn partners and ended up forming an incredibly concrete and dynamic bond. They avoided smothering us with undue pressure and unrealistic expectations, and in return we were able to breath freely and build the business on solid ground. Conversely, we couldn't wait to part ways with the licensor partners that called daily to check up on our progress. Last but not least, I'm a glutton for intense cheese popcorn, and ended up becoming a heavy user of our product so having to travel the country to sell it was more of privilege than a chore.

Let It Simmer ~

1. *Does your product concept provide enough profit margin to fuel the entire race plus leave you with a decent amount money in the bank?*
2. *Can you partner with a likeminded brand that has established recognition, consumer loyalty, and realistic expectations?*
3. *Is being first to market in the cards? If so, are you doing what's necessary to protect your lead?*
4. *Can you tap into an established consumer usage ritual to reduce your time investment and avoid steep consumer product education costs?*
5. *Does your product concept add material value to the category you hope to play in? Will it add incremental sales or will you have to fight to source all of your sales volume from a competitor?*
6. *Is your product innovation clever enough to evade, or at least mitigate, some of the retailer's more arbitrary financial demands?*

7.   *Standout! Can your product be placed in an area within the store that will serve to help generate complementary and impulse purchases?*

8.   *If you're tapping into a connection with a close friend or family member in the industry that can help you get to market, try to ensure that it's mutually beneficial or you'll risk putting an undue strain on the relationship.*

9.   *Do you enjoy breaking bread with the key players in your game? Recognize that if the battle breaches your own organization and inner circle, breathing easy and functioning freely will become increasingly difficult.*

CHAPTER 8

Pope Goes The World

Lessons From Failure

Our grand goal was to sell 20,000 bags of freshly-popped Kernels Popcorn from July 23rd to July 28th, 2002 at the 17th World Youth Day in Toronto—a celebration of faith begun by Pope John Paul II held on an international level every two to three years. It was also Pope John Paul II's final World Youth day celebration. Although the event was designed for Catholics, it attracts sizable numbers of youth from other faiths and denominations and is presented as a multi-faith celebration of young people from all over the world.

'Come on! Are you sure we'll sell that much popcorn?' I asked the event organizer. *'20,000 bags will fill up an entire 48' tractor trailer container!'* It was then carefully explained to us that our forecast model should be built on how quickly we can reach out one hand to collect five bucks and then reach out our other hand to give out a bag of popcorn. So, we did the math on the event's anticipated attendance of a few hundred thousand against the percentage of attendees that we projected might want popcorn and somehow came up with a conservative guesstimate of 20,000 bags.

JP and Johnvince Foods were heavily involved in the event as it took place at Downsview Park, which sits only a few blocks down the street from their offices. Among other things, they were involved with providing storage and logistics for the event assets (i.e. think massive crosses), and co-packing knapsack kits chockful of goodies that were distributed to each youth in attendance. It was hard for me not to get caught up in all of the boundless enthusiasm as the event promised to be nothing short of historic. At the time, our only sanctioned source for securing the crazy number of bags required was directly from the handful of Kernels' retail kiosks located in shopping malls within a 30-minute drive from the event. To boot, fresh popcorn packed in tent-top-folded theatre-style paper bags, especially in the humid summer weather, has a narrow shelf life of only few days so my cousin Chris and I had to orchestrate driving around the city cramming our cube van with what seemed like enough popcorn to fill an Olympic-sized swimming pool. Yes, I know what you may be thinking, but popping popcorn onsite, a la movie theatre mode, unfortunately wasn't a viable option if we wanted to sell the product under the popular Kernels Extraordinary Popcorn® brand name using their proprietary preparation techniques and recipes.

Before this, we spent a couple of weeks in the garage hand-painting gigantic Kernels signage, assembling uniforms, constructing the booth fixtures and laying out our detailed site plans. To pull off the event we knew we needed a team of dependable people (who'd slave for less than minimum wage) who could also follow a strict game plan—we'd need a few smiling cashiers, a couple of healthy runners to re-fill the popcorn display fixtures and someone tough enough to collect and guard all of that cash money. My brother Dave wasn't working for BrandFusion yet but we summoned him to build an MS Excel spreadsheet program to track our hourly sales, inventory, and staff breaks. Perhaps being slightly anal, we even recorded the bags of popcorn our staff ate so that the sales reporting wouldn't be tainted. As most of the staff was comprised of BrandFusion employees and their families (the less than minimum wage compensation should make more sense now), none of us had the compulsory food training the event required us to have by law. Man, what a weird and wonderful sight it was to see cousins, aunts, neighbours and friends sit attentively in a massive city auditorium classroom taking notes on cross contamination and how to properly wash your hands and food contact surfaces. Needless to say, they all answered our call to action and were ready to rock and roll.

Chris and I took our Kernels cube van to the site one afternoon a few days before the event—note, we had a serious Kernels cube van that we leased and decked-out with Kernels Popcorn shaker graphics for such events. After a few months into the lease, however, we ended up using the damn thing more for family moving requests so I got royally pissed off and had to break the lease and lost some serious money ... 'You need me to do what? *Oh No! Please, not another king-sized mattress or 8 drawer credenza.*' We drove up to one of many gates surrounding the 572-acre Downsview Park and noticed a giant *'Do Not Enter'* sign hanging from the swing-gate. Peeking through the chain-link fence, we could see that our assigned booth space was only a few hundred yards or so in the distance.

The truck was crammed with jumbo tarps, tents, signs, bungee cords and wooden folding-tables that we needed to unload to make more space, so we decided to ignore the warning sign. As we slowly rolled onto the field we noticed a horde of officers in military uniform standing beside a serious looking army helicopter far off in the distance. We reached about half way to our site when the van got stuck in a mud patch. I punched the gas so hard that both back wheels buried themselves deep into the wet ground. *'Come on. Damn it!'* I roared. *'Ok, Chris, I'll jump out and try to push and rock the van from the front and then you throw it in reverse, ok.'*

Just as I stepped out of the truck, the helicopter fired-up and took flight. Chris rolled down his window and screamed: *'Oh no, I think they're coming this way!'* My heart raced at a jackrabbit's pace as we were completely alone in a vastly open field and obviously trespassing—and from what I've seen on TV, the Pope packs some pretty heavy-duty security. *'Quick, hit the gas!!'* I screamed in pure panic. Chris hit the pedal so hard that a slab of muddy turf the size of a fat beavertail flung out from under the van's back wheel, tore straight up into the air and then landed flat on my head like a soggy mud-toupee.

The military chopper now hovered 30 feet above my head. *'What is your business here?'* or something like that came thundering over the air-craft's external speaker system. The force of the wind ripping off the propeller generously splattered more mud over my clothes and face— *'Oh Man ... Sorry! We're very sorry. We'll turn around and leave now. Thank You.'* And that, my friends, should have been the first sign that this event was not going to go in the heavenly manner we had prayed for.

The day of the event, we set up a small but well organized tent-city behind our popcorn booth so that a group of us could sleep onsite to close and re-open early the following morning—note, sleeping over was key as the traffic accompanying the transport of 500,000 people was nothing short of nauseating. (Yes, the final attendance numbers had climbed far beyond expectation.) Things were looking decent before the gates opened. There were two or three large food zones that sat a couple of football fields apart. Along with a handful of other vendors —most notably and memorably a fresh red watermelon fruit stand run by some uncompromising fellow Sicilians, our food section was located a hundred feet or so from one of the main entrances on route to the massive centre stage.

Once the gates opened there would be wave upon wave of teens jubilantly marching and singing right in front of our well-stocked popcorn booth. On the way to the port-a-potty 'village' (there must've been hundreds of toilets), I ran into a guy selling bottled water with special World Youth Day labels from the back of his truck. 'Damn, *we should be selling water, too,*' I thought. *'I'd like to buy one pallet, Sir... no wait, what am I thinking ... I'll buy three pallets.'* What a beautiful last minute move, I proudly thought nodding my head in self-approval. Mere minutes before the gates officially opened, we were sitting on 20,003 bags of fresh popcorn and 3,500 bottles of water to unload.

The team was primed and super pumped and I was giddy with anticipation ... and then it happened. We saw the gates in the far off distance swing open. From where we stood, the people looked as small as ants, but we could still see that they were all making a beeline for the main stage in order to get a proper seat and view of the Pope. Twenty-five minutes passed and the gate closest to us remained closed. We then realized the crowd behind 'our' gate had begun to dissolve as people made their way to the open entrances in the far distance. *'Um, okay guys,'* I addressed our troops with confidence. *'I'm sure they'll get hungry and will start exploring the grounds.'*

A few hours passed and we sold maybe 5 bags of popcorn. All I could think of was that we had twenty-friggin-thousand bags and about what had happened to the mound of five-dollar bills we were promised. For the first few hours, Dave and I respected and stuck close-ly to our detailed spread-sheet protocol ... *'Hey man, listen, if you take a bag please remember to record it. Okay!'* As the day wore on and we ac-knowledged that it wasn't exactly going our way, it became more like *'Bruno, how do I record this bag of popcorn I'm taking for my snack break?'* —*'Bahh! I really don't care what you do or how many bags you eat!'* The watermelon mafia were more ostensibly and vocally distraught and dis-gusted. Their war cry, that we still laugh about and use as a catch phrase today was: *'I'm gonna drop the Sicilian hammer when I catch the guys that screwed us over'*—an instant classic line.

As the sun set on our first day, we were deeply wounded but still a little optimistic that the next day would somehow be better. To make matters worse, JP came to visit that night, driving up in the dark on an official World Youth Day golf cart with one of the event's organizers. We desperately tried to share our discontent and to pull him into our fight but he could only focus on how we could and should be merchan-dising the product better. Later that night as our troops retreated to their tents, I tried to grab some sleep in our booth as it was the only available space to lay down. As I stretched out on a spare foldout table and looked up at the curious earwigs starting to crawl around the tent ceiling, my Blackberry Bold rang. *'Hey Bud, it's Joe—you awake?'* whis-pered JP. *'Don't worry, tomorrow will be a better day'*—in his own way, he had called to apologize for not acknowledging my distress call.

Well, the next day came and so did the clouds and rain. I sent home half of the staff as soon as they woke up and unzipped their tents. I also decided to make my own pilgrimage to the far side of the park to see what the scene was like. I bit my lower lip hard enough to make it bleed when I got there. *'Oh Shit! What's this all about?'* I mut-tered as I witnessed the long snaking lines of hungry and happy youth standing in front of Pizza Pizza's booth as well as the other lucky food stations. The other food zones were living our dream and had experi-enced the waves of hungry people we had patiently expected would visit us. I remember thinking to myself: *'I bet they'll sell 20,003 frickin slices of pizza.'* I sprinted back to our camp like an angry panther and shared the news in complete disbelief. I think I remember the red watermelon crew overhearing my conversation and then officially proclaiming that '*the Sicilian hammer was going to drop!*'

In a last ditch effort, we loaded up industrial-sized black garbage bags with our popcorn and travelled deep into the crowds like tired and wet candy stripers. At the end of day 2, we sold something like 75 bags of popcorn and a case or two of warm bottled water—yup, a whopping .3% of our inventory. Based on the dismal sales tally, the persistent rain, our crushed spirits and the fear of curious earwigs, we called it a day and completely packed up shop. The icing on the cake was the desire to be home so very badly but having to sit in 6 hours of brutal blockbuster traffic. At one point, I parked the cube van in the middle of an intersection and slipped out to grab a slice of pizza. When I returned the same car was still idling six inches from the van's front bumper.

Needless to say, despite some half-decent efforts in the days following the event to sell the popcorn before it expired, we took quite a financial and emotional bath on the event. Actually, we could've literally taken a bath as we still had enough warm bottled water to last us two years. To this day, I don't fully enjoy walking through a large event or trade show and seeing all the eager and ambitious small business start-ups in their crowd-less booths. I can literally taste and feel their risk and fragile sense of hope—almost like hearing a distant dog whistle.

Lessons learned. We should have planned to have much more control and flexibility over our production flow—more influence over the basic demand and supply. If we had had the wherewithal to meet the actual volume requirement as it unfolded, and not a delusional forecast, we wouldn't have started the race with so much crippling and distracting weight on our shoulders. Choking on too much inventory, with a ticking shelf-life clock, usually leads to irrational and ill-planned decisions that will weaken margins and compromise brand integrity out of desperation to move product. Would we really have sold that much less if we had popped product onsite as it was needed, offered it in a generic package and then marketed it as 'seasoned with' or 'made with' Kernels' flavours? After all, we were in the popcorn seasoning business. Granted, renting a generator to power up a theatre-style popcorn machine might have also been a risk and limitation if the crowds ended up being too large to properly service, but the cash outlay would have been less than buying 20,000 bags up front—moreover, our breakeven would have been far, far less.

During the introduction stage of a product launch, we'll always gamble with producing lighter inventory quantities even if it means that we short a few retailers in the short-term. Yes, the COGs (cost of goods) will be slightly higher, but it's safer to pull the ripcord if you need to abort the mission and the damage on impact isn't as messy. We've been through situations with contract packers that want to buy the packaging or ingredients unique to our product (instead of having us buy it) and then secretly purchase three years' worth to hold down the cost. Then, of course, they end up sticking you with a hefty five-figure invoice for the remaining components when sales come in weaker than anticipated.

If you can make the economics work based on a temporarily inflated cost and with smaller production runs, you'll be pocketing all the sweet upside when your volumes allow you to start buying and holding more raw material, packaging and finished goods inventory. Do not stock up unless you have legitimate volume commitments (not soft promises) from a retailer. Play it smart and safe until the time is right. Better to break even in phase one of your launch then lose your pants and have to run home to Mommy.

We probably would have and should have enjoyed the rare experience of witnessing Pope John Paul II enlighten half million teens from around the world. Nope, not us. Instead, we ran around aimlessly in circles like circus monkeys while the mighty Sicilian hammer dropped.

Let it Simmer ~

1. *Do you have concrete retailer commitments against your first production run? If not, can you run a more digestible, and albeit less efficient and costlier, amount and still be able to pocket some profit margin?*
2. *Would you be better off to run a more digestible case quantity but lose a palatable amount of money per transaction, or to run a higher*

quantity to lower your COGs and make more per transaction despite risking an expensive chunk of inventory going stale?

3. *If you do decide to start with a larger-sized packaging and production run in order to achieve better efficiencies and to lower costs, be sure to understand the financial threat if you only sell 25%, 50% or 75% of your inventory. Will it only hurt and cripple or completely slaughter your ability to keep the business afloat?*

4. *Do you really need to run full scale production in order to begin selling? Or, can you invest in a set of slick mock-ups (and credible tasting samples) to lock in a sale before you pull your wallet out and start the ROI clock? Note, the other benefit to this approach is that you'll be able to react by incorporating your customers' and critics' suggestions (if they're in fact valuable).*

CHAPTER 9

Lost In New York

Product Placement

Like most entrepreneurs, I'm cursed with an eternally restless mind. When the good ship finally breaks free from choppy waters and begins to sail smoothly, life somehow becomes a tad too still and quiet. Ergo, once we had Kernels Extraordinary Popcorn® Shakers up and running efficiently, we felt a burning need to use our newfound ability, goodwill and infrastructure to drop another powerhouse QSR (Quick Service Restaurant) brand into our hungry grocery basket. Wanting to keep the expansion blueprint simple, and to better leverage both our existing in-market positioning and manufacturing capabilities, we thought to approach New York Fries® (newyorkfries.com) about doing a French fry seasoning. On the face of it, the idea of smattering potato-inspired flavours on freshly cut and fried French fries seemed as relevant and meaningful as offering chip-inspired flavours for fresh popcorn. Both concepts were anchored to popular and intensely flavoured seasonings for common comfort foods that consumers were accustomed to enjoying at our brand partner's restaurant, but that weren't available for sale in grocery stores.

Given that Kernels, in particular the fiery and very loveable founder, Scott Staiman, gave us our first shot in the big leagues, I felt it was prudent that we had his certified blessing to start popping our business beyond popcorn. Of course, it didn't hurt that Scotty also personally knew the President of New York Fries, Jay Gould. Gratefully, not only did he support our aspirations to grow, he picked up the phone in his office with me standing in front of him to make the introductory call. *'Listen Jay, I'd like to introduce you to Bruno Codispoti from BrandFusion. He's a good guy who's done some very good things for our brand'*—or some supportive commendation, more or less, similar to that.

Jay and his loyal crew were a slight bit more austere and governing than the perhaps easier to work with and congenial family at Kernels. Their longtime VP, Warren Price, was an outwardly astute and somewhat charmingly pensive man that was as acutely attuned to his iconic brand and its consumer as ketchup or malt vinegar is to French fries. At the outset, I found it challenging to completely relax in front of him as one might find it awkward to spend one-on-one time with their high school math teacher. In time, however, I grew to admire his deep comprehension of the business and all, well most, awkwardness eventually melted away like Quebec cheese curds doused in hot Poutine gravy.

Following a few months of collective deliberation, we agreed to launch two of the most popular fry seasonings offered at their counter, *California* (a Sweet BBQ profile) and *Cajun*, and also crafted two more original flavours from scratch, *3 Cheese (Cheddar, Parmesan and Romano)* and *Smokey Bacon*. The packaging design was modest and straightforward, but also extremely recognizable as we relied heavily on the brand's classic and omnipresent yellow, black and white taxi cab inspired checkerboard pattern. Droves of faithful fans generously doused their premium russet potato New York Fries in the very same savoury seasoning each day at one of their nearly 200 tasty locations. The seasonings were so well-liked, they actually had a persistent problem with customers five-finger discounting the seasoning shakers from their condiment counters to enjoy at home. At $2.99 to $3.49, our suggested retail in grocery was right in line with our Kernels retail program.

So, why did the product helplessly struggle for a couple years and then eventually burn up and perish in deep fryer? In hindsight, the leading contributing factor with our failure was somewhat obvious and simple, but also difficult to pre-calculate and fully control: a fundamental variable we luckily got in the pocket with Kernels Shakers, but failed to understand the importance of until we started to nosedive with New York Fries—in-store product placement and the consequences of in-store product placement inconsistency. We just couldn't pinpoint, build from and protect the right retail shelf-space location.

New product concepts, particularly unique and unproven concepts, require more logical and consistent homes within a store—a cozy little spot where consumers will, at first intuitively, expect to stumble on it, and then demand to find it there each and every time. Shoppers shouldn't be expected to dig too deep for their treasures. When it comes to in-store placement, a big and clear 'X' should clearly mark the spot.

Out of the gate, we fought hard with retailers to be lined-in alongside the ketchup or malt vinegars. Why not? So we thought. Aside from salt, these are two of the most prevalent North American French fry condiments. It turned out, however, that most retailers weren't altogether thrilled with merchandising small seasoning jars next to ketchup, plus the stipulated listing fees (cost of entry) were rather punishing from a workable ROI perspective. Going back to the listing fee economics we discussed in *Chapter 2: Grocery Math*, how many months of conservative sales will it take to make your investment back. In this case, the timeline was nearly two years. I suppose it should've been more foreseeable that we'd score very little ground against this first placement strategy.

Licking our wounds, we then came up with a superior and more relevant in-store placement location. We'd try to hang the product on the glass freezer doors directly in front of the walls of frozen French fry bags. No brainer, right? The correlation should've been just as natural and fertile as our popcorn shakers living next to microwave popcorn. We invested heavily in designing, manufacturing, and placing customized gravity-fed wire racks that hung securely from the freezer doors.

After a month or so, we noticed the change in course started to click with consumers as our product reorders began to steadily strengthen. Folks were noticing, buying, trying and then coming back for more. And it could've slowly flowered into another success if the company that owned and leased the freezer units to grocery stores hadn't flexed their frozen muscles. It turned out that suspending wire racks from the large glass doors created a slight opening that allowed cold air to escape. Game over. Both the retailers and the freezer company had zero degrees of interest in hearing about possible racking remedies.

Our last stop on this trip was to spud-town, adjacent to the fresh potato bins in the produce section. Looking back, this was a starchy stretch as we were counting on the consumers who bought potatoes to make homemade fries—which we now realize is a much smaller, and simple butter-and-salt, kind of crowd. To boot, we already had two messy strikes on the board so retailers were now dubious of our ability to bring this one home. We went so far as to try to forge a cross-promotional driven partnership with the Province of Ontario's potato growers' co-op association, but our pitch fell flat.

More than five years after we discontinued the line, I received a call from Warren Price: *'Are you still selling the French fry seasoning? I was told an independent grocery store still has product on their shelf!?'* Turns out that there was still exceedingly old product hiding in dark corners in the marketplace and it was now rock solid. I imagine that Warren was just reaching out to make sure that we didn't fire up the business again under the radar. Needless to say, I was more surprised to hear about the surviving French fry seasoning than he was. I guess neither of us should've been surprised as potatoes tend to grow best when you bury and forget about them. All kidding aside, take note of the lingering damage and brand denigration that a botched concept can bring you should you not take full control of the clean-up process.

During our short-lived fling with the gang at New York Fries, we developed and launched a handful of other food concepts, and even had a few promising ideas die in the R&D hopper. Jay Gould was very keen on introducing a best-in-class potato chip under his brand. We resisted the temptation for a couple of years as succeeding in the chip-world takes deep both ultra deep pockets and an aggressive infantry platoon outfitted with direct-to-store-delivery trucks. We eventually surrendered, gave it a shot, fell short and in the process burnt yet another decent savings account over nine months of squandered work.

The one tasty concept that never did graduate from the scribble-filled pages of our big idea journal, that I'd still like to see come to life, was a deluxe poutine kit complete with premium Quebec cheese curds and New York Fries kickass gravy. Oddly, and quite contrary to our modus operandi, one of our most successful and profitable New York Fries' branded initiatives was a premium hot dog. Yep, go figure, a friggin' wiener. How seemingly unoriginal and uninspired is that? It was a fresh eye-opener, however, as the product's success was perhaps solely predicated by the fact that we offered it exclusively to A&P / Dominion in Ontario (acquired by Metro Inc. in 2005)—i.e. the product could only be purchased at their stores.

That summer BBQ season, they pleasantly pushed our fabulous frankfurter of their own volition by offering aggressive special feature pricing in their weekly flyer ads that they completely self-funded. The valuable takeaway was our fortunate glimpse into the very good things that come when you provide exclusivity to a retail chain—a strategy that has the potential to trump our belief in needing to focus on innovation or catching trends ahead of the curve in order to earn our place in the store. I'll save this tasty topic for the next chapter.

Let It Simmer ~

1. *Can you work with retailers to carve out a productive home within the store that's both consistent and instinctual with the consumer's expectations?*
2. *If you achieve success by securing a new, virgin in-store placement location, will you be able to continually protect your newfound home or will you eventually become vulnerable to external forces?*
3. *Before making the mistake of following-up a successful product launch with a seemingly similar concept, appreciate that it only takes one fickle ingredient in the recipe to spoil your entire dish.*
4. *If preserving the credibility and value of your brand after you exit from the market is important, take care in thoroughly mopping up your mess.*
5. *If your concept is somewhat of an uninspired me-too product, what can you anchor its success to? Can you offer it exclusively to a retailer with an ability to move enough volume to make it worth your while?*

CHAPTER 10

Opa!

Retailer Exclusivity Programs

A
h yeah, the blistering sound of Eddie Van Halen's thick and monster crunchy guitar riffs shaking my car stereo to the brink of explosion. It's a much-needed confidence building ritual I rely on when driving to a make-it or break-it meeting—ever try to watch a super hero movie on mute? On this particular cold and rainy morning, we were in talks to bring Ontario's most popular Greek restaurant chain, Mr. Greek Mediterranean Grill® into A&P / Dominion grocery stores. Securing the business would dramatically open up BrandFusion's product portfolio allowing us to reach deep into multiple food categories—e.g. protein products via pork shoulder and chicken breast souvlaki, deli products via tzatziki and imported feta cheese, fresh produce via ready-to-eat Greek salad kits, and into frozen foods via moussaka (layers of ground lamb and roasted eggplant topped with a cheese sauce) and stuffed phyllo appetizers.

We had lined up a meeting to pitch our big-picture-plan, alongside Mr. George Raios (President of Mr. Greek), to a handful of executives and category managers. The meeting went exceptionally well (thanks EVH), and I exited the building knowing we had locked ourselves into something special and meaningful with the retail chain. Unlike many other stories in this book that end in mild discontent and prolonged frustration, the Mr. Greek at A&P saga was an immensely gratifying and profitable toga ride that equipped us with an exceptional and powerful go-to launch recipe.

Loblaws is Canada's leading innovation powerhouse in the sport of grocery, especially when it comes to introducing and then wooing the market with untapped premium and avant-garde food trends. In 2005, grilling up juicy souvlaki (skewered meat) and serving it on authentic Mediterranean pita bread with fresh tzatziki was all the rage. As usual, Loblaws met the consumer demand early in the game with its line of *President's Choice* branded products. At the time A&P / Dominion had its own esteemed private label brand called '*Master Choice*' (yes, Master not Master's). At any rate, with respect to the group of products that we aimed to launch, we believed that their brand didn't carry as much punch and allure as the President's Choice program so our pitch was simple and super straightforward—provide A&P with a well-known, authentic and respected culinary Greek brand so that they could compete more aggressively with Loblaw Companies. The Mr. Greek brand would become their customized instrument to play with in grocery, and theirs alone.

Disclaimer: offering a retail chain brand exclusivity, and to an equal extent, offering exclusivity on a particular product (if the brand it's under is also sold to other retailers) is more of a clean slate strategy that's better served for newfangled launches with no baggage. Most retailers, especially the larger national chains, will frown heavily upon you generously handing their competitors an advantage that they cannot have access to. Before letting things fly, make certain that you can avoid falling into this inopportune hot seat, and that you can make a financially solid go of things based on the sales volume with a single retailer.

A brand and/or product exclusivity program may seem like a basic notion on the surface, but it can be a very persuasive and powerful device if you can encourage all the players in the game to embrace the arrangement at a level where they wholeheartedly believe that the program is their own to both aggressively flaunt and to protect. Try to frame your role and relationship with the retailer as being more of a mutual partner and brand ambassador than a traditional vendor. Angle to work shoulder to shoulder with them, as opposed to the sometimes more usual and uncomfortable foot to ass connection.

Actually, to be honest with you, most buyers working for larger retail chains tend to operate and negotiate cordially and collaboratively. We have many productive and longstanding relationships with prestigious individuals over at Longos, Loblaw Companies, Walmart Canada, Sobeys, Safeway and Costco. However, I'll also make no bones about the dying minority of ball-breaking buyers who unfortunately exist with what seems like a quiet thirst to keep you feeling dejected. Thankfully, we no longer have any such sour grinches in our circle of influence. Ok, I feel better now. Enough with the ranting.

In exchange for agreeing not to offer your program to another would-be buyer, try to frame your opening dialog by speaking in tones that affirm your unique role and increased impartiality in the deal. If you can set the table properly, the retailer will quickly adopt a pride of ownership in the mission that will pay you back in spades. When your buyer walks into their store and proudly gazes upon your product in the aisle, they should experience the same sensation as admiring a new car parked in their driveway. Sorry, I admit that was a little overkill, just wanted to drive my point home.

Ultimately, that pride of ownership will hopefully translate into much better than average in-store product placement and visibility, an increased frequency of pro bono flyer advertisements, and a genuine willingness to help keep looming product copycats at bay. Put simply, what often eventually develops is that the retailer will apply a greater than average amount of control in ensuring that your product flourishes. Conversely, when you're slugging away to sell that exact same product to every retailer in the marketplace, it becomes increasingly more expensive and challenging as you fight for your fair share of voice with each one.

With an exclusivity program arrangement in tow, you and the retailer are working more with a collective pocket of money to invest in the product's evolution. You're singing from the same song sheet. For example, where getting the buyer to financially chip into supporting an aggressive TPR (temporary price reduction) can typically be futile, exclusivity arrangements can help to relax their purse strings. There's also the case of conjoint accountability and a shared fear of failure. Should the product(s) bomb, it's a reflection of the buyer's capabilities and strategy judgment as much as it is yours. As things go, the pressure for the product and program to thrive becomes a somewhat unofficial, mutually binding pressure. And when your product does make its mark, getting the buyer tightly aligned with a follow-up launch of another product within the program may not only be in the cards, they'll be the ones shouting for an encore.

Granting all this upside, exclusivity deals should be firmly governed by a contractual time limit. After a year, or more likely two or sometimes even three, use the privilege of having achieved a better than average scorecard and impressive product awareness to approach other spectating retailers to open up distribution and kick sales up to the next level.

Let It Simmer ~

1. *Can a retailer exclusivity program work for your upcoming launch? If so, can you frame your role as being more of an equal partner vs. a common vendor?*

2. *Can you get a certain retail chain to share in a pride of ownership with your product?*

3. *If you do offer an exclusivity program, can you convince the retailer to share more in the costs required to promote your product? Can you use an exclusivity deal to improve your product's in-store placement, ad support, and to hold your competition at bay?*

4. *How many years can you afford to offer an exclusivity arrangement for? How will you explain your unique preferential arrangement to other curious retailers?*

CHAPTER 11

Damn Turmeric

Are You Solving a
Worthwhile Problem?

I f you're from Toronto, Canada chances are you'll remember the beloved 80s TV personality, Chef Pasquale Carpino (1936-December 30, 2005). Before the Food Network craze, during a time when most non-Italians had never heard of espresso, there was *Pasquale's Kitchen*. The Chef was an exceedingly passionate and charismatic man, always dutifully sporting a blue smock, a white necktie and a red chef's toque. He also happened to have studied opera at the Royal Conservatory of Music and was able to creatively combine his talent for bombastic operatic singing with his love and knowledge for cooking all things Italiano. During Sunday red-sauce lunches at my Grandparents, we would all gather round the wood-paneled television to watch Chef Pasquale as he masterfully julienned red bell peppers while belting out *O Sole Mio* at the top of his lungs—very impressive and very 80s in a good way. (Check it out: http://www.youtube.com/watch?v=uTOTb8FVrlk.)

Despite our successful foray into grocery stores with Kernels Extraordinary Popcorn, New York Fries and Mr. Greek Mediterranean Grill, I still had too much valuable time on my hands and too much bottled energy to burn. It was only natural, then, that, when JP asked me to take the reins on a new gastronomic venture with Chef Pasquale, I jumped perhaps a little too quickly and enthusiastically at the chance. My Italian heritage upbringing was a big bonus, if not an unspoken prerequisite, with this one. The product was a line of Italian sauce-base enhancers (i.e. add a heaping tablespoon of Chef Pasquale's magic into your pasta sauce to make it sing sort of thing).

Pasquale was very Italian in a way that reminded me of my own Uncles. The speciality food distributor, Molisana Imports, was also exceptionally Italian in a way that made me feel I was visiting Southern Italy each time I had to pay them a visit to talk shop or to collect a cheque for product payment. I'd wait patiently in an eerily quiet and dimly lit warehouse at the bottom rung of a barn-style wooden staircase leading up to the offices. The owner's son, Frank, who I believe still runs the show, is my age and a very convincing guy, smart beyond his years—we hit it off like two good Italian boys sharing their greasy brown-bag lunch in the school cafeteria.

Keeping Chef Pasquale content, God rest his big beautiful soul, was an equal task with trying to build the business. Part of the business plan was to have the Chef suit up in his trademark ensemble to put on in-aisle cooking demonstrations in the numerous grocery stores that supported the product launch. It was sometimes a strange and awkward scene to digest as I felt Pasquale, and rightly so, found this obligation slightly humbling. Of course the shoppers and passers-by wouldn't have picked up on this vibe, especially the older big-haired ladies who swooned over the culinary icon. It was the behind-the-scenes spectacle. To me, watching Pasquale lug pots and pans back to his car in a congested parking lot was a bit like witnessing the department store Santa removing his beard and hat.

The business venture itself was an uphill battle. The volume of product sold wasn't nearly enough for Chef Pasquale, the distributor or myself to start singing opera over. Suiting up to serve pasta out of a grocery aisle on a cold and rainy Saturday afternoon is sobering when you're making some decent coin, but when the commission cheques are a little light, it's just irritating. After a few months, I started to get fairly comfortable with being exceedingly open and honest, as sugarcoating projections and results to keep everyone content catches up with you—I like to sleep peacefully at night, remember.

One of the main snags with the product concept, I believe, was that Pasquale's central audience was Italian-Canadian. While his legion of fans certainly loved meeting and chatting with him while grocery shopping, I'm not entirely sure that they were the best candidates for buying and using the product. To explain, when it comes to cooking, among other things, Italians are colossally patriotic to their own family's recipes and preparation techniques. They are stubborn to a fault. Visit Italy and drive from town to town and you'll notice that everyone has a different recipe and preparation style that they'll protect aggressively and very publically until death. You'll see old men assertively squinting their faces and wagging their wrinkled fingers proclaiming: *'No, the sauce has to be made with freshly picked, not dried, oregano or it doesn't taste right. Bah, I refuse to try it!'* Do yourself a favour, avoid debating religion, politics and the proper preparation of tomato sauce with Italians at all costs.

So it's only logical that a proud (and overtly stubborn) Italian-Canadian woman or man wouldn't want to modify or embarrassingly experiment with their perfect and sacred family recipe. *'Hey, don't you know you can't improve on perfection!'* Sure, they'll politely smile and nod approvingly in front of the Chef as they chew his dialled-up rigatoni, but they're still walking out of the supermarket with crushed San Marzano tomatoes, fresh garlic and basil, black pepper and a really good olive oil—real Italians don't do quick and easy.

Ultimately, it was Chef Pasquale's own patriotic protection of his recipes, and perhaps one too many glasses of red wine for us both, which ultimately caused us to part ways. While in Montreal, I received an untimely phone call from the Chef at 10 p.m. while resting in my hotel room bed. *'Bruno,'* he began in a quiet and unsettled voice. *'Who put the turmeric in my sauce? My recipe does not have turmeric!'* I replied calmly: *'Pasquale, which sauce are you referring to?'* *'On the jar, it says turmeric in the ingredients.'* (He's sounding increasingly more irritated now.)

I understood that he was referring to the ingredient deck published on our retail product. I imagine he'd just detected that our contract packer ended up including turmeric in the commercialized version of the recipe without his blessing. The product and packaging were already developed, produced and in the warehouse when I was brought on board so this was also news to me. Be that as it may, maybe it was because it was late and I had been travelling all day. Or, maybe because this felt like a deleted scene out of the *Godfather*, it was enough to unhinge me and give into the writing on the wall. I saw red. *'Listen Pasquale,'* I said in my best Michael Corleone voice, *'I've had enough of this! Please. Relax!!*

Do not take this out on me. I respect you immensely and have been trying my very best to help sell the sauce! It's not my fault that it's not selling.'

We eventually simmered down and calmly apologized to one another. I genuinely adore the man and still hold him in high regard. After all, if I was hoping to play a young Pacino in our relationship that night, he would've been playing the esteemed king Brando. But, perhaps the old axiom holds true: beware should you meet your heroes.

Let It Simmer ~

1. *Are you gauging the true size of the potential market that you'll be going after, or are your assumptions dangerously overstated?*
2. *Does your product concept look to solve a consumer problem that may not want to be solved? If so, should you be tweaking your product or changing your sights to a different target?*
3. *How relevant and useful is your product concept to consumers outside of the core target group? Is there a strategy to widen your net without watering down your concept?*
4. *Take heed before you peek behind the curtain.*

CHAPTER 12

A Slice Of Pizza Pie

Getting it Right

J P and I sat in Michael Overs' boardroom like anxious school kids waiting in an 8th grade classroom for the seasoned and stalwart principal to make an appearance. After all, this was the same brilliant Michael Arthur Overs that founded the Ontario-omnipresent Pizza Pizza® restaurant chain and helped to pioneer the ingenious centralized single-number ordering system now used by oodles of restaurant chains throughout North America ... sing it out loud, you know the jingle ... '*967-11-11*'. After six months of courting one another, we were down to the short strokes with signing on Pizza Pizza to have BrandFusion introduce their illustrious pizza dipping sauces into grocery stores—a product, especially the creamy garlic, with a strong cult-like following in Ontario, Canada.

Michael and his gang were among the first on the block to offer dipping sauces for pizza versus today where every pizza restaurant chain offers their own riff on the popular concept. A few months beforehand, we had almost signed a contract with their restaurant rival, Pizza Nova, but decided to cut bait and roll out the dough with Pizza Pizza when they showed real interest because of their stouter market presence. Making the letdown call to Michael Primucci at Pizza Nova was one of the most agonizing calls I've had to make to date. He was a solid guy, a real gentleman, and had been open to a brand licensing deal with us. When he found out what our plans were, and especially with whom, the conversation and our rapport melted like mozzarella really, really fast. Sorry Michael, no hard feelings, I hope.

Sitting at the boardroom table with JP, my only real worry was getting through the product sampling as he has a disdain for most cheeses —especially the melty, drippy and dippy ones. As Mr. Overs squeezed a walnut-sized cheese blob onto JP's paper plate and handed him a plastic tasting-spork to sample it with, I cringed and quietly giggled simultaneously. We looked at each other like juvenile brothers at the dinner table wondering how we'd ever eat our pile of boiled broccoli. I love cheese and was happy to clean my plate, and thankfully, like always, JP pulled through. After much discussion we left the meeting with a firm handshake and agreed to the basic economics and terms of our deal.

To this day, we consider our Pizza Pizza Dips program one of our most successful retail endeavours and continue to delve deep into why and how the product and program worked in hopes that we can help creamy-garlic-lightning strike twice. The only unfortunate account in the Pizza Pizza chapter was the loss of Michael Overs (1939-March 31, 2010). Being in the same room with the man was always nothing short of edifying and entertaining as he was somewhat of a J. Peterman storyteller in food and restaurant circles ... and I'm a sucker for life lessons through storytelling.

So what made our Pizza Pizza Dips successful? Why have we enjoyed consistent sales growth year over year for the past ten plus years since the launch? Why has preserving the growth and our shelf space been somewhat easier and less inexpensive to achieve relative to most of our other product launches? It turns out, there are a host of good explanations—some intentional and others purely accidental. Arguably, the most important contributor was leveraging the deep-rooted ritual that Pizza Pizza engrained into its legion of loyal fans. With our humble consumer budgets, and without the brand, it would have been near impossible to educate and cultivate pizza eaters to dip and dunk their lonely pizza crust into a non-tomato-based sauce.

Even if the concept, packaging and flavour experience was a direct hit, creating a population of loyal dippers and dunkers doesn't happen overnight—it takes repetition, significant time and big money. How would we have reached enough pizza eaters to make a decent business out of it? Without Pizza Pizza's expansive customer base, frequency and reach, we wouldn't have been able to influence enough consumers at the grocery level to accomplish a worthwhile volume impact. Believe you me, over the years we've launched plenty of aspirational concepts using brilliant packaging designs and recipes that we loved and believed completely in that ultimately nose-dived because they had no established consumer ritual to spawn and grow from.

As illustrated in the previous chapters, carving out a relevant and consistent home within the store that's intuitive to consumers is nothing less than compulsory. For the pizza dips, we sliced out a zip code right next to the take n' bake fresh pizzas in the open-bunker refrigerators positioned in the home meal replacement (HMR) department —grab a fresh pizza and you're likely to toss the dips into your cart along with it. Part of the magic was that the dips needed to be refrigerated and are packaged in a convenient single-serve deli-style cup format. This helped us to generate a fresh and better ingredient underlying narrative. More importantly, Pizza Pizza packed and served the same dips to their consumer in the same deli-style cups, giving our retail format an instant familiarity and credibility. Put another way, if the dips were shelf stable, packed in a salad-dressing bottle and sat in an aisle far away from the fresh pizzas in another part of the store, they'd be collecting dust.

If you plan and tackle the first six months of sales wisely, being first to market, especially when you're operating with a limited budget, can give you the head start you need to dig your feet in firmly. After six months or a year's time, you can bet that either the larger corporate CPG vultures or scrappy start-ups working from their garage will be fervently circling your lunch. At the time, there were already similar cream-based dips sold in the deli department, but they were positioned as more all-purpose and not expressly made or promoted for pizza. Planting the first flag allowed us to more or less define the product and space that we wanted to own and play within (i.e. pack size, packaging format, retail price point, etc.)

Conversely, if you're attempting to enter a category with other brands vying for, or protecting, the same space and message, the product concept focus is usually placed more heavily on trying to match or improve on costs, retails, serving size, packaging design or on pretty much any distinctive product or program benefit that you can push —e.g. ingredient and/or recipe quality, health benefits, merchandising vehicles, or superior consumer and trade spending, etc. It's not easy to create a truly new platform every time you go to market, but it sure as hell helps make the long climb easier when there's nothing but sky above you. With our Kernels Popcorn Shakers, and now our Pizza Pizza Dips, we had managed to achieve a worthwhile first to market advantage once again.

Depending on the size of the retailer we're planning on selling to and where we want the product to end up in the store, we often use specialty direct-to-store (DSD) distributors to get to market. Selling and shipping product directly to retailers versus using a distributor to sell and ship your product is a sales topic worth tackling separately—see *Chapter 26: Planting Seeds*. For now, let me say that there are decent arguments to make for both cases; however, your situation and view on this decision will certainly change and morph dramatically over the life cycle of your product.

In the beginning, it's usually easier to give 15 percent up to a more common 30 percent of your beloved profit margin so that a distributor with a large, well-established retailer customer base and a well-oiled delivery infrastructure can purchase and warehouse an attractive quantity of your product. It's also less onerous, stressful and cash-flow-friendly to sell pallets of product to a single distributor and carry one large receivable instead of chasing multiple accounts who will ultimately and inconsiderately hold your money for way too long and then pay you far less than they agreed to. As your volume and ability to stage and ship orders grows and the economics start to suggest that you can eliminate a distributor's margin, you'll inescapably toil over the decision of making more money at the expense of taking on a lot more work and responsibility.

At any rate, in the case of Pizza Pizza Dips, we found the perfect distribution partner in Western Creamery (eventually acquired by Liberté in 2006). At the time, they were the right sized partner who valued what we brought to the table. Note: coercing a distributor, or a retailer for that matter, to take on a product almost always ends undesirably (and expensively). When a distributor wants your product and can see the finish line, the communication and your relationship have a better chance of being open and mutually constructive. Unless you're desperate, which I respect can be the case, you never want favours; you want a partner that shares your vision and appetite for the mission.

We sold the Pizza Pizza Dips concept into Wal-Mart, Loblaws and Sobeys head office while Western Creamy hit the ground running at the store level and drove the stake in nice and deep. Going back to the 6-month timeline rule, they helped initiate enough success in the onset to create the momentum required to endure the retailer's unofficial probation period—thanks Louise McIlravey and Angelo Eleusiniotis.

At any rate, looking back, I now clearly see that the most pivotal moment and telling crossroads in this story was when JP, despite his disdain for cheese, managed to gulp down the blob of Jalapeno Cheddar Dip that Mr. Overs served up.

Let it Simmer ~

1. *Does your product concept tap into an established consumer ritual? If not, can it survive on the shelf until you build one? Are your pockets deep enough and your persistence strong enough to hold on until a ritual catches on?*

2. *Can you build a case for having your product displayed in a consistent and relevant home where it will benefit from an impulse purchase with another established anchor-product? Think ice cream and sprinkles, salsa and tortilla chips.*

3. *What's the subtle and unspoken messaging to the consumer as a result of your packaging format and where you'll be merchandised? Think fresh versus processed.*

4. *Is your product an original idea? If not, are there enough unique and meaningful points of difference that you can lean on to stand out against your competition?*

5. *Do your distribution partners believe in your product and vision? Are they interested and engaged or do they seem bothered and unenthusiastic? Will they continue to support you if the mission takes longer than six months or a year?*

CHAPTER 13

Cocktail Dreams

Reality Checks

I t's bright and early on a sunny Friday morning in June. Van Halen's soul-lifting song *'Dreams'* (my favourite tune since age 14) is dutifully waking me up on route to the office. While flying down Highway 400 South, it hits me square in the chest like one of Eddie's wailing guitar solos: *I should get into business with Sammy Hagar. Seriously!* To explain, the day earlier, while nosing around on the website for his Mexican cantina resto in Southern Baja California called *Cabo Wabo (cabowabocantina.com)*, I noticed they offered a few trademark items on the menu (e.g. Sammy's Tequila Shrimp). A month earlier I had just completed reading Sammy's autobiography (*Red: My Uncensored Life in Rock*) and had been pleasantly surprised to learn that, aside from his role as the former Van Halen front-man, he was quite the consummate businessman. For complete disclosure, I'm a Van Halen diehard and now I'm thinking: *'Who wouldn't buy a delectable Cabo Wabo frozen shrimp entrée at Loblaws or Sobeys? Of course it'll fly, it's a rockin' foolproof concept. Right?'* Anyhow, I sold myself enough to speed to the office, squeal into my parking spot, bolt through the front door and dive for the phone.

After a month or so of depositing overzealous and persuasive voice-mail messages, the then President & CEO of *Cabo Wabo* Enterprises, named Barry Augus, called me back. I'd like to think I at least sounded cool and composed on the other end of the line. Truth be told, I was standing in my chair sporting a Cheshire grin. I explained to Barry that

I felt introducing a line of *Cabo Wabo* frozen entrées into Canadian grocery stores would both shoot a little extra royalty cash into Sammy's rock n' roll empire and also serve to create consumer interest in visiting the Cabo Wabo cantina.

Barry quickly and politely shot down the frozen entrée idea, but then offered up a super cool consolation prize for my consideration. At the time, the cantina's namesake tequila was making its mark in the alcohol industry selling nearly 40,000 cases in its inaugural year. As such, Sammy was contemplating expanding his *Cabo Wabo* brand via offering a high-end margarita mix. *'No problem,'* I said assuredly. *'Leave it with us for a few weeks, and we'll come to the table with something worthy of the challenge.'*

Despite BrandFusion's hopper being congested with other much more laudable projects and our resources being spread way too thin, I called in the boys for a download session. *'This is it, fellas. This is the big ship and it absolutely has to sail.'* Archie proceeded to brief our flavour house and beverage supply partners and within two short weeks we had a few stubby glass bottles filled with a unique, albeit kind of murky and mysterious, natural lime margarita mix in our impatient little hands. *'There's some weird stuff collecting at the bottom of the bottle. Is it okay to drink?'* Barry asked. I answered instantly: *'No worries. It's natural fruit juice pulp, give it good shake and give it a go.'* (Side note: as you'll read in *Chapter 28: Fruit Pulp Clouds & Chocolate Bloom*, pasteurizing a natural fruit juice containing any traces of pulp typically results in what's called flocculation, which in fact can be off-putting to consumers.)

We waited a couple days or weeks for some constructive feedback. And then, we got the call (to paraphrase): *'Sammy tried your margarita mix. He said let Bruno know it's way too sweet and tastes more like Limeade than the more refined taste profile that we're looking for. But, you know, please remember the tastes buds of a seasoned rock n' roll star have been exposed to more wear and tear than most of us. Can you make it less sweet?'* I customarily would've responded with something like: *'No problem, we'll bring down the sweetness and have a new tasting sample to you within a week or so.'* I, however, stopped biting down on my knuckle and probed further: *'Did Sammy actually say let <u>Bruno</u> know?'* 'Yes, yes, I believe he *addressed you by your name,*' he said. '*Just checking,*' I confirmed, beaming back at my subtle reflection in the laptop screen.

I leaned way back in my big, cushy leather chair after the phone call and rested my feet up on the desk. Staring out the window for what seemed like a good half hour, I knew exactly what the next step had to be. Disengage immediately. Carefully bow out as quickly as possible. Sorry, did I lose and confuse you? Why, you ask. This story could've perhaps ended with Sammy and me holding the same bottle of margarita mix high over our heads on stage with '*Dreams*' blaring in the background during the official product release PR event.

Here's what I asked myself and realized in that pivotal half hour staring out the window: Was I doing this because it was good for the company and for our bottom line, or was it a mission straight into Vanity-Ville? Was I using our limited resources wisely or wastefully? Had we really combed through the opportunity to understand the market size, cost of entry, our point of difference, the brand's strength outside of Sammy's core audience, etc.? Or, had I overlooked every single touchstone to fight for that moment to be up on stage at the release party? Perhaps, most importantly, if the deal went south or tanked miserably, would I be able to listen to Sammy's music and experience that same jubilant take-no-prisoners feeling? Or, would the songs just completely piss me off every time I heard them? Hubris baby, it's a dangerous little sucker.

Who knew that years later, Dave and I would craft *Crazy Uncle*® culinary cocktails (see *Chapter 19: Catching A Buzz*), as it would have been a much more natural cobranding effort. Sammy, if you're listening, we're still interested. It should be noted that in 2007 Sammy sold 80% of *Cabo Wabo* tequila to an Italian beverage company called Gruppo Compari for a reported $91 million.

Let It Simmer ~

1. *Have you carefully scanned the impetus for pursuing your product concept, or is your mission driven by self-indulgence?*

2. *If your mission is driven by self-indulgence, can it still be supported with a sound business strategy and a worthwhile financial reward? If not, should you consider disengaging before the damage becomes irreparable?*

CHAPTER 14

Not So Easy Peasy

Lessons From Failure

A good year or two before the passionate and spirited superstar chef Jamie Oliver became super-popular in North America, our people reached out to his people in the UK in an effort to strike a licensing deal. After a few calls, we managed to generate some curiosity with a woman named Tessa Graham, one of Jamie's business administrators at the time. Although she was based out of the UK, Tessa was originally from Western Canada so I thought we'd have a little homeland advantage. We booked a meeting a month out which would take place in the Jamie Oliver headquarters located above his philanthropic restaurant project '*Fifteen*' in London, England. It would be an expensive meeting to attend and execute properly, but the mission felt promising and, to say the least, different and exciting as I had never been to the UK.

I rushed to the closest Chapters bookstore to acquire his cookbooks and immersed myself in his colourful TV shows to understand what made him tick and to determine what leading product concepts would connect him with Canadians. We ended up with three starting concepts. Artisanal, yet approachable—alternative cooking oils made from nuts and fruits with high mono-unsaturated fats, and a line of funky spice rubs packed in metal shoe polish-like containers, both of which have since become prevalent in the marketplace. The main thrust was a Home Meal Replacement (HMR) program where Jamie would provide trendy and healthy recipes for supermarkets to prepare on site and sell fresh as part of their hot-table counters. Information leaflets would be offered gratis alongside funky Jamie Oliver counter displays. Admittedly, both concepts seemed either marginally niche or slightly ahead of their time. Nonetheless, they were crafted to showcase our understanding of Jamie's growing brand and that we weren't about to milk or diminish his name on the typical tropical salad dressings and pork marinades.

I purchased my $2,650 plane ticket, an affordable hotel room and a slick new navy blue single-breasted suit and headed for the UK. By now, after delving into so much of his work, I had become somewhat of a fan and was looking forward to breaking bread with the man. I hadn't been to London before, so the day before the meeting my travel mates and I painted the town red and took in the usual tourist sites. My cousin Chris had secured a meeting with one of the larger movie theatre chains in an effort to sell the Brits on our popcorn seasoning program.

Side note: The top salty snack flavours of the day in England were markedly more complex and ultra savoury than what we're used to in North America—roasted lamb with mint yogurt, and spicy curried chicken were a couple of interesting flavours that come to mind. These were unheard of and unsalable recipes in Canada and US ten years back, and a far cry from the much more one-dimensional flavoured salty snacks back home. I imagine that today, these funkier flavours would bode well. Not surprising, given that the UK seems to be perpetually ahead of us by a number of years with respect to grocery food trends.

The next day, I slowly peeled open my eyes to check the clock on the night stand and realized my meeting started in less than an hour somewhere across the other end of town. 'Oh Shit. Oh No! ... Oh Boy.' I cursed out loud. I had prepared extensively, flown 5,728 kilometres and bought a new suit for this meeting; being late wasn't an option. Despite crafting my tie knot and combing my hair in the cab, I made it to 'Fifteen' with a couple of minutes to spare. I announced my presence to the maître d' and waited in the restaurant lounge for someone to come and escort me upstairs into Jamie's office. I was thankful for the twenty-minute wait as it allowed me to calm my jet-lagged nerves and to forget the stressful blur of the past hour. After all, I was about to jam on some culinary ideas with the Naked Chef.

As someone marched me up the narrow staircase, I took in a super deep breath and smiled hard. *'Who would've thought BrandFusion would flourish to a point where Jamie Oliver would want to sit and chat about having us build his brand in Canada?'* I'll never forget the next proud moment. As the boardroom pocket-doors quickly parted open, I felt the climax of the journey burning in my belly. It's show time, baby! Surprisingly, however, Jamie wasn't in the room yet. Tessa was sitting there, poised, ready and waiting to hear me out. Dispensing with the pleasantries, I grinned politely and inquired: *'Where's Jamie?'* *'You just missed him,'* she responded. *'Oh. Huh.'* I swallowed hard and paused for what seemed like too long of an awkward moment. I felt my body temperature uncomfortably rising and in my head I'm grunting: *'She does realize I flew in from Canada for this, right?'*

Anyhow, wrong or right, it threw my mojo way off centre. I'm sure my presentation had all the flare and charm of a guy discovering his blind date is still married. Removing the heart and passion from your pitch is like yanking the engine from your car. Your chances of failing are now better than average. I truthfully can't recall how the meeting actually went. I only recollect shaking her hand and reading her facial expression and body language. To me, it said: *'Kinda interesting, but fat chance my fellow Canuck.'*

Feeling majorly snubbed, I also found it slightly challenging to enjoy Jamie Oliver's shows or to watch his guest appearances on talk shows. However, once his mini-series on the Food Network called *Jamie's Great Italian Escape* aired, I began to admire the guy again. I'm a sucker for both food travel shows and for unadulterated, simple Italian food, so it was only a matter of time. Soon after that, Jamie launched his very successful global *Food Revolution* campaign (jamiesfoodrevolution.org) which aims to educate children about healthy food choices, as well as protect them by lobbying government and industry to do the right things.

By this point, I've gradually converted back into a full-fledged fan. Perhaps more vindicating, I noticed that in the years that followed my less-than-fruitful meeting in the UK, Jamie ended up launching an avocado oil and a line of funky spice rubs. More impressively, at least to me, in the summer of 2013, Jamie announced a partnership with Sobeys Inc. '*designed to educate, inspire and empower Canadians to eat better.*' This was the very core and essence of our presentation pitch nearly ten years earlier! We were either ahead of our time, didn't package the concept with enough clarity and credibility, or simply didn't make that much needed special and unspoken connection with Tessa. Live and learn, I suppose. Although if I do score another shot to sit down with Jamie, I hope the meeting is no further than in London, Ontario.

Let It Simmer ~

3. *Tactfully selling yourself before selling your product will always help to produce a more optimistic outcome for your pitch.*
4. *If making a solid personal connection with a prospective partner or buyer isn't achievable, try not to get rattled and screw up your pitch. Keep moving forward with a smile!*
5. *Timing is everything. Are consumers ready for your product concept or is it perhaps ahead of its time? Unless you have the muscle and clout of a sizeable company or that of an established retailer, it's hard to properly convince and educate consumers about something truly new and pioneering.*

CHAPTER 15

Chicken Wings & Other Things

Too Many Cooks Spoil The Broth

When Hooters® Canada unexpectedly reached out to chat about bringing their signature namesake butter-based chicken wing sauce into grocery stores, I said: *'What the ...? Listen, I'm sorry, buddy, but we don't want to meet with you because we find your brand innuendos much too offensive and downright chauvinist!'* ... Yeah, right, that's exactly what I said. It was more like: *'Yep. I'm free in five minutes, can you come over.'* During the intro meeting, the most memorable part was when the chief Hooter stopped speaking in midsentence, paused, and declared: *'We all know Hooters can also mean big boobs, right? We have to be very careful about that.'* I bit my lower lip and nodded my head in what felt like a very Chevy Chase manner. *'Yes, of course. Please proceed.'*

The wing sauce was good, really good—loads of fatty real butter resulting in a satisfying richness compared to the very overly tart and vinegary options in the market at the time. The brand, despite your initial dirty thoughts, is meant to be fun, cheesy and cheeky. It was also hard to overlook that the exact same retail line of sauces and wing breading was already well-established in US grocery stores and was pulling in millions. We liked the play. We liked the guys. And heck, who doesn't love a good chicken wing? To help vet out and validate the concept's viability, we packed up a few big baskets of piping hot wings, fresh made from a local Hooters restaurant, and fed them to Sobeys' Deli manager. If I remember correctly, she totally dug the product and saw past the big boobs thing. So why did we waste nearly a year and not sell a single drumstick's worth? Well, there were a couple of double-D sized problems.

Our main contact at Hooters, and would-be business partner in the venture, was well-versed and highly effective at running his handful of licensed Hooters restaurants and had what seemed like a concrete relationship and respect from all, or at least some, of the original six brand founders in Clearwater, Florida. He was both super quick and super gracious to share the retail opportunity with us, along with two of his local food supplier friends. More impressively, he offered us a decent number of shares in the business they formed to eventually house the monies coming from grocery store sales.

That said, I'm always apprehensive and on high guard when offered a piece of the proverbial pie when it's divided into too many slices—especially before scrubbing the true economics of the opportunity, and knowing everything about all the players at the table who will receive a slice. Contrarily, I find it agonizing to dish out a slice of my unbaked pie unless it's the absolute last option left on the table required to secure a player for our team that promises to have an invaluable talent or contacts. No way, there's a million other much less-committal solutions to adequately move and motivate a candidate to action. Otherwise, I'll protect each and every share point like the last few drops of fresh water in a canteen.

At any rate, each time we met as a team to discuss our game plan, I'd ask to see a formal agreement and the comprehensive COGs to ensure that we were getting a thick enough slice for our role in the chicken wing parade. We weren't virgins when it came to getting worked over as a direct consequence of choosing to operate without a signed contract. Getting our hands on an agreement sanctioned by all the players who were promised company shares, most notably a shadowy figure in the US that we hadn't met, proved to be over a year-long hunt. Perhaps more conspicuous and telling, the US figure also happened to be the master licensor of the Hooters brand for retail with exclusive access to the manufacturing co-packer(s) that produced the wing sauce in question.

The retail product COGs, basic ordering parameters and requirements remained undefined. How much would the product cost us to buy and would we be left with enough margin to pocket for ourselves?

What was our minimum production order quantity commitment and who would be responsible for buying the Canadian-tailored packaging design? Would the co-packer award us with workable payment terms or would we need to prepare to fund the orders upfront? Despite the camaraderie with the fellas involved, and the plentiful free baskets of deep fried buttery drummies and flatties, the gravity and probability of the mission began to vanish with each wing-pull. Definition: one of my only publically celebrated talents is called the 'wing-pull'; it involves shoving a flatty chicken wing into my mouth and then quickly hauling it back out with absolutely zero meat left on the bones. Don't laugh, I'm very proud of this party trick.

It seems obvious now, but the more the Hooters team was unable to present us with a proper agreement and the basic operational mechanics of our involvement, the less engaged we became. At the time, I suppose that the attraction of being associated with an internationally celebrated brand, and potential size of the jackpot, kept us hanging around for a lot longer than usual. In retrospect, however, I can also appreciate that the group's inability to consummate the deal allowed us to peer deeper into the crystal ball to get a clearer understanding of how our future dealings with the new company and our would-be partners might operate.

Considering that actions speak louder than words, I'm relieved for having had the accidental opportunity to conduct a proper, albeit too lengthy, due diligence if the alternative might have been to try and build the business without a firm hand resting on the steering wheel. It was all for the best, as once the COGs were finally nailed down, there wasn't nearly enough meat on the bones to keep us from eventually going hungry. The Hooters crew were a real hoot to hang with. A solid bunch of guys that I'm certain we would've had many good times with—but when it comes to business, I'm not a fan of wingin' it.

Let It Simmer ~

1. *Before you dive into a new venture, insist that you meet and get to know every player in the game that will have a stake in the business.*

2. *Be suspicious should a prospective partner offer you ownership in their company too quickly and easily, particularly if the fundamental costs and metrics are not yet understood.*

3. *No margin, no deal. It's amazing how far and deep into a business courtship people will go without knowing if there's enough meat on the bones.*

4. *If you're thinking of offering someone ownership in your new company to secure their commitment, slow down to consider if an alternative motivation is possible; at least until a generous period of examination has passed.*

5. *Beware of lip service. Before locking yourself into a long-term commitment, carefully take stock of what a person does and doesn't do vs. what they repeatedly promise you. In the words of Ralph Waldo Emerson:* 'What you do speaks so loud that 1 cannot hear what you say.'

6. *Put a strict timeline in place, particularly once the rope starts slipping from your grip—if it ends up being missed by a mile, it might be a blessing in disguise and provide you with the time required to flush out the facts.*

CHAPTER 16

Rotten Fruit

Even the Smartest People
Make Big Mistakes

One bad apple can spoil the whole damn bunch. Hastily surrendering ownership in your start-up mission in an effort to recruit business partners and to secure their resources is somewhat of an exposed nerve for me. Ok, relax. I realize that we've just covered this subject in the previous chapter, but at the risk of overdramatizing, I'd like to spend a little more time on this to nail down my point. Don't be short-sighted; think long and hard before offering a precious piece of ownership in your newfangled firm. Too many start-ups give away a slice of their company, and then eventually their ability to operate freely, much too easily and early in the game in an effort to help them climb that first monster step. Whether it be for a lack of financing, sales relationships or industry experience, I've seen capable food entrepreneurs with super strong and promising personalities and product platforms hand over a set of spare master keys to their front door like it was no big deal.

The decision on handing out an ownership offer to someone that might be able to help you advance in the game shouldn't be taken any less seriously than deciding to slip an engagement ring on your date's finger. Okay, well maybe it's not that serious, but it can be damn near close in some instances, especially when you factor in the divorce repercussions. Consider that once you clear that first seemingly giant step, you may not need a partner as much or even want them at all. I can also tell you that once you finally clear the first few steps that there are an infinite number more, shifting and winding up an endless stairway to financial-heaven. And with each new set of obstacles, a partner with an entirely different skill set and familiarities may be needed to help to advance. Keep in mind that, once the honeymoon is over, you have to learn to live and compromise with that person for the long haul while they continue to share your burgeoning bank account.

I've had the fortunate opportunity to have either accepted or have been offered ownership and a voice in dozens of considerable food company start-up undertakings. Other than those with my brother and JP, each chapter has ended in a prickly and costly separation. I know what you may be thinking, but it wasn't always me that was the problem. Hold on to each and every percentage point of your company's ownership until you're absolutely certain that it's time to pull the golden ring from your breast pocket. Hold on to your ownership and operating control like a kid clutching his pillowcase full of Halloween candy. Offer an overinflated commission incentive, tie in a handsome performance based bonus, or put them on a plane with their spouse to Cabo San Lucas, but try to keep your company undivided until the long-term picture reveals itself. Remember, even the smartest, most experienced and well-funded partners will make great mistakes and drive you to drink.

We've had our share of prematurely getting down on one knee to make an offer. Here's a story of someone else impulsively asking for our hand in partnership. When Nick Antonopoulos called to ask if we'd be interested in having him fly us out to Montreal to hear a business pitch on a packaged premium frozen fruit concept for retail I said: '*Sure, why the hell not.*' Having worked with Nick on another food related mission, I knew first hand that he was an exceptionally successful and prudent businessman in the Quebec restaurant and food service scene, plus I love visiting Montreal anytime I can—especially Old Montreal; if you're ever in town, make a point of having your morning cappuccino and croissant at Olive & Gourmando.

When he picked Dave and me up from Pierre Elliott Trudeau International Airport, looking very spruce in his crisp, mauve Lacoste pullover and designer jeans, Nick was noticeably keen to fill us in and set the stage for the meeting he had organized with Hans Schmid. Hans was a veteran in the fruit importing business. Having held a senior procurement position at Danone, he was well-connected and exceedingly well-versed in the game of sourcing produce from the four corners of the world.

As we pulled up to Hans' stunning lake front-home, situated in a picturesque and charming community, Nick pointed out the lakehouse-turned-office at the back of the property which sat a mere stone's throw from the water. *'Man oh man, I could get used to having our meetings out here,'* I whispered to Dave as Nick finished taking a phone call in his car. It was even more spectacular inside. Custom carved wooden boardroom chairs and grand cathedral ceilings overlooked sprawling views of the lake. As we sat on the weathered leather couch in his dimly lit and most godfather-esque office, we were introduced to another two seasoned and well-established venture capitalists that were to be part of the mission.

Nick and Hans proceeded to paint a fruitful picture of the opportunity at hand. A company named Europe's Best® had taken the freezer section in Canadian grocery stores by storm with its introduction of premium frozen fruit assortments packed in attractive re-sealable stand-up bags. Big and luscious medleys of strawberries, blueberries and mangos were selling like Eskimo Pies® back in 1922 and the fellas wanted a crack at shaking the money tree. With Hans' knowhow and international contacts, Nick and Co.'s financial resources and counsel, and our sales and retailer relationships, it was tabled as a no-brainer.

Our point of difference would be to offer retailers a like-product, if not a superior one, at a better value for their private label (store brand) program. It was a difficult offer to refuse—and not only because we were sitting in an office worthy of Don Corleone. We were being offered ownership and equal control in a new company without having to invest our own money and it was backed by established, motivated and sincere partners with proven track records. *'What's the risk?'* we asked ourselves. The following week, we formally accepted their invitation to join forces.

We would start drawing a decent salary once the first billable sale was secured and collected. Despite advising the group to register the company name as *Nature's Fruit* (singular), the company was officially registered as *Nature's Fruits* (plural)—which, to us, sounded a tad peculiar and comical, but then again I just re-read *Chapter 6: Eat in Moderation, Not Deprivation* and do realize that I shouldn't be so quick to call the kettle black when it comes to peculiarity.

Within a month or so Nick & Co. each deposited a nice chunk of cash into a Toronto-based bank account that Dave and I would be responsible for managing. As our first order of business, we all gambled on ordering a container of assorted frozen fruit samples from overseas, designed and printed a few thousand colourfully branded stand-up resealable bags to house the sales samples, and strung together a rather technically impressive sales pitch that spoke to Hans' global procurement procedures and plans. By this time, Dave and I had become suspicious of Nature's Fruits' ability to match, let alone beat, the incumbent brand's pricing. We had spent the month tapping our industry relationships to better understand margin requirements, volume expectations and the likelihood of penetrating the category—which, by the way, we would've been wise to do before choosing to sign on as official partners willing to work pro bono until the profits were ripe for the picking.

Our discoveries suggested that our sell prices might actually end up erring on the side of being more expensive. We attempted to counsel the group, and proposed to cancel the ten-thousand-dollar investment required to secure the container of fruit samples we had ordered until our position of strength became clearer. It was decided, nonetheless, that we should move forward with the investment in order to build momentum and to be properly prepared. Worst case, we'd have to unload the product at a discount. Nevertheless, from our perspective, the honeymoon had ended and we were left feeling anxious about marriage.

Looking back, I feel more for Nick & Co. as they had put their trust in our contacts and capabilities. Sometimes I wish I wasn't so good at selling myself upfront because it typically leads to having to live up to an expectation that I haven't the time or impetus for. Fearful of failure, I circumvented the usual chain of command, and called for a sit-down with Mr. Al Cussen, one of our most senior vice president contacts at Wal-Mart Canada, to present our program. Note: Going above your buyer's head is a risky card that you can't play too often, and is one that should be reserved only for certain tactical situations—it's sort of like floating aimlessly in a dingy at sea and knowing when to fire off your only flare in the emergency gun.

On any other day, I would've tried to lock in a meeting with the appropriate private label buyer, but this situation was somehow different. I felt the pressure of the group weighing heavily on my integrity and wanted to both prove my worth and to flush out our new company's potential. Could 'we,' and perhaps more important to me, could 'I' pull this off? I wanted to fast track the usual drawn-out vendor-buyer tango to flush out the truth about our chances for success. That afternoon, however, we left the meeting knowing that Walmart didn't consider our big opportunity as much of a no-brainer as we had sitting in Hans' lake-house office. A couple of weeks later, we left Sobeys' National head-office knowing that they too were on Walmart's *sorry fellas, it's no-go* page.

On top of everything, as we had predicted, our pricing was in fact higher than our would-be competition. Wasn't our *raison d'être* better pricing and value? Isn't that why we all wanted to climb this fruit tree? We tried to be as open and candid with the group as we could by explaining that, in light of the preliminary feedback from retailers, the mission wasn't as promising as we all had imagined it to be. Looking back, I wonder if the drawback was us? Would the results have been the same had Nick & Co. recruited someone with a deeper understanding of selling in the fruit business? Given our sense of accountability and ability to see a few steps ahead, we stressed that we should give consideration to taking our ten-thousand-dollar loss in samples and time versus taking a hundred thousand dollar hit in the foreseeable future. Again, looking back, would the right partner with a stronger know-how and drive for the mission have begun to pull the plug at this point in the game?

I recollect Nick responding to our admission of defeat with something along the lines of: '*Really guys? Let me tell you of a little frozen fruit company called Europe's Best that started from nothing and that is now worth tens of millions of dollars.*' I remember firmly palming the phone receiver to mute the call and looking over to Dave and saying something along the lines of: '*How is that any different than saying, let me tell you about a little computer company called Apple Computers that is now worth tens of billions? Okay, so now what?*'

By that point, we just wanted out. I'm always amazed at how quickly relationships can spoil despite everyone's absolute best efforts and interests to get along and to build something great. I suppose it's how and why wars can start. At the time, I remember thinking that, if Nick and Co. had focused on flushing out the accurate product costs and uncovering realistic selling prices before unleashing their expectations and offering Dave and me a share in the business, the story may have unfolded a little differently. And then again, in hindsight, I can also now appreciate that's why they brought us on board and now realize that a more motivated and determined partner could have perhaps used the company's resources at his disposal a little better to devise a revised game plan. Nonetheless, we quickly found ourselves at odds and, within a week or two later, had totally separated from the company. The group was left with a container loaded with frozen fruit, a slightly bruised bank account and the deflated hope of trying to shake any fat fruits from the tree.

It's years later now and I continue to wonder how such a well-established and experienced group of entrepreneurs, myself included, could make such poor business decisions and be so blind to the facts. Our pricing was just too high to take a big bite out of the competition. Why didn't they appreciate this fundamental flaw in the plan? The original working title for this chapter was actually 'Even the Smartest People Make Mistakes.' But, as I started to reminisce and write down the nuances of this story, I began to appreciate that we may have just been the wrong partners, with weaker than required relationships and talents for this particular mission. Maybe I was the smarty-pants who had made the greater mistake. Maybe I was the rotten apple. Having said this, I'd still much rather be on the receiving end of an ownership offer. If you can't already tell, I'm that kid clutching his pillowcase full of Halloween candy—well, apparently, except for the one or two apples that folks sometimes give out.

I know it's tempting to offer someone seemingly better suited for the mission a piece of your company pie in exchange for a better chance of real progress. But if and when your hopes are dashed and your pockets are lightened, consider that you may regret inking a formal partnership agreement and signing over even a few points of ownership in your company. There are many other less committal ways to secure and compensate a valuable member of your team and to ensure that they feel both the benefits and pressures of having some skin in your game. Be careful what you wish for. I'd rather call off an arrangement with someone over the phone or in a coffee shop rather than after a honeymoon in paradise with the first joint-mortgage payment waiting in the mail.

Let It Simmer ~

1. *Can you offer a creative incentive, other than sharing ownership in your start-up company, and still get what you want out of the relationship?*

2. *Will your partner be as good of a match down the road, or are you tempted to offer them ownership simply because they are what you need at this very moment?*

3. *Hold off on offering, or at least on officially signing over, ownership until a few key pieces of the puzzle are revealed—e.g. accurate costings, retailer interest, volume assumptions, minimum product guarantees, etc.*

4. *When the story changes and the climb becomes trickier, will your candidate still be up for the mission? Or, has their vibe and approach quickly dampened?*

5. *As the factors and gameplay become clearer, ask your candidate questions that expose their evolving mindset instead of instinctively pushing them towards your goal? Does their analysis and drive align with your own, or are they trying to convince you otherwise because they've lost interest?*

CHAPTER 17

Milkin' It

Pushing Too Far With
Product Line Extensions

<p>

A</p>ny veteran storm observer will explain that lightning can, in fact, strike in the same place more than once. It may take only a few months or up to multiple lifetimes, but it is possible if you wait it out long enough. When it comes to trying to repeat the booming thunder of a successful product launch, you may not have to wait a lifetime for another solid hit, but chances are that it won't occur as quickly or as naturally as you want or need it to. Following up a big win with a product line extension (*a product under the same brand name within the same category*) and/or a brand extension (*a product with the same brand name in a different category*), or a seemingly comparable brand or product strategy (*a product with a different brand name in the same category*) is a common strategic reaction. But storm chasers beware, unless you're in Venezuela where the Catatumbo River meets Lake Maracaibore, relocating the strike zone is a rather elusive game.

A few years into building our Kernels Popcorn shaker business, we tried relentlessly, and fruitlessly, to create another successful seasoning product line. The sales volume, profit margin and our growing production capability and supply partner network (i.e. contract packers and suppliers of raw material ingredients and packaging) for all things shakers was just too appealing and obvious to ignore. In under three years, we struck brand licensing deals with QSR (Quick Service Restaurant) giants New York Fries® to create a French fry seasoning, with Golden Griddle® for an unlikely breakfast egg seasoning, with Teriyaki

Experience® for an exotic Pan Asian rice and protein seasoning, and with Sbarro® for an authentic Italian seasoning.

With the exception of the Teriyaki Experience and Sbarro seasoning shakers, the other products collected a thick layer of dust on the grocery shelf. Despite using the same distinctive shaker container as our Kernels line, our best-in-class flavour recipe approach and our let's-make-boring-seasonings-look-funkier-than-the-norm strategy, we couldn't generate another positive electrical charge. As discussed in *Chapter 7: Pop Goes the World*, our success with Kernels Shakers was built on much more than solid brand awareness, patented recipes and good-looking packaging. We enjoyed first to market status for a product concept that stood on the shoulders of a well-established consumer ritual, and in the process succeeded in filling a meaningful category void.

The market was not only ready to add intense flavours to their naked popcorn, they were avidly seeking a solution. Kernels had been selling flavoured popcorn for nearly twenty years before our foray into grocery; movie theatres had also been offering moviegoers complimentary popcorn seasonings for years before we decided to shake things up. Consequently, consumers had acquired a taste for popcorn seasoning but had no option to purchase it outside these two arenas. And whereas sprinkling established chip-like flavours onto hot and fresh microwave popcorn wasn't much of a stretch for consumers, it seemed too foreign to shake exotic and unestablished flavours onto their French fries, scrambled eggs, fried rice or pasta. Instead of leaning on other well-established eating rituals to help satisfy a genuine consumer demand and to fill a category void, we aimed to invent a new demand but ended up missing the mark each time.

When our Mr. Greek® frozen souvlaki line started to fly out of A&P / Dominion's freezer bunkers (see *Chapter 10: Opa!*), we assumed that consumers would naturally take to all things Greek and would readily support brand extensions marketed under the popular Ontario restaurant name. Store managers seemed to openly rally behind the notion that we had given the Mr. Greek line exclusively to their company. As a result, we enjoyed better-than-average product in-store placement and aggressive flyer ad support. At the time, there were no qualms over whether or not we should invest more time and money into a few additional tasty baklavas. After completing the first season, it also became clear that we had earned the trust of our buyers and of the coveted senior management (a hat tip to Tom Williams, Tony Morello, Paul Del Duca and the late and great Paul Fortin). The door was held wide open and we knew it could close unexpectedly at a moment's notice.

Thus, we proudly threw on our togas and laurel leaf crowns and dove straight into the Parthenon of brand extension development. In just over a year or so, we worked intensely with Mr. Greek's congenial founder and President, George Raios, to develop the following ostentatious list of Greek delicacies under his restaurant's brand name—moussaka, spanakopita, breaded shrimp, breaded kalamari, tzatziki, feta cheese, souvlaki burgers, Greek-style potatoes, Greek-salad kits and Greek-inspired seasoning. A&P green-lighted each and every one. To boot, this list doesn't include the product concepts that we worked on that didn't end up on the shelf because of either sourcing or manufacturing snags—whole wheat pita bread, taramosalata, baklava, kefalotyri cheese, and bottled Greek salad dressing to name a few. Needless to say, we jumped the Greek shark.

To this day, thinking about all the convoluted contract packer agreements and the list of unique ingredients and packaging guarantees makes my laurel leaf crown spin. Now, we did have a couple of valuable, Olympic runs with the Mr. Greek Tzatziki, Feta Cheese and fresh salad kits because I believe our timing, quality, pricing and packaging held its own against the competition in the respective categories. Despite receiving a decent level of product launch awareness from the retailer, the volume of the other misfit products paled in comparison to our inaugural brand launch with the frozen souvlaki line. In most cases, we had to discount the introductory shipment to help stores clear their inventory. This also meant that our collective return on investment for these products wasn't too attractive. We had spent more money to cultivate recipes, procure ingredients, design and build packaging, and to guarantee minimum production runs than we were able to pocket in profits.

More damagingly, we overloaded and eventually soured both the consumer and the retailer with the brand's new product blitz. Had we focused on protecting our core souvlaki line and recognized the budding success of the three new brand extensions earlier, our energy and money would have been invested elsewhere. Luckily, in the end, after a stellar three or four year outing with the Mr. Greek brand at A&P / Dominion, we did end up hauling in a Herculean profit despite the unexpected dead weight associated with the failed concepts.

It took me over ten years to learn how to firmly say *NO* to a seemingly interesting offer from a willing brand licensor or an eager retailer and still feel at peace with my decision. It's in my nature to say *YES* when my gut says otherwise as I'm the type of guy who wants to desperately please people, or at least I used to be. Nowadays, it's exceedingly difficult for me to accept most offers—admittedly, it's now to a fault. As I revealed on the first page on this book: '*You learn more about what not to do when you lose money doing the wrong thing. I can tell you how I've lost a boat-load of it over the past 20 years playing this game of delusional buffet-sized profits.*'

The usual hitch with those who table us offers to shepherd them into grocery stores—whether it be a prospective restaurant brand partner, a critically acclaimed chef, or a humble home chef—is they find it impossible to comprehend the flagrant distinction between what's possible in their kitchens and dining rooms versus what's probable in a crowded grocery store aisle. I regard Pizza Pizza® Dips to be one of our most celebrated and long-standing accomplishments. The Pizza Pizza brand is an extremely well known restaurant chain in Ontario that moves copious amounts of dough, tomato sauce and mozzarella through their busy commissary. Their dominant share of the crowded restaurant pizza market is remarkable to say the least. Perhaps not as commonly acknowledged, Pizza Pizza also procures and sells a staggering quantity of chicken wings.

Nonetheless, when the veteran crew at Pizza Pizza suggested that we follow up the successful launch of our creamy garlic dipping sauce with a frozen chicken wing program, we instantly sensed that it would be a dubious and over costly undertaking. Their opportunity paradigm was based and built on the fact that they sell more chicken wings than probably any restaurant in Ontario. The potential consumer interest in a grocery program was supported by the droves of repeat orders and high consumer praise that the restaurant enjoyed on a daily basis. I imagine that they may have also been stoked by their strong poultry supplier relationships and buying power that we'd be able to tap into and leverage.

We, on the other hand, instantly sized up the mission a little differently. The frozen chicken wing category in grocery was already chockful of both competitive and competent national and private label brand offerings. The cost of entry into the frozen protein aisle was much costlier than it was to play in the dairy category where we had established the brand in grocery—upwards of $50,000 per sku compared with a more digestible $5,000 per sku, respectively. Yes, Pizza Pizza's chicken wings are of high quality, a nice size and are damn tasty, but what would our key point of difference be against the established incumbent brands?

Most importantly, when assessing whether or not we should take a recipe into grocery, we ask ourselves this question—would a consumer react the same way about a product if they had to buy it outside of the restaurant's busy four walls or off their high traffic website? When consumers are standing at a restaurant's order counter, or chatting with an order-taking operator on the phone, or clicking through their online-menu order system, they're making an uninterrupted purchase decision within a brand vacuum. Walk out of the restaurant, hang-up the phone or power down the smart phone and stroll into a retail store and the rules of engagement dramatically change. Your captive audience is now overstimulated and confused by too many choices and, unless you give them a compelling reason, they'll default to what they know; to what feels most comfortable.

It's about quality, price, packaging, in-store placement, share of shelf space, and established purchase rituals. It's about competing with, and trying to disrupt, an emotional connection a consumer might enjoy with another brand. In our case, licensing the Pizza Pizza powerhouse might have scored us some initial product trial because of the brand's ubiquitous consumer awareness. However, if the product should fall short on realizing the other equally significant purchase metrics, scoring repeat orders would have been challenging.

It's for this reason that we wince when a popular restaurant or chef, or more painfully, an overzealous home cook presents an opportunity by starting the conversation with: '*Everybody that's tried this recipe goes absolutely crazy for it and insists that I should try selling it in grocery stores!*' In my head, I'm saying: '*Well, listen here, my wife can crank out an impressive homemade arrabiata tomato sauce that's hands down the best I've had the joy of shovelling into my mouth—but ... the only way I'd invest in bringing it to market is if Chef Boyardee was my only competition.*'

Let it Simmer ~

1. *Have you peeled away enough layers and looked deeply enough to understand why your product was a hit before trying to clone its success? Get to the very bottom of it because 'only the spoon knows what is stirring in the pot.'*

2. *Are you in jeopardy of taking your product extensions / brand extensions too far and to the point of souring and tiring retailers and consumers?*

3. *Will your recipe perform as well in a retail store environment jam-packed with comparable products as it does in your restaurant or at home with friends and family?*

4. *Can your product extension / brand extension maintain the same key points of difference from your competition as your original product introduction?*

CHAPTER 18

Boiling Over

Quality Over Quantity

The path to profits and prosperity isn't always about launching as many new product concepts as your budding company can bear to handle. While fostering innovative new product development is the engine for big growth for many established companies, try to go for meaningful depth over significant breadth until you have both the necessary resources, financing and time in your corner. Don't get too brave or cocky when you start to see and taste a little palpable success. Avoid letting the new product pot boil over because you have too much cooking on the stove. Assign a serious chunk of your newfound revenue stream wisely to help strengthen the roots of your core product; otherwise, you'll risk burning up your cash and ability to stay afloat.

Of the more than one hundred foodstuff skus that we've managed to squeeze out into retail, we have cupboards more stuffed with half-baked concepts that somehow siphoned our bank account and clogged our calendars with make-work—all at the expense of stealing that extra oomph from building and protecting our core lines. We have a row of abandoned cupboards in our test kitchen filled with mock-ups and franken-samples of products that either died suddenly after the first order, or that have never seen the light of day. We call this culinary gravesite 'The Lost Pantry.'

Crack open the cupboard doors without letting any boxes, bags or cans come tumbling out, and you'll find Booster Juice® Smoothies, Hooters® Chicken Wing Sauce, Jack Astor's® Spinach and Artichoke Dip,

Eating in Japan Stir Fry Meal Kits, Golden Griddle® Sausages and Plant-ers® microwaveable glazed almonds. Heck, we even have an entire corner cabinet dedicated to our Kernels Extraordinary Popcorn® mishaps. Praise our loyal and understanding partners at Kernels, especially Eli and Scott Staiman, for having supported the majority of our big bright ideas. Scan those lost shelves and you'll unearth Tornados® puffed corn snacks, Swizzle chocolate drizzled caramel corn, packs of paper popcorn bags for kids' parties, Spring Fling fruit glazed popcorn, Kernels Karamel pop-corn topping, and my all-time favourite, Kernels chocolate covered cara-mel popcorn packed inside a jumbo foil-wrapped Easter egg—all duds.

Granted, I'd be remiss not to mention that for every few misfires, we've managed to hit the bulls-eye. And by the way, launching a dud takes no less time, money and effort than unleashing a grand slam sell-ing product onto shelves. We've also had to redistribute hard earned profits from our successful core lines to feed these ill-fated escapades.

Ironically, most of our meaningful financial growth has come after we've misfired by concentrating on way too many new initiatives at once, causing us to recoil, re-energize and refocus. To be clear, however, innovation can and should equal big growth, so always keep at least one strong and hopeful product innovation in the hopper, and work to fos-ter and protect it. As your resources and ability to pick out fighters from the litter strengthens, cultivating more than one or two new concepts becomes less risky. Hush-hush, I'm actually munching away on a new Kernels inspired killer concept as I'm writing this chapter. If all goes as planned, we'll be unchaining it, alongside Staiman & Co., around the same time that this book is set to be released.

During the mid 2000s, at any given moment, we had a minimum of twenty new and ambitious product concepts on our development list —or as we chose to dutifully refer to it at BrandFusion, our 'FusePath.' I respect that an NPD (new product development) list of this magnitude isn't anything extraordinary or ambitious to most medium or large sized companies. We, on the other hand, had a team of one or two some-what inexperienced staff tackling the list (who, by the way, were also accountable for sales, manufacturing, and accounting responsibilities).

As the face behind our growing company, courting and negotiating with illustrious restaurant chains for the licensing and use of their brand mark became my thing. Over the course of two very prolific years, we must've tried to woo every popular restaurant chain in the country to join our food fight in grocery stores, as well as a few chains south of the Canadian border. Although I shouldn't whine as in most cases we typically scheduled our meetings in their restaurants, allowing me to happily sample everything off the menu. Putting on a passionate pony show while scarfing down a cornucopia of appetizers and mains became a most welcomed weekly ceremony.

Holding meetings in Hawaii with Cilantro Mexican Grill and in Fort Lauderdale, Florida with Muvico Theatres also had its advantages. I knew that the wheels had started to come loose from our caboose when I began to screw up the basics and thoroughly embarrass myself in the process (and, of course, when my Levi's began to tighten around the waist from all the Friar-Tuck-style gorging). One of my colleagues at Johnvince Foods had secured a meeting for JP and me with two senior VPs from Allied Domeqc, who at the time owned Baskin Robbins®—the world's largest chain of ice cream specialty shops. Our game plan was to license the Baskin Robbins brand for a line of premium retail ice cream toppings.

Normally, I would have made it a key point to prepare for the inaugural meeting by visiting one of Baskin's busy locations to study the menus, sample ice cream flavours, and to snap pics of marketing signage for future use and reference. For this particular get-together, however, I did not prepare whatsoever. I had dined and chatted with a handful of other prospective restaurant partners in the weeks leading up to the Baskin Robbins meeting so I hadn't the time or energy and arrogantly felt that my wheels were good and greased enough for another spin around the discussion table.

As I slid into the room a la Cosmo Kramer from Seinfeld, JP had already begun to chat with the folks from Allied Domeqc. In well under the first five minutes, I would single-handedly kibosh our chances for inking a contract with the ice cream moguls. The first words out of my mouth were: '*I have to tell you; my family and I are huge fans of your ice cream. I just love that new Caramel Apple product that you recently introduced!*' There was an awkward pause, and then one of the two ladies politely retorted: *'Um, that's not ours. I believe you're thinking of Dairy Queen's new product.'*

JP shifted his eyes in my direction and shot me the same clenched teeth stare that my Father used to give me as a kid when I asked for ketchup on my eggs (a big no-no at a Calabrese breakfast table). *'My apologies, what was I thinking. Actually, I was referring to your new Grasshopper Mousse Pie!'* I said trying to put the cool-train back on the tracks. *'Nope. Sorry. That's also one of Dairy Queen's flavours!'* replied the other lady. By this point, JP is stepping on my toe under the table. As you can imagine, we didn't end up launching the ice cream toppings. We just had too much on our plate for me to give the opportunity the appropriate attention. I should've played it safe and opened with giving props to the Peanut Butter 'n Chocolate ice cream shake, as that's always been my bag at Baskin Robbins.

I also find that, when we're involved with too many new concepts, it's tough to completely stay madly in love with them all. And if I don't completely love and believe deeply in a product and its purposefulness, sitting in front of a squint-eyed and sceptical buyer to sell it becomes next to hopeless. I'll say it again: until you have the resources required, it's about the depth, not the breadth. When you've toiled over every minute detail and it literally feels like you've finally given birth to a perfect and beautiful product, you're not out there selling it per se. It's more like you're sharing your infectious enthusiasm with the customer —which always makes for both an easier and triumphant presentation.

After years of taking a good beating at the hands of wanting to do too much, we've tightened the development sieve to a point where we'll only support the advancement of two new food concepts at the very most. Based on our available resources, our NPD garden has become less about growing as many varieties as possible, and more about cultivating a couple of blue ribbon contenders. We also appreciate that growing conditions will change overnight and either prolong, or even end up killing the harvest.

Whether it's because of a sudden change of players in the game, a fading expectation in your contract packer's capabilities, or an interminable launch timetable, the path to market will constantly elude you.

When the boutique burger joint Lick's® decided to launch a retail version of their Home burgers in A&P / Dominion, consumers couldn't get enough of the meaty stuff. The over-the-top ten-dollar restaurant hamburger craze we're seeing today was still years from hitting the dining scene, and Licks was cashing in on the unexploited category in grocery.

It was hard to overlook their accomplishments in crossing over to grocery so we decided to follow suit by approaching Webers burgers with a plan to develop a retail version of their iconic burgers for sale in Loblaws grocery stores to give A&P / Dominion a run for their money. The landmark hamburger restaurant was established in 1963 and sits on a highway just north of Orillia, Ontario. Webers was so popular that in 1983 it installed the first and only privately owned pedestrian bridge built over a public highway in Ontario so that it could accommodate more folks jonesing for a good burger.

Paul Weber—son of the restaurant's creator Paul Weber Sr.—and I hit it off instantly. It didn't come quick or easy, but on a Canadian-cold January night, as we strolled through the International Car Show with our wives, I eventually convinced Paul to accept the food fight mission. Just a few weeks later, however, we regrettably learned that Paul had decided to sell his longtime family burger business. By this point, we were already in discussions with his meat processing plant contract packer to duplicate the family's famous recipe for retail. We met the new owner of Webers during a product cutting at the plant. Where Paul had been charming and collaborative, I could instantly see that the new mayor of burger-town wasn't digging our tune much. He spent most of the hour-long meeting using his pencil eraser to tap on his calculator to assess our significance in the deal. By the time we reached our car in the parking lot, I had decided that we would cut bait and move on.

I hate leaving money on the table, but I hate working through unrest far more. In my experience, the conditions for a healthy launch have to look and feel just right during the courting and initial collaboration stages. Don't get me wrong; I realize that choosing to stay in the ring to fight for your prize can pan out too. It's just that I'd rather save my energy to fight an opponent that's not on my own team. Later that year in early summer, while shopping in Loblaws with my wife Lisa, I stopped dead in my tracks as I caught sight of the Webers® burgers display in the freezer bunker. This wasn't the first unmerited case of someone else taking a food product concept that we started to the finish line without us, and it would be far from the last. Don't get me started on East Side Mario's! Based on the level of exposure and merchandising support, the burgers seemed to sell modestly for a couple of years and then slowly faded away.

The path to market is very rarely a straight and measurable line. The more complex and ambitious your product concept, the more you'll end up chasing the launch date. Unless you're launching a relatively simple and straightforward concept, or a simple line extension (i.e. new flavour for an existing product line), the finish line will continue to keep moving further way. But then again, does the world really want another boring citrus vinaigrette, bran muffin mix or spicy pasta sauce? Well, I'm sure they might but will it be a five-hundred case opportunity or can it be the fifty-thousand case monster you want it to be?

Whether the magic lies in your distinctive recipe and preparation style, or the packaging format and design, it's important to remember not to let deadlines completely steer the ship or dictate the ultimate quality of your product when you're on the verge of launching something truly original. Be patient. Get it right the first time. Consumers and retailers will be unforgiving and quick to remember your failures. When Dave and I teamed up with BeaverTails® to create a unique retail item for grocery stores, we operated with the weight and awareness that we'd be judged unforgivingly if the concept didn't properly capture the iconic brand's deep fried dough addiction and Canadiana narrative. After well over a year of dragging a couple of willing manufactures through countless recipe iterations we refrained from giving into our restlessness to punch the big red launch button despite seeing a formidable interest in some of the product submissions that came out of our test kitchen. Our goal was to keep on digging deep until we unearthed exactly what we were looking for.

A few years back, the pressure of cycling through our prodigious list of twenty-something concepts would have clouded our judgment. This time around, the conditions for patient cultivation were bang on —our relationship with the good folks at BeaverTails was exceptional, our new product hopper wasn't choking with caramel and apple pie ice cream and the brand's relevance and originality remained relevant and inspiring to us throughout our development journey. So we continue to tweak, tinker, polish and taste until we get it just right.

If all goes well, I'm hoping there's a BeaverTails baked grocery goodie in your local supermarket by the time you're reading this. If not, it's either because we couldn't nail the results we wanted, or because we missed the mark again and it's already come and gone without you even noticing. Listen, when I launched Kernels Popcorn Shakers back in 2000, I loved the brand, the concept and the people involved in the mission. It turned out to be a painstaking obsession for nearly two unpaid years. It was also the only product that I fixated on in the that time. I dug super deep, past the heavy layers of supply partner and retailer scepticism, past the concern that others seemed to have for my crusade. If you're a one-person-army, focus on building your food empire one single crop at a time.

Let It Simmer ~

1. *Have you gradually bitten off more than you can chew at the expense of neglecting the evolution of your core product(s)?*
2. *Go for depth over breadth until you have the adequate resources to spare. Prioritize your new product development list by profit and volume potential. Investing in new product development is a critical piece to increasing your business, but realistically weigh out your reserves and finances against what you'll also need to cultivate and protect your core product(s).*
3. *Prepare or be aware! Are you offering each food product in your incubator the devotion and energy they need to evolve, or are you in danger of heading towards your own 'Baskin Robbins blooper?'*

CHAPTER 19

Catching A Buzz

Staying the Course &
Rolling with the Punches

After more than 10 years of raising someone else's prized brand high up on our sore shoulders, Dave and I began to hear the same inner-voice urging us to whip up something magnificent from scratch. A food brainchild, with a cool brand name and image that we believed in and obsessed over so deeply that we wouldn't, or physically couldn't, compromise our vision for—one that had the potential to eventually garner a legion of loyal foodie-fanatics. The end result would be different in a grander and more meaningful way compared to the other, tamer in-house creations we had introduced along the way—i.e. *Eating in Japan* stir fry kits, *Nature's Fruits* frozen premium fruits, *361°* Magic Miso and *Flavour Station* salty snack toppings to name but a forgotten few. It's a colourful story built on a foundation of classic axioms that speak to embracing constant change, stubborn persistence and the difference in outcome when you choose to drive instead of navigate from the backseat. This is a significant and career defining story that we continue to write today.

We sat down for a much-needed espresso break in the busy trade-show hall to reboot and discuss all the new and funky food products we just sampled at the SIAL show in Montreal 2011. Despite eating close to my body weight in free Belgian chocolate and Italian charcuterie samples (yet again—sigh), we came up empty on potential new ideas and inspiration. It's always more of the same, just packaged in a slightly new way. On the plane ride home, however, Dave and I came across an article in *Saveur Magazine* (a subscription must for any respectable foodie). It was on 'Paletas' which are basically fancy Ice Pops sold roadside in Mexico. The flavours, however, are made from wonderfully sweet and savoury recipes and, unlike most of our frozen-fructose-crap in North America, are made from purely natural and often local ingredients—for example, there's a popular flavour called *'Chamoy'* which is a sweet-spicy mixture of mango and red chilies.

By the time we touched down in T Dot, we penciled a game plan on the back of a cocktail napkin (which is, by the way, the best place to pencil a plan). Our idea was to create a line of funky Paleta flavours; the added twist was that we'd infuse the pops with premium alcohol —fancy-schmancy adult ice pops if you will. The idea was far out enough from the norm to make a meaningful innovation statement, yet not so far that consumers wouldn't understand the concept—which is really that desirable sweet-spot you want to play in. Either way, it was one of those neat ideas that still felt mission-worthy a few sleeps later.

Time passed and our excitement was tempered only because we couldn't find a small batch juice contract packer that also had the ca-pabilities and the alcohol license required to produce the frozen beast we were chasing. Until, Bartly James Murphy, one of my closest child-hood friends, swung by our office with an interesting juice pouch pack-age. It looked and kinda-sorta functioned like an upside intravenous bag. No straw required, just rip, invert n' sip. What's more, the pouch was freezable so the juice could be served as an ice-slushie treat. Bart had just begun to work for the company that packaged the pouch and was instrumental in setting up a meeting with its affable owner, Darryl McDaniel.

We eventually pitched Darryl our alcohol-laced Paletas concept and he graciously agreed to help us flush out the concept and to commer-cialize it. It turned out that the pouch was being used for a vodka-based frozen beverage so his company was also in the process of securing their alcohol license. And to that end, all of our ducks seemed to be lining up. Following our initial get-together, however, many months passed with zero progress as the company was too busy with more pressing and worthwhile business, and to boot, still hadn't secured their alcohol license. If an idea is strong enough, set-backs can also allow you and the idea to breathe and to change course on to a more accessible and down-hill road. A vital lesson we've learned on a number of occasions is that if it's meant to be, the simplest milestones with your supply partners shouldn't be impossible or painful to achieve. When you've locked into the right person or company, the easy steps feel somewhat easy and the hard ones eventually get sorted out.

At the crux of our fascination with the Paleta concept was the idea of mixing common, yet sexy, ingredients in surprisingly uncommon ways. It was also about mixing seasonal and natural ingredients with booze in a crafty and artisanal fashion that appealed to foodies (of a legal drinking age, of course). Perhaps it was only natural then, that our concept eventually morphed into a culinary mission to create and pion-eer best-in-class, all natural, mixologist-inspired cocktails into retail. A mixologist, or a bar-chef, is the bar equivalent of a culinary chef. They extend the creativity and quality of cocktails by utilizing culinary con-cepts and exotic, often premium, ingredients with chef-like skill.

We jumped from alcohol-laced Mexican popsicle bars to chef-in-spired crazy cocktails—go figure; but the point here is that this type of unplanned progression shouldn't be an unwelcome surprise. It is, in-stead, to paraphrase the great David Lee Roth, what happens when you *'jump and roll with the punches to get to what's real.'* A couple of weeks later, Dave stumbled upon a glowing article about a much lauded To-ronto drinking establishment called BarChef, located in the city's eclec-tic and electric Queen Street West. Frankie Solarik, the bar's co-owner and resident mixologist, was being heralded as one of Canada's bright-est stars in the industry—a master flavour-wizard concocting magical elixirs in his hipster lair. *'Let's try and score a licensing deal with Frankie,'* Dave suggested.

Up until that point, we had paid well-known restaurants a royalty rebate based on our net sales for the use of their brand-mark, propri-etary recipes and category expertise; why not use the same licensing model to pay Frankie a royalty for his cocktail recipes and our product's endorsement? At first, I was indisposed to having someone else join our booze-cruise given that I knew we had to sail the seven seas before seeing a profit and would have to do all of the navigating and bankroll the excursion. In the end, we realized that the alcohol sector was uncharted waters for us so we decided to invite Frankie aboard. Dave made the call to Frankie and he accepted the invitation to hear us out. Knowing that we'd be consuming multiple weeknight-cocktails, I bribed my wife's younger cousins to chaperone Dave and me to the bar and picked up their dinner tab while they dined nearby.

We also invited Leigh Bailey, a seasoned specialist from one of our preferred flavour development suppliers (a company that takes a chef's recipe and helps bring it to commercialization in an efficient and economical way; and, if they're good, in a way that doesn't lessen the impact of the chef's original recipe). Frankie also invited his agent to sit in. Yep, that's right. Total Rock Star. The man had an 'agent.' We sat at the back of his dimly lit and posh bar and sampled four or five of his most popular and potent libations. If I look back at my meeting notes, I can tell that by the fifth drink I was feeling slightly buzzed as I can hardly read my tiny scribble. We all left the meeting inspired to work together. It was settled, we'd develop three flavours, a 'Basil, Honey & Lime Daiquiri' a 'Spiced Cola & Mint Julep' and a 'Vanilla, Lavender Tequila Sour'—each bevvy complete with its own artisanal rimmer made of citrus rinds, cane sugar, sea salt and various floral aromatics.

Aside from spending the following couple of months trying to replicate Frankie's recipes en masse, seeking out unique bottles, alcohol-licensed bottlers, sales agents, distributors and industry consultants, we tried to figure out how to connect with the LCBO. To my friends living outside of Canada, the government in Ontario not only governs all sales and distribution of alcohol (including to restaurants, which are referred to as on-premise customers), they retail it themselves; aside from licensed wineries, select grocery stores that sell beer and wine, and a handful of other ambiguities, consumers buy their spirits from a, albeit exceedingly attractive and well-merchandised, government-run store. This is also the case with many other Canadian markets, but not all of them.

The deeper we delved into what was required of us in order to conduct business with the LCBO, the more alien and overwhelming the project became. Most folks in the industry we looked to for counsel looked at us the same way you smile at your six-year-old kid when he insists on taking over the stove to make Saturday morning breakfast: *'So cute and ambitious but you're gonna get burned badly pal!'* As a side note, all three of my kids, especially my son, Gabe, cook like mini-molto-Marios despite having to stand on a chair when making proper gently folded scrambled eggs and crispy Canadian bacon.

After we navigated through and completed the never-ending government forms and mandatory requirements, and successfully acquired our official agent's license, we were ready to face the alcohol's industry's oligopoly giant in Ontario—the LCBO, the single largest purchaser of alcohol in the world. They also represent nearly half of the country's sales for many alcohol companies. We filled out what we could of their on-line product submission process but knew that an old fashioned face-to-face was needed if we were to stand a chance. As a side-note, over the past ten or so years, selling food and alcohol has become more of a clerical-sport in filling out ever-changing Excel spreadsheets and on-line forms—what ever happened to cutting a deal in the dimly lit stockroom over a makeshift upside down milk-carton-table? Get ready to fill out forms—seemingly useless short forms and appallingly long multi-page, multi-tab and multi-painful forms; for the most part, being a key account sales manager means you'll regularly be bashing in your computer screen with your mouse trying to figure out if the sale is actually worth the aggravation.

Our growing army of sceptics insisted that, without an established relationship, being awarded a coveted face-to-face meeting was a pipe dream. Nonetheless, I kept calling the buyer, carefully depositing eager voice messages. *'I realize you must receive a ton of requests,'* I started with in one such attempt, *'but this lil' sucker is right in the pocket with where you want to take the one-pour cocktail business. Give us a shot, we'll make it short, sweet and worth your while.'* At the time, we knew the LCBO was both ready and hungry for RTD (ready-to-drink) craft cocktails because they had started to feature more ambitious recipes in their widely read and highly regarded, *Food & Drink* Magazine. In the end, the buyer graciously granted us a meeting. Deep breath. *'Ok. We're on, Dave ... two weeks from today,'* I hollered from my desk over to his.

Now, this is where you separate the men and women from the little boys and girls. This is the big juncture on the road to launch-town that gets me all fired up like a soft taco loaded with ghost pepper salsa. In the beginning, cold-call sales pitch meetings gave me instant nervous pangs. However, after years of practice and acclimatization I've grown to love and respect the dance. In a more corporate setting, agreeing to a meeting with the world's largest purchaser of alcohol despite having no industry background, no legitimate product samples, no packaging designs, no pricing or no plan just isn't done. Period.

It's all nonsense, I say. The only things you need neatly packed in your attaché case is genuine passion, credible knowledge, an infectious vision and … big brass balls. Our flavour development supplier was months away from presenting us with a workable tasting sample, we had no idea what style of packaging, let alone a brand or design vision, we wanted. Here's how we strung it together *tout de suite*. That weekend, Dave and I were in San Francisco at the Fancy Food Trade Show. Thirty minutes before we had to leave for the airport, we came across an alcohol contract packer, stationed in Canton, Georgia, that was at the show unveiling their new, unique shaped aluminum can. We liked the look of it. They agreed to bottle a beverage for us under our own brand name. We swindled three can samples from their booth display and jammed them into our carry-ons, already bursting with food-samples (most of them plane-ride snacks of course).

We also come across a contract packer with the capability to pack liquids into small squarish pouches with a re-sealable spigot. '*Hmmm, perfecto,*' we thought, for the bitter herbal extracts we thought we wanted to include with our original beverage concept. For the brand name, we went with '*Bar361°*'—named after 361 Degrees Inc., the company we had incorporated to sell alcohol products. Time was short, but more importantly, we didn't want to invest serious cash until we knew there was concrete interest to fall back on, so I asked my neighbour's boyfriend to whip up a couple of design concepts. He had come to see me for career advice a few weeks earlier as he'd just graduated from graphic design school.

It was a win-win as he got the chance to design something meaningful for a start-up brand to add to his portfolio, and we scored a fabulous freebie design within a few days—when you're starting out this type of experience should be considered valuable 'career-currency'—JP drilled this notion into my head at an early age. He'd often declare with fervour: *'Listen, you're not getting financially compensated for being involved with this project. In fact, I should be asking you to pay me for the ride!'* I bought some matte black spray paint from The Home Depot, went out to the office parking lot, gave the aluminum cans we scored at the food show a few coats of paint and spray-glued the label design on —voila! For the tasting samples, we asked Frankie to mix-up a large batch of the cocktails and then poured them into some fancy apothecary bottles adorned with '361° LAB SAMPLE' labels.

Piecing together the actual pitch wasn't an issue. I love building a compelling case for a product concept that I believe in. Ask me to pitch something I don't dig and you'll see right through me like my wife does when I sneak a few tablespoons of Nutella after the kids have gone to bed. If I believe in it, and know the retailer and consumer will benefit, I'll stand on the buyer's desk and tap dance like Danny Kaye—controlling and properly channelling my energy and enthusiasm is my daily challenge.

As we slowly trailed the buyer from the quiet lobby waiting area to his office, we walked past a myriad of classic neutral coloured cubicles happily occupied by conservatively dressed and astute looking LCBO personnel. I remember being five minutes into the pitch, gently kicking Dave under the table and throwing him a very subtle smirk as if to say: *'We're actually flowing pretty nicely here.'* The clincher happened when we moved our pony show from the buyer's office into a special room the LCBO uses for bevvy tastings.

As we were about to crack open our tasting samples, the buyer said: *'Hold on a sec, fellas. Let me grab my boss and a couple of other colleagues.'* Boom baby! This is the moment. The one that comes along every few lunar eclipses or so. Do or die. Always be prepared with a two-minute tune of your sales pitch—a 'best of' track. With our adrenaline kicked into monster high gear, Dave and I continued to riff back and forth. And then, the tasting itself—I can only remember the group raising the glasses to their lips in super slow motion. That first swirl and sip, followed by an eventual revealing facial expression that immediately follows. Yes. Yes! YES! They loved it. Well, at least two of the three as the 'Vanilla Lavender Tequila Sour' had too much of a perfume-y potpourri thing going on.

Despite loving our other two craft cocktails, they explained that it was regrettably too late in their buying season to accept any new spring and summer themed products and that it would make more sense to introduce a winter themed flavour as our inaugural one; retail chains evaluate and work to build their seasonal product assortments six to nine months ahead of time, so you'll be pitching a Christmas concept over the phone with your feet dangling in the pool. Remember now: 'You've got to roll with the punches ...' We left the building with a handshake agreement that, if we could properly polish the product concept with relevant and attractive packaging and pricing (AND now come up with a completely new holiday themed flavour), that we'd be awarded a shot on the big booze stage.

The LCBO meeting was on a Friday. Leaving the house for work the following Monday somehow felt strangely different, in a rare and special way. By this time, we weren't strangers to being given the coveted green light by a retail chain giant, but man-o-man this was the LCBO, the world's largest purchaser of alcoholic beverages. We needed a kickass brand with a strong voice and a brand narrative that people actually cared about. We needed to create a lifestyle brand, not just another message in a bottle lost in the sea of competition we were about to face. I needed to place a call I'd been reserving to make for a lunar eclipse spotting like this one. My childhood mate was, at the time, the president of one of Canada's most celebrated advertising agencies called TAXI.

I'd never dared called Jeremy Gayton in the past, as I knew his agency's fees would be hopelessly out of reach and we never had an opportunity that I felt was worthy. 'Jer, I need a favour buddy.' As he always does, he listened carefully before speaking and then, when I was done explaining our position, he asked all the right questions. 'Let me digest it, see if we can spare the resources and get back to you' were his closing remarks. Needless to say, he called back a few days later, laid down the rules of engagement and came to our rescue—and then some. *'What about the fees?'* I asked hesitantly. *'Let's not worry about that for now,'* he replied. *'This is also a rare and relevant opportunity for TAXI to create a meaningful brand from scratch. One that we can use to canvass our company's talents.'*

He then proceeded to assign a Creative Director (Dave Watson), a designer, a copywriter and an account manager to our project. Together, under Watson's über inspired guidance, we drilled deep into who we would target, why they would or should care about our brand, and how we could stand out and make a difference on a shoestring budget. In the end, we shortlisted the brand name to be either *Batch No1* or *Crazy Uncle*—the latter, a name someone had half-jokingly blurted out in a previous creative meeting that we all had snickered over. *Batch No1* felt right, and categorically much safer than the riskier and mischievous *Crazy Uncle*. Nonetheless, we toiled over the decision for a solid week. *'How the hell are we going to call up the LCBO to tell them we decided to change our brand name from Bar361° to, um ... Crazy Uncle?'*

We called Watson to half-heartedly declare that our choice was Batch No1. Later that evening Jer called me on the drive home. *'I rarely interfere at this point with the client's decision, but the team and I are feeling like we're on to something bigger with Crazy Uncle.'* Long-car-ride-story made short, he convinced us to roll the dice and take a chance on the Uncle and we agreed—thankfully.

Once we locked into the brand name and messaging, the design and personality started to take shape. The team's desire to create something that Watson affectionately called 'shabby-chic' led us to an elegant, yet fun design inspired by dandyism—the *'shabby'* part was our old-world moonshine jug: the kind your European grandfather uses to bottle his homemade gasoline-wine. (Note: somewhere along the line, we dropped the unique shaped aluminum can, among other options, and opted for the jug.) The *'chic'* part was the handsome custom-calligraphy logo drawn by world renown lettering design artist Ian Brignell, and the crisp men's pocket-square influenced patterns. Here is the copywriter's summation of Crazy Uncle® that ultimately sealed the deal for us:

We all know the eccentric uncle. He wears a captain's hat but doesn't own a boat. He boasts about his impressive Russian Jazz record collection. He marches to the beat of his own drum. It's that same unpredictability and uniqueness that inspires this drink. Our Crazy Uncle one-pour cocktails have deep complex flavours and a bitter undertow. With an appreciation of detail, and an artistic expression in liquid form. Why be like everyone else, when you can be something completely different?

In between the brand building exercises, glass bottle hunting, bottler negotiations, production challenges and sales meetings with our new distributor, we spent months, and a few sleepless nights, trying to commercialize our cocktails. Frankie had come up with a little holiday number that both we and the LCBO thought was seasonally splendid —Blood Orange, Rosemary & Maple Punch:

Perfect for the punch bowl at a suave cocktail party, or a cozy winter night by the fireside, this sophisticated punch has the tart acidity of blood orange infused with deep wintery spices like clove, cinnamon and cardamom, and finds its balance in the rich, natural sweetness of Canadian maple syrup.

We sat on the cozy couch in our family-room-style strategy room (complete with a fireplace, acoustic guitar and a wet bar) to taste the third hopeful iteration of the beverage prepared by our flavour development supplier. It was still far from perfection. Much too heady-sweet and watery, without nearly enough flavour depth—where were the subtle back notes of clove and cardamom? Why couldn't we taste the pure maple syrup? We were aiming to push the quality of ready to drink cocktails to a previously unreachable level where they tasted as if they were mixed with care and love in a bar by a pro. The flavour lab was in Kentucky a mere hour and a half flight away. I looked over at Dave and then at Leigh. *'It's clear that we have to visit the lab, sit down at the table with all those involved, and then tweak and taste until we nail it. There's just no time to go about it any other way at this point in the game.'*

I had been in this very same hot seat many times before and knew the benefits of a well-planned and intentioned plant visit would far outweigh the costs associated with carving out a few days of travel. Even if we provided meticulous tasting notes and direction to the flavour experts and chefs in Kentucky, the risk of waiting another three weeks only to be thwarted once again was one we couldn't afford to take. When it's crunch time, insist on a full-day tasting and tweaking session. Leigh pulled some strings and we were off to Erlanger, Kentucky. It's also highly constructive and recommended to take the time to explain your vision and expectations to the team. Let them jump on your carpet ride so they can better see and believe in the magic. It was worth the trip. We left the session satisfied that we had captured the quality, versatility and the true essence of Frankie's cocktail recipe—we also left the meeting with a fierce buzz after having sampled over ten different attempts.

After a few more heartaches and handfuls of uncomfortable production related ups and downs—namely the stubborn metal cap removal caper, the cockeyed bottle-label fiasco, the not-so-sticky adhesive on the custom elastics that fastened the rimmer sachet to the bottle, the too-thin-for-LCBO corrugated cases, and the surprise presence of unwanted flocculation (i.e. floating sediment clouds caused by exposing the juice pulp to high heat in the pasteurization tunnel), we were ready to ship our first order. LCBO had positioned our entry into their stores as a test that they'd be following closely.

In order to secure a listing in their Spring 2013 program, they mandated us with a sell-through target of forty-five percent of the order by December 17th (nearly 4,000 bottles). If we were able to achieve a sixty-five percent sell-through by the same date, we would be awarded two new listings. Based on Crazy Uncle's uniqueness and originality of the product, memorable brand name and packaging, LCBO chose to showcase us in their high profile 'What's New' section in the Holiday edition of its Food & Drink publication. Our brand name and package design played a pivotal role in securing a decent amount of prominent print and television media appearances. With TAXI at our side, we also ended up being recognized in the design world scoring a few nods such as one of '*2013 coolest packaging deigns*' and '*Top 10 Inspiring Packaging Designs.*'

Dave and I spent a few weeks visiting four or five key LCBO stores per day with our sales reps to chat up the store staff and ensure we pushed, what the industry refers to as, liquid to lips. Many key locations chose to showcase Crazy Uncle as a '*Staff Pick*' resulting in prime merchandising locations (i.e. next to the check-out counters); taking the time to visit and meet the staff in these stores was time well invested —something we still insist on with each new launch.

For a few weeks in December, I started each day by jumping out of bed with my heart in my throat while making a beeline for my laptop to check the previous day's sales. By the target date, despite a paltry, yet logical, forced push by the LCBO into only a couple of hundred of their nearly 700 locations, we exceeded the requirement and reached a seventy-five percent sell-through. By New Year's Eve we hit 97%. As such, the two flavours we'd originally presented to the LCBO (*Basil, Honey & Lime Daiquiri* and the *Cola Bitters and Mint Julep*) were green-lighted for the following Spring.

We ended up selling the Blood Orange, Rosemary & Maple punch over the next four consecutive winter seasons with nearly the same results. It was a prodigious win for us as the road had been dark and long —we had started the journey from nowhere without a map. In the years that followed, we pushed hard to defend and nurture our new baby brand by continuing to introduce whimsical and unexpected flavour combinations made using best-in-class ingredients. It's years later and I still smile at the faded black spray paint splat tattooed to the parking lot asphalt as I walk into the office each morning.

Let it Simmer ~

1. *Should you be changing course in light of new facts or are you stubbornly holding steady because of your ego and the inconvenience associated with changing direction midstream?*
2. *Are you in bed with the right supply partner? Do the easy steps feel easy?*

3. *Before you open your wallet too far for costly prototypes and the like, think 'clever arts & crafts' and make it work with super-snazzy mock-ups backed by a proper and compelling story and plan.*

4. *When your supply partner is in a development-rut, can you jump on a plane, train or automobile and visit them to help things move along and stay put until the job gets done?*

5. *Ignorance is bliss and can sometimes work in your favour. Are you backing down or changing your approach or slowing your speed because you should, or only because someone's told you 'that's not the way it works around here?'*

6. *Even if you're ready to launch your product, is it the right time of year? Will waiting another few months or more increase the degree of your success? Take a breath and rethink before you pull the trigger.*

7. *There is no task beneath you on the road to launch—visit stores one-by-one if you must to get the job done.*

8. *Believe in your mission and its purpose deeply and it will go light-years further.*

CHAPTER 20

Worst Thing Since Sliced Bread

Proper Due Diligence

A smoky, salty, meaty and gooey cheese revelation—this was my first impression of my first heaping mouthful of the Reuben sandwich from The Bread Vault Bakery. Let me explain. This was no ordinary lunchtime sandwich; the fat-ass cut sourdough bread was baked in-house in a wood oven using an ancient recipe that incorporated a two-week-old pre-fermented 'poolish' dough starter. The primo smoked corned beef brisket and tangy Russian dressing were also made in small batches with love. Their finishing move, however, was the culinary clincher—whipped butter generously slathered on the outside bread slices to sear the entire sandwich on a flat top grill and seal in the goodness with molten Gruyère cheese.

The result was a crusty and chewy golden food-porn masterpiece. To boot, it was served on an attractive reclaimed-wood plank. Despite our initial trepidation with investing in the business, Dave and I stared at each other confidently after downing the first bite with nostrils fully flared as if to say: *'Hot damn, this is too good! Way better than we expected.'* If it weren't for that corned beef narcotic, we wouldn't have lost $80,000 in less than three months.

Jimmy was beyond intense, he was a borderline madman—but we liked him instantly. We quickly got the feeling that he was grossly misunderstood (by literally everyone) and took on the demanding role of becoming both his protector and his interpreter to the outside world. After a meeting, we used to say: *'Okay, let's try to decode what Jimmy actually meant.'* Or: *'Did you run that one through the Jimbo-filter?'* In the beginning, we blindly trusted his capabilities; after all, he'd once been the President for a number of years at a successful and well-known power tool company. Now, he was a skittish entrepreneur desperately looking for guidance and a quick capital injection to take his budding, but bleeding, upscale quick service bakery / restaurant concept into the black and on to the next level.

It was something fresh and different, but as always, still all about great food. We are forever searching for that extra degree of passion that causes a true foodie to dig deep to find those culinary gems. To find the too good to be true and to make discovery of the rare and great and then to share it with like-minded consumers. Our interest, however, wasn't in taking over the restaurant's operations—instead, it was in polishing the concept so that it was marketable on a much larger stage as a franchise restaurant opportunity.

With its fresh baked artisanal breads made from ancient recipes, extravagant sandwiches and sinfully decadent desserts, we had the feeling there could be a lot more neighbourhood street corners inhabited by The Bread Vault. As we sat across the white-and-red-checkered table in the local diner down the street from our future investment to close the deal, I should have paid closer attention to the fidgety guy sitting next to Jimmy. He was a key staff member at The Bread Vault that had tagged along with Jimmy for moral support—or so we thought. Thinking back, we also should have paid more attention to the Head Chef's odd behaviour.

A week or so before offering our agreement terms, we walked through the restaurant to get a sense of the assets, the processes, the people and the problems. Chef Ted pulled me aside in secret to explain that the restaurant's concept, the wonderful recipes and the staff were all his doing, not Jimbo's. Although I recognized his actions and angle to be peculiar at the time, I thought he was just trying to impress me or lobby for early support and respect—boy, was I wrong with this one too. In the end, the condition we used to structure our agreement would prove to be a life (and bank balance) saver; namely, complete strategic control in exchange for general guidance, business planning and capital investment via a line of credit that could be converted into fifty percent ownership in the business at our option within a certain period of time.

The key was that we didn't sign on as legal partners out of the gate. We were lenders with a set of house keys and a significant voice—this type of deal structure is called a convertible debenture—I suggest googling it before you sign on as an official partner to an existing business in need of capital and guidance. Just think of it as living with your potential spouse before officially tying the knot. If they turn out to be nutso, you can pack up your things and bolt. You may have to leave behind a high-priced cappuccino machine and fancy Dyson vacuum, plus a few months' rent—but it's cheaper, quicker and less painful than hiring a divorce lawyer and getting dragged through the mud.

Before we officially visited the restaurant to address the staff and key suppliers, we took it upon ourselves to call up every person on Jimmy's list who was owed money. The list of irritated suppliers and lenders holding out their hands for money was plentiful. I was honest in my approach: *'Listen, I'm not the new owner. Our company is lending money and guidance to help The Bread Vault from going belly up. If you wait this thing out, you get a big fat zero. Good luck taking legal action as there's not even enough value in the business to pay the secured creditors (i.e. the banks, the equipment leasing company, etc.). Agree to take half (or less) today, and we'll cut you a cheque tomorrow.'* Aside from an uncompromising Calabrese-Italian food supplier (surprise, surprise), the lion's share of supplier grievances was mopped up—or so we thought based on what was formally shared with us during the due diligence period.

A few days before signing the agreement, it became all too clear that Chef Ted and Jimmy were at great odds. Daily disputes and a power struggle between the two were taking a toll on the staff, and ultimately, on the business. Jimmy felt that he had had no control over the business he had bled for to build. What's more, the Chef found that ensuring Jimmy stayed out of the building on deliveries and menial chores was mandatory to keeping the peace.

The genuine problem, as it is with most restaurant start-ups, was the financials. Each week, it was costing twice as much as the sales they generated to keep the doors open. A deeper exploration revealed that the Chef's salary was a huge encumbrance. Jimmy felt confident that he could strap on a Chef's apron without having the restaurant lose a beat. *'I know how to make most of the menu, and we can learn the rest,'* he assured us. Parting ways with the Chef, although risky, was inevitable. The Chef called me shortly after he was asked to leave. It was difficult, but we were able to reach a place of mutual respect and I agreed to help him transition elsewhere with regards to money he was owed, among other things. By this point, Dave and I contemplated cutting bait as we hadn't invested any serious funds and began to smell something funky, but then decided that the risk was still tolerable and held off on releasing our catch.

As we pulled up to the restaurant on a crisp and early Monday morning in September, we were genuinely excited to meet and address the team. We had flown to New York the week prior to scout out a few popular bakery concepts and returned inspired. We had innovative ideas, unique designs, clever promotions and fresh recipes in tow—all crafted to make The Bread Vault sexier and more marketable as a franchise opportunity. We knew a good year or two was needed to let the new direction settle in and take shape, but we were game.

As I stepped out of the car, I noticed Chef Ted nervously pacing back and forth in front of the restaurant. *'That's interesting and unfortunate,'* I thought, as I knew Jimmy had let him go the week before. How did the staff feel about his sudden departure? How would they feel seeing their ship-less captain bobbing around the restaurant window? Not good, it turns out. Not good at all. As I addressed the young men and women wearing their baker's whites, Jimmy's uncle and that fidgety guy who sat beside Jimmy during our contract signing watched awkwardly from the sidelines. The more I explained that Jimmy would be assuming the reins as the rightful heir to his bread throne, the more his subjects seemed in pain and discomfort. And then ... bada bing, bada boom —the brown bagels hit the fan.

Some staff decided to quit and storm out while making a dramatic exit, while the others seemed distantly interested, yet very much guarded. From that point forward, it was a downhill ride to mouldy bread town. Every day, beneath every small and large stone we unearthed complications and silliness. Solving them should have been easier than it was, but we also had to operate within the mental quicksand that the 'Jimbo-filter' added to the equation.

Weekly sales routinely fell short by about fifty to sixty percent of covering the restaurant's basic overheads. Our first order of business was to understand the production processes with a fundamental goal of restructuring labour, challenging food costs and the menu itself. The amount of spoiled and unsold goods, and the labour it took to prepare them, was ugly. The thing about baking artisanal fresh bread the way The Bread Vault was preparing it is that you require an experienced baker or two to work throughout the night. To boot, without Chef Ted, Jimmy and his adorable uncle had to try and figure out how to prep and bake, in addition to running the bakery during its hours of operation.

As you can imagine, trying to run a struggling business on next to zero sleep, few breaks or sign of daylight is like leaving your buns in the wood oven until they burn black and dry up. Instead of focusing on what made the bakery unique and popular, Jimmy panicked and tried to find solutions by concentrating on new ideas and investments. Instead of worrying about why we were losing $1 for every beautiful homemade butter croissant that we sold for $2.50, we spent exhausting hours convincing him that we shouldn't renovate the second floor into a private dining / event space; or, despite their apparent popularity, taking his uncle's famous cheese and wiener windups off the menu so that he could hone his skills on executing the menu we wanted to eventually franchise.

What should have been an undertaking that cost us the equivalent of investing a full day or so per week, quickly mutated into a full-time responsibility that, above all else, was hugely physically and mentally exhausting. Dave and I would leave the restaurant feeling like we'd just stepped out of a boxing ring—dazed and confused. On the days we didn't visit The Bread Vault, we'd both spend our car rides to work and back home, and everything in between, on the phone trying to get Jimmy aligned with our thinking. Near the end of our short journey, we were spending more time trying to correct wrongs and dodge perilous bullets from a handful of parties owed money that weren't 'captured' on our original clean-up list.

By this point, we had been sufficiently warned about Jimmy's peculiar modus operandi by staff, suppliers and even store customers. Buying the business outright didn't make sense either as aside from the warped baggage and inconvenient travel time, Jimmy's compensation expectations were out to lunch compared with what the business was actually worth.

Of course, the circus eventually had a destructive, time sucking effect on our core business at BrandFusion. Once we realized this, we pulled the ripcord hard and fast. Yes, it hurt, but after a few days or so, we felt our energy return and decided our financial loss should be viewed as an investment to further our food education—four years' tuition and residence fees squeezed into a quarter of a year. Most importantly, and the reason for our relatively easygoing departure, was the structure of our deal. The convertible debenture allowed us to disengage and move on without the fear of further penalties or exposure with the host of new conflicts bubbling and brewing. Although, in all fairness to Jimbo, that damn Reuben sandwich and those bedevilled beautiful butter croissants were off the chart delicious.

Let it Simmer ~

1. *If you are investing in an existing business, can you structure the deal so that you can walk away relatively easily and inexpensively if it's not what you thought it would be?*
2. *Do you trust your inner voice or are you ignoring it and your gut instincts because it's too difficult or uncomfortable to cut bait and disappoint others involved?*
3. *Have you worked to expose all the rotten layers before taking the reins, or should you listen and observe more before taking the stage?*
4. *New opportunities take time and patience before they can stand on their own. Can you be there and be fully engaged and involved until the business can survive with less of your time?*
5. *Is your core business suffering as a result of newer and perhaps more 'seemingly' exciting prospects? If so, can you divide your time wisely and competently?*

6. *Will your prospective new business partner bring value and save you time or create additional work and avoidable anxiety?*

7. *If the business owes unsecured creditors money, have you tried to settle or simply assume the liabilities at face value as part of the deal?*

CHAPTER 1 | Gathering Substance. **TOP LEFT:** Standing on the front steps of the Beta Brands candy factory in London, Ont. — aka my CPG Food Industry University (June 1998, photo credit: Derek Ruttan); **TOP RIGHT:** *Strategy Magazine* photo shoot with JP (Aug 1998, photo credit: Stephen Uhraney); **BOTTOM:** Good times (Summer 1999). My Beta Brands farewell bash: Unbeknownst to me, coworkers had the local radio station (FM96) broadcast that the woman to eat the most Lifesavers candy off my body wins tickets to a Matthew Good Band concert. After feeding me a few too many barley pops and decking me out in a hand-sewn ensemble, a pack of she-wolves was unleashed. Check out the hungry lady snacking on a candy chunk from my armpit!

CHAPTER 6 | Eat in Moderation, Not Deprivation. **TOP:** An open window with a colourful view, taken from my office at BrandFusion. **BOTTOM:** Grand opening of Gabo Wabo's Popsicle Bar. My Son, the little bugger, must've raked in more profit than BrandFusion that day—and that's even after factoring in the rent we charged him to set up shop.

2000

2004

2008

2014

CHAPTER 7 | Pop Goes the World. Keepin' it fresh. Packaging evolution of Kernels Popcorn Shakers.

CHAPTER 8 | Pope Goes the World. **TOP:** Popcorn pop-up shop at World Youth Day (Toronto 2002). **MIDDLE:** Popcorn purgatory: Over 500,000 hungry mouths and we end up selling a whopping 75 of the 20,000 bags of popcorn procured for the event. **RIGHT:** Events van—aka dreaded family moving van.

CHAPTER 9 | Lost in New York. **LEFT:** Gravity-fed wire racks created a slight opening that allowed cold air to escape from freezer—game over. **RIGHT:** The *New York Times* Headline ... Potato Chips Chase Goes Stale. Underdog Wiener Wins!

Grilling ... Mediterranean Style.

Available exclusively at these fine stores:

We're fresh obsessed.

CHAPTER 10 | Opa! **TOP:** Retailer exclusivity programs may seem like a basic notion on the surface, but can prove to be a very persuasive and powerful device. **BOTTOM:** The guys and I serve up souvlaki to A&P / Dominion head office staff in their office parking lot. Yep, that's me, 3rd from the right, standing beside Mr. Raios (President of Mr. Greek). And yes, I'm well aware that I look a tad, um, George-Costanza-stocky? Blame it on the ultra-strict diet of barbequed jumbo pork souvlaki and Kefalotyri cheese! Listen, I take my work seriously ;)

CHAPTER 11 | Damn Turmeric. The original television celebrity chef and our family's first food hero, the much-loved Chef Pasquale Carpino (1936-December 30, 2005).

CHAPTER 12 | A Slice Of Pizza Pie. Creamy garlic gladiator: Thanks to tapping into an untapped consumer eating ritual and to finding the perfect space in the grocery store, our Pizza Pizza Dips have endured many years in the deli refrigerator.

CHAPTER 13 | Cocktail Dreams.
TOP: A decade after I pulled the plug on my chance to collaborate with Sammy Hagar, I was able to share our Crazy Uncle Über Caesar with him.
LEFT: Full circle — although we never did launch a Cabo Wabo lime margarita cocktail mix, we ended up creating a Basil, Honey & Lime Daiquiri under our Crazy Uncle culinary cocktail line.

CHAPTER 17 | Milkin' It. Ease up on the gas pedal. Avoid embracing too much, too quickly: *'Fast is fine, but accuracy is everything'* — Xenophon, Greek Historian of the 4th century BC.

CHAPTER 18 | **Boiling Over**. Luckless patrons of The *Lost Pantry*: Kernels chocolate covered caramel popcorn packed inside a jumbo foil-wrapped Easter egg, Golden Griddle Breakfast Sausages, Booster Juice Alphonso Mango Smoothies, and Eating in Japan Stir Fry Meal Kits.

CHAPTER 19 | Catching a Buzz.
TOP ROW: The birth of Crazy Uncle—from quick n' dirty retailer presentation mock-ups to an award-winning packaging design.
MIDDLE LEFT: Strength in numbers—Dave and I visit our flavour team in Kentucky to put a final spin and approval on the recipe. **MIDDLE RIGHT:** Our Blood Orange, Rosemary & Maple Punch finally hits the shelf in the LCBO.
BOTTOM RIGHT: *The Globe and Mail* newspaper photo shoot with Dave (Oct 2013, photo credit: Jennifer Roberts).

CHAPTER 21 | Stinky Cheese & Anchovies. **CLOCKWISE FROM TOP LEFT:** (1) Magic Miso marinade packaging design dilemma; (2) Kernels Blue Cheese challenge; (3) 'Do you like my green eggs? No, we do not. We would not, could not eat them anywhere!'. **BOTTOM RIGHT:** Crazy Uncle All Natural Über Caesar. **BOTTOM LEFT:** Dave and I (left) chat with Michael and Guy Rubino about our newfound partnership in advance of the launch of the latest Crazy Uncle product (*Vaughan Citizen*, May 2014, photo credit: Adam Martin-Robbins).

CHAPTER 22 | Tomato Potato.
TOP: Rimmer seasoning sachet fiasco.
RIGHT: Butter oil packaging and
product positioning debacle.
BOTTOM: jack-o'-lantern candles
NOT included.

Brothers Bruno, left, and Davide Codispoti launched Crazy Uncle Hard Root Beer in Toronto this spring as "craft soda for grown-ups."

New drink a conversation piece

CHAPTER 24 | Feeding the Beast. **TOP LEFT:** *The Toronto Star* photo shoot with Dave (June 2016, photo credit: Melissa Renwick). **TOP RIGHT:** all natural Hard Root Beer. **BOTTOM LEFT:** waterbed-sized floor retail display. **BOTTOM RIGHT:** Following our serendipitous one-minute-sidewalk-pitch, *The Thirsty Traveler* snaps and posts a pic of our chance encounter. Photo credit: Kevin Brauch.

CHAPTER 28 | Fruit Pulp Clouds & Chocolate Bloom. Despite best-in-class ingredients and packaging, our Hail Mary pass, *Crème de la Crème*, quickly spirals into *Crème de la Crap* because of humidity issues.

CHAPTER 30 | The Candy Man (Almost) Can. LifeSavers *NSYNC Sweet Sounds of Summer promo results were far more prosperous than my one night as a music mogul.

CHAPTER 31 | Milk Money. **ABOVE:** $120,000 for YTV's Marty the Mad Flavour Scientist provided zero sales lift. **RIGHT:** Limited Edition movie themed promotional shakers proved to be a win-win campaign, year after year, for both us and the movie studios.

CHAPTER 32 | Family Table. **TOP:** Family Circus: Cousin Chris, Enza Pulla and I participate in the Maple, Ontario Santa Claus Parade (Nov 2002). **BOTTOM LEFT:** Dave fires up the office grill to barbeque Korean short ribs for yet another bloody magnificent, yet typical, office lunch. **BOTTOM RIGHT:** A familiar face: My wife Lisa, lending Johnvince Foods her smile for a Sam Mills gluten free pasta TV commercial.

CHAPTER 33 | Putter or Butter. **TOP:** Choosing the butter over a putter: hanging with the boys around a smoking cauldron of Brother Milan's 'Beans Plus' soup simmering over an open fire. **BOTTOM:** Dave teaches a class on Neapolitan pizza making using Brother Milan's hand-forged-iron stone pizza oven at Waupoos Estates Winery in Price Edward County.

CHAPTER 21

Stinky Cheese & Anchovies

Cast a Larger Net

Personal taste can be awfully subjective—just because you love and crave a certain food or dish, it doesn't automatically mean that others will, or should, too. Archie, our long time BrandFusion associate, once told me his former boss at one of the leading Canadian grocery chains aimed to launch products under the premise of '*feed the masses if you want to eat with the classes.*' In other words, you'll need to move as many cases as you humanly can if you want to uncork that bottle of Bruno Giacosa Collina Rionda, Barolo DOCG. Yep, I know. I completely realize that this sounds super shallow and uncomfortably pretentious. That said, it's an accurate and brutally honest rule to remember if your endgame is to move volume. Incidentally, I've yet to uncork a Bruno Giacosa.

Speaking of wine, for example, I typically serve my homemade reserve when family and friends, less concerned with an appreciation of oenology, come over to dine. Once again, it's not that I'm shallow or pretentious, it's just that it truly pains me to watch a freezer burned ice cube bobbing up and down in decent glass of red. Once in a while when I do uncork a real beauty with the same crowd, and refuse to offer ice, the glasses remain nearly full. '*What's wrong with your wine?*' I'll inquire. '*It's too bold and barnyardy,*' they'll reply to which I'll then apologetically shrug my shoulders and retort: '*But, but ... that's a good thing!*'

Having said this, I'm the only one bothered at the table while my guests cheerfully sip their refreshing wine-coolers. The point being that they are in fact my guests (my customers) to please, so why should I force them to like or want or appreciate what I do. Conversely, when I was in high school and university, I made it a very premeditated point to order party-sized pizza, half with extra anchovies, as I knew it would guarantee me half the pizza, plus a couple of slices from the other side of the pie. When I worked at Quaker, one of our most popular *Crispy Minis®* Rice Chips flavours was Salt & Vinegar. The acidity level in the vinegar was so robust that it could make the roof of your mouth momentarily raw. After receiving a few consumer complaints, we decided to lower the acidity bite only to find that our most dedicated Salt & Vinegar fans stopped buying the product as frequently because they craved for and missed the burn.

In this particular case, our most dedicated fans drove enough of the overall sales volume that we decided to reinstate the vinegar-punch; go figure. It's difficult to assess how consumers will respond. Our experience suggests that, if you have the slightest inkling that consumers will nag about something, they eventually will; and let me tell you, there are some pretty aggressive and vocal people out there who spring at the chance to let you know how they feel. The good news is that most of the time, a speedy and favourable reply can ease the most boorish of critics. Who are you hoping to serve your dish to?

The story that leads up to Archie's '*feed the masses*' lesson is a good one to start with. He was part of a product development team that set out to re-engineer the Oreo® cookie by making it out of superior ingredients. The cream filling was made from pure Madagascar vanilla bean paste and the biscuits out of real cocoa and cane sugar. Amazingly, the consumer taste panel results were less than unacceptable. '*It just doesn't taste like <u>my</u> Oreo!*' consumers protested.

Scott Staiman (Kernels Popcorn Founder) refers to this situation as '*the burnt chocolate cake*' syndrome. He grew up eating and loving his Mother's chocolate cake, which always had a faintly burnt outer crust. No other chocolate cake could give him the same euphoric food-buzz. For Scott, his ultimately satiating recipe was much more about fond and comforting memories than about using good quality cocoa. Now, that's obviously not to say recipes and concepts that aim to elevate the status quo can't work. Today's taste buds have become dramatically more experienced, adventurous and selective.

A good friend of mine, Sal Consiglio, runs an established and popular namesake family business called Consiglio's Kitchen wear on St. Clair Avenue West in Toronto. He's been prominently displaying and selling quality imported espresso machines for well over a decade. It wasn't too long ago that he remembers non-Italian customers fearfully opting out of investing in a machine because espresso just didn't taste like their coveted Tim Horton's blend; it was too strong, too dark and too foreign. Nowadays, Sal is peppered with questions like: *'Are your espresso beans single origin? Is the machine's grinder ceramic or metal? How do I achieve a denser crema?'* Mama mia, are we in Toronto or Milan!?

Come to think of it, this also feels like a good time to quickly touch on the weightiness of product consistency, and how it can even trump product quality at times. Sticking to the topic of espresso, I was once bewitched by a hauntingly perfect cappuccino. The café's owner-barista was a veritable maestro on the *Faema®*.

On an otherwise very routine morning, I stopped in to visit the maestro and to order my roasty-toasty narcotic. Alas, he wasn't there. When the nameless barista handed me my drink, I could immediately tell that the magic was missing just by how the bubbly foam stared back at me in the cup. One tiny sip and ... Yup, I was right, it tasted average at best.

A few mornings later, the maestro was back at the wheel. *'Just so you know, the past few days my cappuccinos haven't come close to your beautiful babies'* I declared with a slight smirk. He glared back at me with a step-off-buddy look. *'What a backhanded compliment!'* he started, *'you don't know how much I hate hearing that! I haven't been able to teach any of my employees to make their coffees look and taste line mine. It's killing my business whenever I'm not here. I can't bloody leave. I've actually decided to lower the quality of my own cappuccinos a bit so that they're at least more consistent with how the other baristas make 'em. That way, eventually, no one will complain, and I can call in sick every once in a while.'*

Unreal. The maestro actually chose to operate below his capabilities and personal standards in an effort to *not* disappoint customers and to keep them coming back. Consistency is king. File and bank that frothless wonder before signing off on your final masterpiece.

I've had my fair share of food creations that have soared high over everyone's head—my first and most memorable was early in my consumer packaged goods (CPG) career at the McCormick's candy factory in London, Ontario. *'I have a feeling this one will be the runaway confection hit of the Easter season!'* I remembered promising Blair. *'I know we can't technically license Dr. Seuss' Green Eggs & Ham property, but ... if we make the egg's chocolate-y coating green and then colour the marshmallow-yolk fillings with a vivid red, purple or blue, folks will surely make the connection.'* Blair looked at me funny. *'Trust me!'* I reassured him further. *'We can even design our packaging in a very familiar, but not exact, Seuss-ian style.'*

I respect Blair for granting me the freedom to try such a stupid idea, and then backing me up with the sales department when they looked at him funny. I remember having such a strong emotional tie to the book and to the idea. I also remember not showing my green eggs around enough when Pam Watson from our R&D lab furnished me with tasting samples. I must've eaten the box and saved one or two for Blair and the sales team. The packaging didn't end up having that *Seuss-ian* vibe I envisioned as apparently no one else made the connection to the popular children's story. Nearly twenty years later, Blair and I still laugh about this fiasco. *'Do you like my green eggs? No, we do not. I would not, could not eat them anywhere!'*

A few years back, Dave and I rallied to launch a blue cheese Kernels Popcorn seasoning. We had become bored of introducing straightforward chip-inspired flavours like cheddar, dill pickle, bbq, ketchup, etc. Outside of the office, our love of good food and food exploration had matured so we wanted to introduce a flavour we thought was more culinary-worthy. *'Who doesn't like a strong and stinky blue cheese?'* We chose to ignore the fact that most of our consumers were kids and families. We gave little thought to better understanding and to respect our existing sales rankings—dill pickle and white cheddar had been our workhorse flavours since the beginning.

Nonetheless, during the flavour development phase, we scarfed down bowl after bowl of blue cheese popcorn in the office and at home.

It was indisputably our new favourite flavour. It ended up being our worst selling flavour ... ever. In a desperate attempt to bolster sales, we changed the packaging design and product name to *Blue Cheese RANCH*, thinking and hoping that the addition of the more chip-familiar 'RANCH' reference would connect with more folks. It actually did, but not nearly enough as it's all about repeat sales and not deceiving someone in order that they pick up another bottle, bag or box.

Similarly, the ready-to-eat popcorn category (popped popcorn in a bag) has been on the rise as of late. Walking the Fancy Food Show in San Francisco a couple of years ago, we couldn't help but notice the number of start-up companies trying to squeeze their way into the clogged category with similar off-centre flavours such as Curry & Cool Yogurt, or Sundried Tomato & Parmesan to name a couple. The flavours sounded and tasted great, the packaging looked fresh and attractive. And yet, aside from a select few brands (namely the ones with either established distribution or deep pockets or both), the majority of product introductions failed when we checked back a year or so later. Show me the volume!

Funnily enough, a number of popcorn companies, both established and start-ups, have recently found success, and the ability to co-exist in a clogged category, with the simplest of flavour approaches—premium popping corn, small-batch popped using a good salt and healthier oil (i.e. avocado oil, expeller pressed coconut oil, etc.). It was frustrating to witness the market entry and triumph of so many new popcorn players with such a simple concept, while we self-indulged in our stinky blue cheese.

The paradox then becomes: When does improving on certain food products fail (i.e. using Madagascar vanilla cream for Oreo cookies), and when does it work (i.e. popcorn made with sea salt and expeller pressed coconut oil)? Consider that the impetus for eating an Oreo cookie (or in my case, an entire row or two) might be reward or stress determined so comfort and gratification in familiarity is key. For eating popcorn, choosing a healthier snack alternative might be the goal, in which case changing the status quo by offering better ingredients is both acceptable and desirable.

These days, we try to hit the sweet spot between satisfying our maturing culinary palates while staying relevant and engaging to a market segment that's large enough to reach the necessarily volume targets. It's about having to be willing to massage and to compromise your recipe and packaging. It's also knowing when to stand your ground and take a chance on pushing something fresh and new. It should go without saying that, if you don't fully and completely believe in your product and its narrative, it'll be a short-lived love affair. When you compromise too much, it'll surface in the form of uninspiring sales pitches, an unwillingness to invest enough money, etc.

One of our fan favourites and proudest culinary accomplishments is with our Crazy Uncle® cocktail brand, aptly named the *Über Caesar*. (Note: the Caesar is Canada's self-proclaimed official cocktail; it's similar to its US cousin, the Bloody Mary, but is made using a tomato-clam-based juice vs. a straightforward tomato base.) At first, we toyed around with dialling up the standard recipe with a clever culinary twist by adding in subtle notes of aged balsamic vinegar from Modena, Italy, and smoky Canadian bacon (a recipe trend that we noticed was becoming common in high-end restaurant prepared Caesars). In the end, we decided to stay true to the classic recipe by leaning on premium and all natural ingredients.

All other brands playing in the Caesar cocktail space were manufactured using MSG (monosodium glutamate), high fructose corn syrup and artificial colours and flavours. Our blend was inspired by the original all natural recipe (invented in Calgary, Alberta 1969), made using vine-ripened tomatoes, clam broth, grated horseradish, Lea & Perrins® Worcestershire and Tabasco®—by the way, I probably put Tabasco on twenty percent of everything I eat. The final result, which we enlisted the help of celebrity Chef Guy Rubino to assist us with, was a veritable culinary accomplishment in the field of pre-mixed cocktails. The experienced taste-panel at the LCBO were blown away. Sampling the cocktail at trade shows, parties and other events was a pure joy as people showered us with compliments and high-fives. Consumers were even willing to accept the slight settling of natural ingredients in the bottle despite being used to the competitor's more artificially homogenized and electric red appearance.

Our main obstacle was the higher retail driven by our small-batch process and expensive ingredients. Depending on how you define success, the launch was both a moderate triumph and a moderate letdown. Had we indulged our personal taste by adding in the aged balsamic and bacon notes, I don't think we would have sold a quarter of the bottles that we did. We were right in thinking that people would rather consume a straight forward, clean and honest Caesar that they in turn could personalize at home by adding other interesting ingredients. However, despite the accolades and glowing reviews from both consumers and media critics (feel free to google *Über Caesar reviews)*, we only sold a quarter of what we forecasted in our first season.

The market segment that found purpose in our mission to provide an artisanal product without artificial ingredients just wasn't large enough. The majority of Caesar fans opted for the safer, more familiar and more affordable beverage—they went for the side of the party-sized pizza without the anchovies. Nonetheless, we still push and proudly sell the *Über Caesar* each spring and summer season. It hasn't made us rich, but it's worth the fight, both financially and strategically. For now, I'll have to hold off on buying that $1,031 bottle of Barolo and be happy with drinking my homemade red (without ice cubes).

At times, the fight isn't worth a long and drawn out battle so you'll have to find a clear path and pull the ripcord early enough to cushion the financial blow. There are a few food product categories that I wouldn't touch with a ten-foot zucchini; shelf-stable salad dressings and imported olive oil, to name a couple. Everybody and their brother has 'the best one ever' to sell and there's just too many players in the category vying for the same precious real estate. I was surprised then, when we found ourselves agreeing to take Chef Guy (and big brother Michael) Rubino's (star of the Food Network's '*Made to Order*' television show) miso-based marinade to market. Guy handed Dave, Archie and I a tasting-spoon each of the magic marinade in the kitchen of his (then) restaurant Ame. It tasted more like a wonderfully silky smooth savoury vanilla pudding than a marinade. What's more, miso paste is packed with enzymes that can efficiently tenderize protein in record time (which comes in handy in the restaurant business).

We ended up developing three skus using three different and unique miso pastes, all blended with sake (Japanese wine), mirin, tahini and cane sugar: a saikyo (golden) miso for fish, an aka (red) miso for chicken, and a hatcho (black) miso for beef. To help make our product stand out from the saturated sea of dressing and marinade bottles, we hired a marketing agency and charged them with the unlikely task of designing a brand and a package that was unorthodox and noticeably different than the norm. Like with most marketing agencies, we first spent a few good months delving deep into who we were both as individuals and as a company, what the narrative of the brand message should be, where we hoped the brand would be in 10 years, yada yada.

It's easy to get swept away in such self-indulgent rhetoric, so much so that you don't end up challenging the basics perhaps as much as you should. I remember reassuring ourselves with their design concept proposal saying: *'Hey, if the head designer and copywriter think we can be more distinctive by not showcasing the product name or flavour description as much as we usually do, let's roll the dice! After all, we did ask for something different, right?'* The agency believed that a simple and bold wallpaper-type pattern and the absence or diminished treatment of common design elements, such as emphasizing the product's purpose or description, would engage consumers and get them to pick up the product.

Well, it was a bad gamble. Consumers didn't know what the heck we were selling. Which, in hindsight, was unwise because we were trying to sell something slightly unknown and ethnic to begin with. Conversely, when we sampled the product at higher end grocers, such as Pusateri's, we couldn't keep the product from flying off the shelf. To be fair, I think it was also a case of falling in love with a niche product that could only cater to a select demographic. We had, yet again, fallen in love with the more adventurous side of the pizza stacked with anchovies and blue cheese.

Faced with the decision of sinking more money into a packaging redesign and increasing our marketing communication efforts, we decided to take a less onerous road. Instead of investing more money and then waiting for a year or two to see if the financial tide would turn, we approached one of Canada's largest food retail chains and offered our magic miso marinade to them exclusively for their more artisanal and selective private label product line. Sure we only made twenty percent of the profit we'd make selling the line under our own brand, but over the next couple of years we recouped the total cost of our investment—around $20,000. Had we continued down the original path, we would have had to dump three times as much in redesigns, listing fees, trade and consumer marketing, and most importantly, our time.

If you don't have the funds to invest in proper third party qualitative tests (a deep dive into what people think and feel) or quantitative tests (a measurement of how many people think or behave in a particular way), take matters into your own hands. Have friends, family, neighbours, your kid's classroom, etc. sample your product and provide structured feedback; just make sure you're getting feedback from the target audience you hope to eventually sell to—my Grandmother loved the Green Marshmallow Eggs but then again, she loves everything that I do. Most importantly, develop a thick skin. Listen, don't speak and defend. When people tell you to change everything that you've done, take a breath and find that one worthwhile nugget to use. When you push the go button and finally move forward, keep your high-five hand in your pocket.

I never get overly excited when the first purchase order finally comes in, no matter how large it may be—it's only the pipeline fill required to stock the shelves. If it doesn't sell, I'm eventually getting the cleanup invoice. I don't even care about the second order—it's only the back-up refill for the retailer's warehouse so they have product 'if' your product should sell. If it doesn't sell, now you're getting an even larger cleanup invoice. Now, the third order, that's something worth grinning about and giving your teammates a quiet low-five over. It suggests your product isn't collecting dust. And remember, in the food business, we make our fortune one dollar at a time. If you're looking to generate volume, consider that it's sometimes best to stick with an affordable and basic good quality cheese pizza and lay off the anchovies if you want everyone to enjoy a slice.

Let it Simmer ~

1. *What does success look like to you? How many cases will you need to conservatively move in order to keep your head above water?*
2. *Is your connection to your product concept mainly emotional or is it a logical and pragmatic one? Remember it's hard to hear and process reality, but it's crucial (and less expensive).*
3. *Is your mission fuelled by a self-indulgent passion play, or do you want to make serious money? Passion plays are okay too, but is there enough volume potential to provide the return required to keep things going and growing?*
4. *Does your product idea strike the balance between something you're passionate about but that many others will love and crave too?*
5. *Where do you expect to sell your product—at a weekend farmer's market or at 11,000 Walmart stores in 27 countries?*
6. *Have you tested your product to a point where you understand how consumers might respond? Have you tweaked and incorporated the results into your final masterpiece? Note: checkout surveymonkey.com.*

CHAPTER 22

Tomato Potato

What's in a Name?

Assigning a clear and clever product name and product description to your packaging design is considerably more important than you may think. Deciding on a perfect vessel to house your brainchild is equally as vital. It can be the difference between selling four hundred or four thousand cases. Consumers always seem to end up being both smarter and more capricious than you might presume. Each time we underestimate the finer points and nuances of what or how we communicate what we're selling on our packaging design, or what we pack it into, it comes back to haunt us. If the key messaging on your package design, or how it physically feels in the hand, overpromises what's in the box, bag or bottle you'll be reprimanded by consumers with softer than anticipated sales. If you offer your product in a jar or bottle when consumers subconsciously expect to buy it in a carton or a box, don't be surprised when it gets delisted six months after it hits the shelf.

Don't stretch the truth about what's actually in the package. Be clear and tell people what you're offering and why they might consider buying your product instead of the one sitting next to it. Taste, and in most cases smell, don't come in to play until the product makes it home, so shoppers will scrutinize your product on at least two basic and instinctive levels before tossing it into their cart—sight and touch. Now, you might fool folks the first time with a mixed matte and metallic printed carton, complete with holographic logos and high-definition images, but building your empire ultimately relies on creating sustainable purchase habits that lead to healthy repeat orders.

Does your product deliver on what it promises? Before making a decision on what to order in a restaurant, don't you study every option on the menu and carefully examine each ingredient and preparation technique associated with each dish? I sure do, and when my plate arrives at the table, it had better deliver on each seemingly little promise —my *carrot, ginger, coconut and lime soup* had better not taste like watered down *carrot and lime soup*. Every published detail becomes an impending consumer expectation by which you will be measured. If you're going to sell the sizzle, make sure your steak is worth the money.

One of the most challenging and chancy missions for a start-up enterprise working on a Slim Jim budget is to introduce products that are perhaps too original and ambitious. It usually takes a meaningful marketing budget and/or ingenious product awareness strategy to educate consumers on the efficacy and superior benefits of a completely original concept creation. Throwing down ten or twenty thousand dollars at a top marketing agency is like shopping at Harry Rosen with fifty bucks in your pocket—the most you're walking out with is a pair of dress socks or a pocket square. There's an army of smaller and more willing boutique agencies out there that are much more affordable— i.e. ten or twenty thousand dollars will get you the full wash and hot wax. In our experience, they seem to be most proficient at deep diving to better understand the relationship consumers have, or should have, with your product and brand. However, the execution and impact of their plan usually falls flat.

After six months, you'll realize that the same program and results could have been engineered in-house for a fraction of the budget. You'll also realize that your money would be better spent investing with retailers on in-store activities—e.g. aggressive temporary price reductions (TPRs), flyer ads, air mile contributions, off-shelf point-of-purchase (POP) displays, sweepstakes and contests, rebates, product sampling, etc. If you do have a truly innovative product concept and a worthwhile story to tell, consider ringing up a PR agency specializing in consumer packaged goods to help you spread the good word. Note: Despite your Mother's incredible excitement for your adventure, most products and stories aren't as newsworthy and interesting to the public as you might think. Be honest with yourself before putting too many eggs in this basket.

Until you build your business to a level where empowering the right marketing agency match is within financial reach, your package and design has to do the majority of the heavy lifting. Before you start piecing together your packaging art brief for the designer, run out to a handful of grocery stores, drug stores and club stores to buy both the products that you'll be competing against as well as any products that have a look and feel that you'd like to integrate into your efforts. What can you learn from their design, messaging and overall approach and how can you improve on it? What mistakes have they made and how can you avoid making the same ones?

In 2001 we developed a naturally flavoured butter oil for both popping and topping popping corn. We marketed the product under our Kernels brand as a no trans fat, shelf stable, easier alternative to using real butter. To make the launch both less risky and more affordable, we decided to use our contract packer's stock plastic bottle to avoid having to invest in a custom shaped bottle. Unfortunately, the stock bottle looked much too conventional and felt more evocative of a cheaper cooking oil so it confused consumers and completely missed the mark: *'Why would I pay $3.99 for a 400ml bottle of cooking oil when I can buy a 1L bottle for the same price?'*

The 'real butter flavour' messaging and the product's 'popping and topping' purpose was also difficult to decipher for the consumer. As a result, in 2004 we decided to source and invest in a more playful bottle and adjusted the focus and balance of the package design. At nearly twelve thousand dollars, the new bottle mould wasn't cheap, but we felt that, with another new and fresh design and clearer messaging, it was worth the risk.

We ultimately failed with this product concept after less than a year in the marketplace. Was it because we launched with an ill-suited and undesirable bottle format? Yes, I think so, in part. But my gut says the main contributor was because we also over promised and under delivered on what was inside the bottle. We over-packaged and over-designed what we were selling. In retrospect, I don't believe the product concept solved a meaningful consumer problem. Popcorn is, more or less, considered a healthy snack alternative, so dousing it in a *'butter flavoured'* oil might not have been a popular choice. If a consumer is looking to occasionally cheat and indulge, they'll reach for the real McCoy and a pot to melt it in.

We've run and tripped through the same motions with our Kernels Popping Corn product. The product was originally launched in a clear and humble looking plastic jar with a simple and straightforward label design. The sales volume was more than worthwhile. Actually, it was our best seller from a per store, per week, per unit perspective. Somewhere down the line we decided to kick the packaging up a notch and called it 'Premium' Popping Corn and packed the corn into a fully printed and re-sealable stand-up pouch. The new design relied less on showing the actual product, and more on flair. It cost us slightly more, so we charged slightly more for it. Consumers responded loud and clear by cutting our sales in half. Once again, we over-packaged the product.

I've always found it challenging to balance personal tastes with what will actually work with, and engage, consumers. I respect that many have succeeded by never compromising their vision. I've read the Steve Job biographies and get the whole 'consumers don't know what they want' mantra. In the consumer packaged goods business, however, I believe it's more of a careful balance between tapping into existing consumer expectancies and behaviours while sticking to a unique vision. Sure, you want and need to be in love with what you ultimately end up with in order to actually believe in it and then sell it. But, at the same time, you have to be relevant and connect with a large enough pool of shoppers to float your boat.

Remember the 'feed the masses and eat with the classes' adage. Let's delve deeper into the misstep on the packaging design for our Magic Miso Marinade that I touched on in the previous chapter. We desperately wanted to avoid looking like every other marinade on the shelf because we wanted to stand out from the competition—the salad dressing and marinade category is inundated with similar looking bottles and jars. Perhaps slightly less obvious, but equally important, we also needed to be different in order to be emotionally attracted to the mission. Contrary to our proven packaging design modus operandi, we reluctantly agreed not to underscore the product's name or even its usage intent—that is, we didn't come out and scream 'Miso Sauce' or 'Miso

Marinade' in big bold letters smack dab on the front of the package. This design relied heavily on being more interesting and eye-catching than obvious and informative.

I remember being at the printers for the press approval thinking that our gamble to be different than the norm would either payoff handsomely or cut us off at the knees before the race began. As I admitted to you earlier, it was the latter. We had sacrificed clarity for trying to be distinctive and paid for it. Had we possessed the consumer marketing budget to spread the good word, we might have stayed in the race for a while longer. More importantly, had we invested in balancing a more utilitarian design approach with a few unique elements, we could've finished the race unbroken.

In Canada, try not to fall deeply in love with a packaging design until you see how it looks and reads with the proper CFIA bilingual labelling requirements. I love Quebec. I love the French language, it's beautiful. To be sure, all three of my kids attend a French Immersion school in Ontario. It's unfortunate then that the implications of having to incorporate this second language onto your packaging design usually ends up upsetting the visual balance and appeal—the smaller the area you have to convey your messaging (i.e. spice jars vs. a cereal box) the more complicated the task.

Make sure your designer doubles up on the English copy before presenting you with any concepts for review. Doubling up on English copy defers having to pay for French translations before you're certain of what you want to say on your packaging design. Once you do commit to your copy and source the French translations, have a French speaking person examine the copy to ensure that it properly captures the nuances of what you're trying to communicate. I'll never forget getting a call one November from a confused consumer who had just bought a carton of our Kernels Halloween microwave popcorn—it actually popped up orange. They had called to let us know the orange candles weren't included in the box? *'Sorry Sir, orange candles?'* I shrugged my shoulders. *'Yes, on your box it says Chandelles orange!'* he explained.

I looked at a box in my office: *'No, sorry. Chandelles orange means that the popcorn pops up orange!'* Are you crazy, he scoffed, *'then your translation should read Éclatement orange? Chandelles means candles! My wife thought that you included candles in your box for lighting up jack-o'-lanterns.'* Needless to say, triple check your translations if you want to accurately connect with the twenty plus percent of Canadians that speak French as a first language. Unless, of course, you can afford to squeeze a couple of candles into your carton.

There's a real finesse in choosing the right shade of a certain colour, or deciding how to express the inclusion of a key ingredient on your packaging design. It can make the difference between the product feeling fresh versus fake, or the recipe coming off as relevant versus tired and boring. I can't tell you how many swatches of orange I've stressed over in an effort to accurately depict the quality and taste of cheese enhanced products. Softer and warmer oranges typically feel more natural than what we facetiously refer to as *'pylon orange'*, which marks a more electric and artificial cheese. Or better still, our number one orange-enemy, 'Brady Brunch orange' which we use to describe oranges that fall into more of a seventies–shag-carpet kind of space—who wants to eat cheddar cheese pizza dip from a 70s coloured container? I'm also constantly amazed at how slightly tweaking a package by changing a colour's shade and a word or two can give a struggling product its second life.

During my brief stint at Quaker Oats Canada, we couldn't understand why our *'Original'* flavoured Crispy Minis® was our worst seller, despite *'Original or Regular'* potato chips representing the lion's share of all potato chip sales. We decided to keep the recipe exactly the same, but tweaked the packaging design by changing its primarily navy blue bag to a more pleasing aqua blue colour. We also changed the product name from *'Original'* to *'Sea Salt.'* And boom, there's your double digit growth. The *'Original'* flavour description and navy blue bag was much too dull against the other, more alive, flavours in the line-up. Our changes were successful in making the product more interesting without over promising what was in the bag.

One of our best Crazy Uncle® cocktail inventions was our *Cola Bitters and Mint Julep*. Up until a few weeks leading up to the maiden production run, the colour of the liquid was a refreshing bright caramel brown. The colour of the foil-stamped copy on the bottle label was set to be a refreshing Caribbean-ocean blue. During production, we made two last minute changes that ultimately killed the consumer's first impressions of what we were offering them. Feeling uncertain that consumers might not connect a cola-themed cocktail with a lighter and brighter brown, we darkened the liquid colour significantly so that it resembled a traditional dark brown cola soft drink. During the press approval of the bottle label, the pressman apologized at the last minute for not having enough ocean blue foil and offered us the option of using a silver foil instead. We agreed. We were wrong.

The cocktail was developed for summertime. It was meant to come across as fresh, fun and refreshing. Instead, the darker liquid colour set against a more serious silver foil gave the product a more refined and mature appearance—instead of screaming pool party, we screamed old guy drinking alone in his living room—we missed the mark. Consumers that actually sampled and purchased the product repeatedly commented on how the cocktail surprisingly tasted so much more bright and refreshing than they had expected it to taste. When in doubt, hit the pause button—even if you have to temporarily upset your supply partners and retailers. Ship your product the way you know it should look and taste, as everyone involved will eventually move on to putting out the next fire. If you push things through because you're not up to rocking the boat, it's over before it's even begun.

It's amazing how one tiny little packaging element can become the single thread that unravels your chances for success. To boot, it always seems to be the most unexpected and seemingly frivolous detail, that one stupid thing that you never bother to have your eye on. It can take years to line up all the various pieces of your puzzle—i.e. recipes, formulas, supply partners (i.e. contract packers and suppliers of raw material ingredients and packaging), designs, retailers, a sales team, marketing campaigns, etc. It seems unfair then, that it only takes a seemingly petty product or packaging calamity to destructively change how your story unfolds.

Picture this: Days before your opening order is set to ship, your manufacturer notifies you that they can't, and in fact won't, pack your order as they can't seem to fit the declared weight into the package.

What will you do when you receive a phone call from your custom's broker informing you that your fully-loaded trailer of goods isn't being permitted into the US as your packaging design should've included a *'Made in Canada'* declaration? What's your plan when a large retail chain commands you to take back your forty pallets of fresh product because it has become apparent that the majority of the bags appear to have broken seals?

Been there, done that. Our most germane story is a painful tale of not-so-sticky elastic bands. When we launched our Crazy Uncle Cola Bitters and Mint Julep craft cocktail, we sold it with a free sachet of artisanal rimmer seasoning attached to the bottle. It should be noted that not many, if any, alcohol brands include a free add-on with their bottle as part of their everyday product offering. Finding a dependable solution for attaching the rimmer sachet to the bottle was challenging. We spent a great deal of time and too much money to get it right. Searching online, we stumbled across a manufacturer of custom elastic attachments out of Worthington, Minnesota.

We worked closely with them to develop a horseshoe-shaped elastic with adhesive applied to each end. We then manually threaded the elastic through the handle-ring on the bottle's neck and attached the sachet to the sticky ends. The system, and sachet of rimmer seasoning, cost us way too much and ate into our margins more than we felt comfortable with—a difficult decision given that the sachet was a free add-on.

Otherwise, everything else seemed to line up in our favour during the inaugural production run. Our carefully crafted small batches of booze tasted fantastically delicious. You could imagine our disbelief and instant heartache when we walked into a store the very day after the product was shipped only to learn that each rimmer sachet was either missing, or worse, was crumpled up and sitting on the shelf or floor. Turns out that, when we tested the adhesive's effectiveness, we used an unvarnished material instead of using the varnished substrate we ended up using for our sachets. The adhesive wasn't sticking to the varnished material.

Nearly two years of jumping through hundreds of mini hoops to get the launch just right, and within three days of hitting the shelf we were fielding irate calls from our sales team, shoppers and (gulp) retailers asking us what the deal was. In the end, we lost a great deal of sales because consumers assumed the bottles were picked over. Once again, it was a classic case of the tail wagging the dog as our free add-on had cost us dearly in both margin and the consumer's first impressions. It's years later and we're still apologizing to store managers for the not-so-sticky elastic debacle.

Please, don't underestimate any detail. The price of being labelled as 'annoyingly repetitive' is much smaller than a not-so-sticky elastic band that wards off consumers. Funny story: I remember trying to explain to one of my first reports at Quaker that holding someone's hand can be a pain in the ass, but it's necessary to minimize unwelcome surprises. Instead, it mistakenly came out something like this: 'You know, Kelly, holding someone's ass can be a pain in your hand, but it's very necessary if you want things done right.' Luckily she had a decent sense of humour.

Let it Simmer ~

1. *Is your product name and its description perhaps too cute and clever, at the expense of being clear enough for consumers to quickly recognize what you're offering? Does everyone get 'it', or is it just you? Mock-up a package or two, and show it around to friends and family. Visit a store and ask the manager if you can put your mock-up on the shelf next to your competition (and quietly snap a picture or two)—which package stands out more? Which one looks more enticing and appetizing?*

2. *Who is your main target audience? Is your product 'dressed' to their tastes, or more towards your own?*

3. *Have you conducted a decent cross section of store checks to better understand what consumers are habituated to seeing and buying (e.g. large chain stores, smaller independents, department stores, drug stores, club stores and convenience stores)? What do you think a shopper's initial instincts and expectations might be? Is your packaging design and vessel in line, or does it miss the mark because it's either too plain, too novel or just too much?*

4. *Have you stretched the truth in an effort to build a superior packaging message or have you accurately described what's in the box? Have you over designed and over complicated your packaging, or does it reflect the standard and aim of your offer?*

5. *Is your product creation actually solving a consumer problem or filling a category void? If so, is your targeted retail premium worth the solution?*

6. *Before you run to invest all of your consumer budget with a marketing agency, have you sufficiently budgeted for in-store trade marketing efforts? One way to avoid this misstep is to assign a set dollar amount per case towards both trade and consumer marketing budgets—skip ahead to* Chapter 31: Milk Money *for more info on this topic.*

7. *Have you judiciously combed over each seemingly trivial detail with an OCD-worthy filter, or are you blindly trusting your supplier partners a little too much?*

CHAPTER 23

Chew With Your Mouth Closed

When to Debut Your Idea

'Work hard in silence, let success be your noise'
—Frank Ocean

D
ave and I have had more than our fair share of bright ideas bla-
tantly ripped off and plagiarized. With each ugly pilfering, we become slightly more jaded and protective. However, most of the
time, we're only pissed off for half a day and then let it slip and slide off.
It's not in our character to harbour destructive feelings and allow them
to cultivate. Our sacred golden rule has always been to operate in a mode
that holds the conscience clear and free. Or, as mentioned throughout
this book, to operate in a way that allows us to sleep well at night. By
this very nature, despite sometimes sacrificing investments and prospective profits, we usually let things slide and then try to unearth and
preserve the lessons learned. We have our Dad to thank for us being
built that way.

I could ramble on about certain episodes where we opened our
mouth a little too early with the wrong guy or gal—like the time we
were too hyped and perhaps too indiscreet about opening a walk-up
window artisanal fast food concept in the charming ski village at Blue
Mountain in Collingwood, Ontario. In search of feedback and advice,
we shared our plans with someone who was already operating an eatery
in the village.

While we waited patiently for the right piece of real estate to free up,
'BAM' along comes the very same funky walk-up window food concept
a mere few months later. Most likely, no one is interested in hearing us
whimper about such immaterial events, as they're all too common. I can

hear you screaming into the book: *'Your fault, buddy! You opened your big mouth and were too slow to the mark. Speed up, or get off the track.'* Okay, I'll give you this one. Reserve your final judgment, however, until I tell you this next little curious affair.

During the final celebratory confetti-filled scenes of the season finale for *American Idol* (Season 8, 2009), I turned to my lovely wife Lisa and whispered: *'I have an idea, Hun.'* I then began to wildly scribble down ideas and contacts for a reality food show that would centre on the grocery sector instead of restaurants, traditional cooking shows or food travel. Note: There were a hell of a lot fewer reality concepts on the food and travel focused networks in 2009. I remember looking over at the digital clock on my nightstand, noticing that the time was now 2 a.m. I had been in a trance, madly jotting down ideas and possible contact names for hours. I'm now thinking: *'I can't wait to share this beauty with the boys tomorrow morning.'*

Gripping my Thursday morning cappuccino too tightly, I proceeded to paint the big picture for the guys. We would conduct a cross Canada contest in search of the next big food idea to introduce into grocery stores from coast to coast. Home chefs would converge in various cities presenting judges with their culinary masterworks. The finalists would be given a set budget to enlist supply partners, built product prototypes, create packaging designs and shape marketing campaigns, etc. Dave and I would sit on the judges' panel. I appreciated—and was well aware—that we would be complete nonentities from a TV personality perspective, but I was banking on a likable and relatable brothers in business, investing their own skin in the game angle. The show would also serve as a stage to expose how challenging it is to introduce a food product into the retail market space.

The day after the final episode, we would have grocery shelves stocked with the winning item that Canadians had chosen themselves. We would most likely approach Loblaws, Walmart or Sobeys as an exclusive partner, but not until we had our ducks lined up in a perfect row. After all, we didn't want the idea to be snatched from our hands before we could properly anchor ourselves to it.

In order to preserve the concept, I strung together a Keynote presentation demonstrating the basic structure of the show, which relationships we could tap into, etc. My childhood mate, Jeremy Gayton, was a shoo-in to play the role of marketing mentor for the episode centred on building a marketing campaign. As mentioned earlier, Jer was the President of TAXI advertising. At the time, we also began a working relationship with Toronto celebrity chefs, restaurateurs and television personalities, Mike and Guy Rubino, and thought they'd be textbook mentors for the recipe-refinement episode.

For a while, the Keynote presentation rested unmoved on my MacBook desktop. Then one day, Dave recalled he had met a television producer earlier that year. We decided to ring him up and asked if he'd be interested to have us pitch him our idea. Sure, it was an extra-long shot, but like everyone, we appreciate and crave the elation that comes along with stepping out of your comfort zone and sometimes colourless daily routine. We met Rich Goodman (whose production company shall remain unnamed) at a charming little Greek restaurant in Bloor West village for lunch. As far as producers go, he was exceedingly approachable and immediately easy to like.

Rich was super interested and wanted to go for the ride with us ten seconds after staring at the concept-telling cover page imagery of the presentation. The big vision clicked for him instantly. We spoke of our industry and what the logical next steps towards developing a perfected pitch for the network station (which shall also remain unnamed) would look like. I vividly remember politely excusing myself from the table to visit the restroom and gaping into the mirror thinking: *'OK, now this could be a refreshingly different ride in a very cool and desirable way. There's a real, albeit very minute, chance Dave and I will be hosting our own TV show.'*

The next few months with Rich were nothing short of entertaining and, yes, refreshingly different. Each week we would convene at Brand-Fusion in our samurai-themed boardroom (or 'bushido war room' as we like to call it) to build and polish our television show pitch. Rich is something of a seasoned script-doctor so he'd challenge us to keep milling and reworking the ideas and episodes until a super clean and pure version was finally extracted. We even compiled a list of celebrities we'd approach for the show's host—Kevin Brauch from *The Thirsty Traveler* and *Iron Chef America*, and George Stroumboulopoulos from *George Stroumboulopoulos Tonight*, were our top choices.

When we felt the pitch document was worthy of our vision, a meeting with the network was scheduled. Although we intrinsically knew how vital being present at the inaugural meeting was, we half-heartedly agreed to have Rich break the membrane alone to get the ball rolling. In hindsight, it may have been a much larger issue than we anticipated. Operating in the dark is always scary, messy and much slower than it actually needs to be. With bated breath we waited for a status report, the final results and an outlook on our future as TV personalities. When Rich finally called with the network's official response, we were told something to the sombre tune of: *'Boys, they really loved your idea, but the issue is that the network's available budget for supporting new content is significantly underfunded by its parent media company. It's strictly a money thing.'*

Despite the holdup, we remained carefully optimistic as we knew that our concept for the show was fresh, very relevant and right in the pocket for the network at that time. We agreed to chill and sit back, collect our wandering thoughts and think of another approach to woo the network with. A few months after receiving the initial verdict, Lisa and I were up north with the kids visiting a close friend of ours at his cottage. He happened to work in the television business. Very early one morning, while our kids and wives were still asleep, we tiptoed out the back porch and made our way down to the dock for a little bass fishing.

As we drank coffee and watched our red and white bobbers sit motionless in the still waters, we traded stories of what we were both up to in our work lives: *'Hey, you're in TV. Tell me what you think of this idea that Dave and I are working on. Let me know if you think it has any legs.'* As I proceeded to tell my friend (who shall remain unnamed), his eyes and mouth began to widen like a largemouth bass. By the end of my fishtale, he honestly looked as if he'd witnessed me reel in a 10-pounder. (FYI, the Ontario smallmouth bass record is 9.84 pounds.)

'WHAT?' I gasped. *'Um, Bru,'* he began, with his eyes still stretched wide open, *'just last week, I read through a new pilot series for the same network that you just mentioned. The concept and episode details are verbatim*

to what you've just described to me. As far as I know, it's been green-lighted [pause]. Uh ... what is the name of your TV show concept.' With my eyes and mouth now strained wide open, I told him the working name for our show. Slowly nodding his head in agreement, he responded in a very low and slow voice: *'Yep, I believe that was the working name ... but they're working on changing it to something else.'*

After that, we sat quietly for a long moment and both looked out onto the still lake. I'm now thinking: How surreal is this? One night I'm scribbling down an idea for a television show and today I'm fishing off a dock, four hours from the city in the middle of nowhere, being informed that it's been 'green-lighted' without me. I called Dave on my way back up to the cottage: 'Morning, lil' Bro! *Are you sitting down?'*

That Monday, I began to angrily compile all my notes, research and the like, that I had accumulated on the project. I had been super enthusiastic over the prospect of getting our own show, and had made it a point, if not an obsession, to accurately document the ride. Despite the gravity of the situation, Rich was reluctant to press the network on the matter. Unlike Dave and I, he had a valuable reputation and a steady pay cheque to safeguard in TV town. We respected that. Period.

As if the situation wasn't weird enough, a few weeks later, I get a call from my childhood buddy, Jer. *'Hey Bud. Thought you should know that I received a call from the TV show you either are, or aren't, a part of. They asked me to be a judge and sit on the panel to help mentor and evaluate the contestants from a marketer's viewpoint.'* A long and awkward silence ensued. *'Whaa? Did you accept?'* I asked, feeling stupefied, but also pleased for my friend. *'No!'* he asserted. *'I just can't spare the time. Plus, if you're not involved it doesn't feel right.'*

Ok, I thought, this thing is moving beyond TV town and into bizzaro-world. All the while, Dave and I remained conflicted about picking up the phone to call our lawyer. Was it all just a grand coincidence, or did the network unconsciously build off our idea with a more credible and established line-up of players?

Whether or not the actions were above board, however, was extraneous to us. It was our big idea and we wanted, at the very least, some credit. That said, just when we thought it couldn't get any more unnerving, during a lunch with the Rubino brothers, the topic came up. We had asked for their opinion and input on the pitch to the network before Rich had fired it off for evaluation. Guy and Mike were television show veterans with their long running food show, 'Made to Order.' Mike acknowledged: '*We were asked by a producer buddy of ours to be part of a new show on that network. After he explained the concept, we figured that it was the thing that you were working on. I asked him if he was working with you. He wasn't. What happened?*'

By this point in the ordeal, all we could do is snicker and think about how much more interesting the story was becoming for posterity and dinner conversation purposes. By this point, the network had begun their marketing campaign for the new show. With the frequency of promotional ads that they were airing to push the show, it certainly seemed that it was one of the properties the network was banking heavily on for the new season. We ended up calling a lawyer that specialized in the entertainment industry. Upon laying out my chronologized collection of notes, research and the like, it was clear that she was wetting her chops. After the one meeting with the lawyer, however, we agreed to release the 10lb smallmouth bass back into the lake.

Could it have all been just a giant star-crossed coincidence? Maybe. Be that as it may, there were enough fish to fry back at the office so we decided to focus our energy on the positive rather than get sucked into a long-drawn-out, expensive and epic David-and-Goliath battle. It was our miscalculation in deciding not to push harder to be present during the pitch—rookie mistake. Had we scored some face time with the network, I'm confident that our chances of being involved, even remotely, would have been measurably better.

When the show finally aired, I couldn't get myself to watch it. When I finally did, I realized that our original concept had been watered down to a point where the show's vibe felt much more contrived vs. the more relatable and likable entrepreneur attitude we had cooking in the pot. When I came across the first winner's product concept staring back at me in the grocery store, I picked up, bit my lip and then put it back on the shelf.

The very next morning, in the locker room at my gym, a colleague that worked for the grocery chain that supported the winner's new product was addressing someone's question about the TV show. No one in the room knew my history with the show. *'Oh ya, it's a great show.'* Then he said something like: *'The product isn't setting the world on fire, but the show has been a surprising success.'* Unbelievable, I thought to myself, standing there in the buff. I guess it's best to leave the rest up to karma, pull up my socks and move on.

Let it Simmer ~

1. *Keep your big mouth tightly zipped until you are absolutely and positively certain that it's safe to debut your big idea.*
2. *You are the best person to represent yourself, your ideas and your capabilities. You are your own brand. Go to the pitch and don't take no for an answer.*
3. *Protect your ideas and position until they are ripe for harvesting. When in doubt, insist that a non-compete agreement is signed, especially if you're on unfamiliar ground and in the company of unfamiliar players.*
4. *Before you pull the legal-trigger, aside from the financial repercussions, time investment and slim odds of winning, consider how the negative energy may wreak havoc on your ability to perform in other areas of your business.*

CHAPTER 24

Feeding The Beast

Maximizing Rare Opportunities

A riddle for you: What do you get when you combine impeccable timing and nearly flawless product execution with sassafras and vanilla beans in a frosty mug and then top it with a big creamy dollop of luck? Well, in our case, you get one final and fortuitous chance in the booze biz that ends up being the rainmaking difference maker that you were praying for. Despite what you may be thinking, 'feeding the beast' thankfully isn't about how to cook for your ungrateful father-in-law. Nope, it's a story about what it feels like when you've been floating aimlessly at sea for what feels like forever, and then finally catch that mythical *Humunga Kowabunga from Down Unda* wave off guard.

In *Chapter 2: Grocery Math*, I made mention of rare and extraordinary circumstances where the absolute perfect product is unveiled to a ripe and ready marketplace at precisely the right point in time and space. It's a wonderfully magical combination that defies conventional wisdom and strategy. Like a solar eclipse, the spectacle may only last for a brief period of time so being prepared, avoiding the blinding bright lights and knowing how to react becomes the game. This little ditty is also a hefty reminder to keep swinging hard for the fences regardless of how many times you strike out—don't give up after the 20th embarrassing disaster, because your 21st shot could turn out to be your moment in the hot sun.

We had just received an inopportune notice from the LCBO stating that, after four successful holiday selling seasons, our Crazy Uncle®

Blood Orange & Rosemary Maple Punch would not be supported in their 2016 winter program. On top of everything, in spite of a loyal and steadily growing fan base, sales for our Über Caesar cocktail weren't nearly on pace with what we, or the retailers, had expected. Our future in the alcohol business wasn't looking too bubbly.

Meanwhile, back at the ranch, Dave and I had been messing around in the kitchen with a female-focused cocktail concept that we christened 'Spritz-ology' which was, more or less, lightly and naturally flavoured vodka-based seltzer water with spa-inspired flavours such as fresh mint, basil and lime. At the same time, we were also toying around with hard (i.e. alcohol-laced) craft sodas made using natural bitter extracts and stumbled on a pleasantly familiar flavour profile that tasted very much like creamy root beer.

A few months later, while visiting a supply partner in Chicago, we also stumbled upon a hard root beer brand that was catching fire south of the Canadian border. We asked a seemingly too-young store clerk in a nearby liquor store how it was selling. 'Man, we can't keep this stuff in stock, it's totally flying off the self!' was his enthusiastic Bill & Ted's Excellent Adventure sounding reply. Weeks later we inevitably found ourselves sitting in the LCBO's big boardroom pitching the idea of introducing both cocktail concepts under our Crazy Uncle brand mark. After proving to the LCBO, repeatedly, that we were capable of properly and quickly executing on our ideas, the alcohol retail giant quickly developed into a tremendously supportive and proactive partner for us—especially our direct contacts, Lisa Chapman, Jeryca Dillas, Stacce Roth and Alanna Bailey. When it was all said and done, our Crazy Uncle Hard Root Beer: Craft Soda for Grown-ups was green-lighted, but the 'Spritz-ology' spa-inspired cocktail line prospect eventually fizzled out.

For the record, though we didn't end up scoring an approval on the latter concept, it seemed that we were tightly aligned with what the marketplace was looking for. Later that same year, another brand, backed by Arlene Dickinson (of CBC's Dragon's Den) launched a cocktail line concept with pretty much the same flavour inspirations and positioning targeted specifically to women.

In this particular case, however, being granted a chance to bring a hard root beer to market in the summer of 2016 was the luckier of the two choices and a genuine godsend. We put our game-faces on and obsessed over perfecting our product, specifically the flavour profile. As Dave put it plainly in one newspaper interview: *'If we're doing a hard root beer, we want it to be the best root beer out there. We're not just trying to put a product out there in time to ride the trend.'*

At first, we blindly thought that Crazy Uncle would have the category cornered with a first-mover advantage for at least the lion's share of the inaugural selling season. As usual, fat chance. As our launch date loomed, we learned that not only would we not have a first-mover head start, we'd be one of three local Canadian brands launching that summer, along with a handful of other US hard root beer brand entries. Surf's up! Everybody and their uncle (pun intended) into the sudsy water!

No worries though. Rest easy my friends. It turned out that the benefits and fanfare associated with multiple hard root beer product entries generated way, way more noise, outweighing the voice and volume that we would've brought to a table set for one—think Marty McFly in *Back to the Future* when he slowly turns the overdrive knob to 100 on Doc Brown's gigantic guitar amp.

Within our first few weeks of shipping product out to stores, we immediately recognized that the ride would somehow be different than our other crusades. For starters, our opening order case quantity was forecasted to have lasted well over a month or so to comfortably meet the volume demand which was to be driven by a marketing promotion that we invested in with the LCBO—i.e. prominent in-store product placement supported with summer-themed signage, backed by an out-of-store consumer advertising campaign. Without any communication to consumers of our product's debut, and even before the big LCBO promo had begun, store inventory was immediately sucked up by thirsty consumers.

We had launched the second or third week of April, and by the middle of May we had been awarded with a handful unsolicited write-ups in various national and local newspapers. The *Toronto Star* newspaper ran a fun editorial piece on upcoming summer cocktails worth opening your wallet for. Among other product group evaluations, it compared the taste and overall drinking experience of the three Canadian hard root beer brands and declared us the winner. In years past, we had grudgingly thrown our brand's savings account at promising PR agencies in an effort to drum up such activity, and now there we were basking in the limelight for free.

Needless to say, Dave and I weren't prepared for the *Kowabunga wave.* We had been gearing up for the better part of a year, working with our supply partners to order and build, what we had thought, was plenty of stock to pacify the demand for the summer. Lordy lordy, were we ever off our mark. Imagine having only one or two cheese burgers to satisfy a famished Shaggy and Scooby Doo. Our social media platforms started to light up with hard root beer enthusiasts who had either purchased and loved our product, or with folks who just couldn't get their hands on an ice cold can. In retrospect, this was a very fortuitous thing —well, at least at first. The inventory hiccups served to create both concrete store and consumer demand for the product.

The exceedingly nerve-racking and imminent reality, however, was that it took way too much time to receive the required raw materials and packaging orders that we needed in order to stay in the game. What good is a 10-week lead time when the peak summer selling season is only 15 weeks long? To boot, although our contract packer was giving us more than our fair share of production line time, it wasn't nearly enough to manufacture what was actually required to douse the quickly spreading fire. It was our big shot, and probably the biggest one we'd have for a very, very long time. Talk about feeling helpless. Too much drama for hard root beer, you say? Hmm, maybe for most, but try to appreciate that before the hard soda storm, we were nearly five years and countless dollars and hours invested into the brand without a prayer of making the steep climb into the black.

With the pressure and tally of lost sales continuing to mount, we proceeded to work closely with our sales agents across the country to plug the slowly growing holes in our fragile boat. In an effort to pacify hot pockets of sales activity in and around certain urban areas in Toronto, we attempted to re-allocate inventory from a handful of liquor stores that had succeeded in hogging crazy amounts of inventory for themselves. I recall one such store in Ottawa having 1,000 cans on display despite a handful of stores within driving distance having next to zero product. It was late one Friday afternoon, so I asked a sales rep to collect a decent number of cans from the Ottawa store in question and then to redistribute them into a few nearby stores that following Monday.

It was the week leading up to Victoria Day. Pending the weather, this is one of the biggest weekends for alcohol sales in Canada. To my surprise, that following Monday, the store had sold nearly the entire 1,000 cans. Turns out that weekend, before the Victoria Day weekend, we had pushed through 10,000 cans in 400 or so liquor stores. Talk about an impressive early fireworks display. Dave and I were nothing short of stupefied. The weekend following Victoria Day, I was visiting London, Ontario with Lisa and the kids for my son's baseball tournament—Go Vaughan Vikings!

In between the ball games, under the sweltering summer sun, the team would retreat back to the hotel to recharge with their exhausted families in tow. With a rambunctious gaggle of eleven-year-old boys tearing up and down the hallways riding on luggage carts, I decided to quickly and quietly slip out to conduct a few liquor store checks in the area. Lo and behold, each and every store I popped into was completely out of stock. Not a single can anywhere to be found.

By this point in the summer, the grand, and grandly expensive, promotion that we had invested in with the LCBO was just starting. Our Crazy Uncle Hard Root Beer price tags were in fact prominently displayed in the front of each store I visited, but behind each lonely, white $2.95 ticket was a big, deep empty slot. We had invested some serious coin for in-store promotional artillery to make a loud statement, but ended up firing all our rounds straight up into the air, miles away from the target. Of special interest, the store staff in each of the stores immediately knew of the product and made mention of its popularity.

The next morning, after the tournament, Lisa and I decided to visit the beautiful lakeside village of Port Stanley, located on the north shore of Lake Erie, before heading home. We enjoyed a chicken wing and pizza patio lunch with the kids at a fun little beachside bar and grill called GT's On The Beach. *'Hey now!'* I thought to myself, *'This place would be perfect for selling our Crazy Uncle Hard Root Beer float program.'* Hard root beer ice cream floats also happened to be the creative thrust of our marketing and brand awareness program for restaurant accounts. The majority of our competitors made their hard root beers using a malt-base, where ours was fashioned with craft soda—a much more logical vehicle for preparing a proper ice cream float. So much so, that we brought JP's son, Vinny, on board that summer in an effort to forge as many partnerships as possible with willing ice cream, BBQ and burger joints.

I singled out the manager working the floor at GT's and confidently strolled over to him. Immediately, I sensed and could see the expected *'what in the hell does this guy want to sell me'* facial expression. The moment I mentioned hard root beer, however, his demeanour immediately lightened. *'Hard root beer, Eh! Which one do you sell?'* To which I proudly replied: *'Crazy Uncle!'* After a very short pause he smiled and said: 'That's *funny, I just bought your product last week and I actually really liked it. It's too bad that I printed my menus for this summer as I would've included your product. Come see me next year, ok.'* Seeing as it was only a few weeks since we had shipped the first orders out, had literally just begun the awareness campaign, and every nearest liquor store was sold out, the fact that he was already presold on our mission was a strangely foreign, yet emancipating, chance encounter for me.

On a more serendipitous note, one crisp and sunny afternoon, Dave, Vinny and I fought the usual disgusting gridlock traffic from our uptown office into the downtown Toronto core to deliver a pitch to Claudio Aprile (celebrity chef and judge on *MasterChef Canada*) on serving our Crazy Uncle Hard Root Beer float in his critically acclaimed restaurant called *Origin*. Alas, he was caught up elsewhere and was a no-show. What's that? You're having Jamie Oliver no-show déjà vu moment, you say? You and me both.

Leaving *Origin*, on the way back to the parking lot, and feeling somewhat deflated, we end up passing celebrity bartender Kevin Brauch on the sidewalk. You may recognize Kevin from such TV shows as *The Thirsty Traveler* and *Iron Chef America*. *'Hey! Wait up, Kevin!'* Long story short, we handed Kevin the last can in our bag and gave him our best one-minute-sidewalk-pitch (aka elevator pitch). He was extremely gracious, a true gentleman, and seemed very interested in what we were up to. *'Listen boys,'* he professed, and then said something like: *'I don't usually do this, but let's snap a pic right here so that I can post our encounter and your product on my social media feed.'* *'If that don't beat all!'* we laughed to ourselves as he walked away. *'Talk about a great Food TV celeb consolation prize.'*

At any rate, the stories continued to pour in like sweet, frothy root beer. Our Calgary, Alberta agent, Mark Kuspira, was also experiencing the same zealous reaction with our product in his marketplace. Here's a quote from a retail chain in Edmonton that was sourced for a newspaper interview:

> *Our customers cannot get enough of the Crazy Uncle Root Beer! We tell them that it's all natural and made in Canada and the response has been overwhelming! Every time we taste people on it, they get hooked and we literally can't keep it on the shelves. We love root beer, and we love the Crazy Uncle Hard Root Beer!—Ryan Tycholas, BASELINE Wine & Spirit Co.*

Jeryca Dillas, our supportive and reliably upbeat buyer at the LCBO, also provided an official quote for the media:

> *The Crazy Uncle producers pride themselves on their foodie, all-natural approach to beverage alcohol and with one sip of their hard root beer, this is very clear. During Crazy Uncle Hard Root Beer's brief time in market, this product has already made quite a name for itself!*

In accordance with the title of this chapter, 'feeding the beast' speaks to corralling, controlling and pacifying product demand when consumers are behaving like a hungry pack of wolves. In some ways, if you're managing the flow of inventory and order fulfillment properly, it kind of feels like a back and forth choreographed dance between you, the retailer and consumers. Bear with me here. Give them too much product at once and you might step all over their feet and smother 'em. Give them too little too late, and they might lose interest, become annoyed and look for another partner. And just like the magnificent Mikhail Baryshnikov, you'll need to know how to skilfully lead, tempt and playfully flirt with your partner.

In our case, the unpredictable out of stock episodes and teasing stores with hardly enough inventory seemed to help build serious interest, intrigue and genuine cachet for the product. By the way, teasing retailers with 'hardly enough inventory' wasn't all completely by design. It was, in truth, all that we could manage to have produced despite begging our raw material and packaging supply partners for better lead times and our contract packers for more line-time. Nevertheless, and hallelujah, the dance also succeeded in provoking substantial, and very unplanned, pantry-loading among both stores and consumers.

In fear of constant and looming out of stocks, many stores began ordering unprecedented quantities of product to ensure that supply was secured. By way of illustration, some locations built towering, massive 3,500-can displays. Despite selling our cans individually for $2.95 each, as opposed to selling them in the more traditional four or six packs, many consumers stocked up and bought full twenty-four count cases—that's over $70 of hard soda! Despite all the craziness, and of course, our family and friends calling to congratulate us on our big win, Dave and I remained cautiously optimistic and more guarded than usual. After all we had been habitually and badly burned so, so many times before in somewhat hauntingly familiar situations.

We knew all too well that there still could very well be an ugly outcome that had to do with us sitting on a warehouse of deserted, unspoken for inventory. Meanwhile, retailers were imploring us to hurry up and build more product: *'What? Can't you just build more and ship it in next week? Don't you want to take hold of this rare opportunity?'* Our largest account actually told us that if we couldn't ship a truckload a day that they would either put the product on hold, or delist it altogether. With each such fair warning, we accepted, acted and achieved what we needed to. Chris Churchill, our agent in Ontario, called us up one frantic afternoon to recognize our determination and commitment to the mission.

'Thanks boys. Most other companies your size would've turtled up in the face of such chaos.'

Quite honestly, I was on the other end of the phone, sitting in the office parking lot scratching my head and thinking: go figure, it took us nearly twenty years to score a beauty of a hit and now we're in danger of being punished for not being able to make enough product instead of not being able to sell enough. After the first six weeks of sale, we had concluded that despite having shipped a conga-line of transport trucks, we had actually lost more sales volume than we had cashed in on because of an incapacity to produce enough product.

Ironically, we had spent so much energy and money on our Über Caesar cocktail as we knew that it was a far superior product to any other Bloody Caesar offered on the market, yet we couldn't muster up a fraction of the numbers we had projected. Now, with our hard craft soda platform, we had succeeded in casting a much wider consumer-net. As evidence, nearly three times the number of stores decided to carry the hard root beer within the inaugural three weeks, compared to the total number of stores supporting our Caesar after nearly three years of sale. Looking back, it's clear that, where our Caesar may have been slightly too niche, the hard root beer in some way hit that ultra-sweet spot in-between niche and mainstream.

More importantly, when would the soda tap shut off? When would the music end and the dancing stop? Would we only be given another week or two to bust our moves out on the floor, or could the party last the entire summer, or even longer? Would one of the other looming competing hard root beer companies begin to gain the high ground amidst our period of product shortage? We were dealing with a fast moving target. We appreciated the fact that the potential for us to mismanage the opportunity was still very much at large. The competition seemed to be nipping at our heels three times as fast as they usual did. If our out of stocks continued on for too much longer, we'd have royally pissed of everyone eating at our table. A few more slip-ups and we would've spent the entire summer setting the dinner table beautifully for another hard root beer company to sit down and eat our supper.

Understand that it takes a 10-week lead time for printed cans, with big upfront—pay before delivery—money. And when it's not your manufacturing facility and you're producing with a contract packer, it also usually takes a ton of massaging and sweet talkin' to squeeze in more valuable line time. I'll never forget how Dave and I felt that summer in June: each day was a test of our character and mental stamina. We seemed to be trapped in one of those haunting stuck in slow motion nightmares: we saw the promised land, but just couldn't reach it as fast as we wanted to. I felt like a starving hound, chained to a brick wall with a huge bowl of primo chow, unreachable, just inches from my nose. It also takes deep pockets, or more sensibly, clever cash flow management manoeuvres, to string together the finances needed to tango.

On top of everything, one bad move and we'd lose the ability to pay ourselves and our lenders back. Heaven forbid, we'd need an emergency exit plan, should the fun abruptly end. All this to say, regardless of our financial and supply partner resource vulnerabilities, it was high time to grow a pair and just flat out go for it. In spite of the risk of having the proverbial plug pulled before we could successfully convert our investment into saleable finished goods, we dropped the Sicilian hammer and invested in serious, serious raw material ingredients, packaging and in finished goods inventory.

Our sights were now on the bigger, long-term picture. We weren't interested in trying to recuperate the small fortunes we had sunk into our brand. We were more concerned with digging our heels in even further. It was time to go long on our position. We had grown tired of the feast or famine sales pattern that the Crazy Uncle brand had been mocking us with. We needed a more predictable, stable and strong cash flow rhythm to help secure our future in the business. So what did we decide to do next? Well, in response to the risks and pressures, we actually decided to up the ante by betting on a number of new follow-up Crazy Uncle product line extensions.

In other words, instead of leaving the blackjack table, we decided to double down. Despite the constant urge to cash in, and to pay ourselves for the years of investing in the brand, we believed it would pay us back in spades if we continued to invest every penny into the business. I wish I could tell you how this story ends, but we're still smack dab in the middle of the sarsaparilla storm. If all goes well, you should be able to still walk into a liquor store in, and possibly outside of, Canada to buy a can at least a few years after this book hits the shelf. If you can't find it anymore, it's hopefully because the product has naturally run its course and we've used the momentum to *funnel gunnel* (that's Crazy Uncle lingo for 'parlay') the business into another connected opportunity. If you remember only one message from this story, it's to keep dancing, even when the music stops, the lights turn off and they launch you out the back alley door.

Let it Simmer ~

1. *Are you feeding the beast properly, or do the wolves have you cornered?*
2. *Can you leverage your temporary inability to supply enough product to help create more demand, interest, intrigue and cachet with retailers and consumers?*
3. *Have you planned for a possible high volume success scenario with your supply partners that takes their lead times, payment terms and other order requirements in account? i.e. consider asking for a floor stock agreement (for more info, see* Chapter 25: Only Salmon Swim Upstream).
4. *How can you parlay the awareness and momentum of a successful product launch into another connected opportunity before the music stops?*
5. *When the rainmaking difference maker that you've been praying for finally arrives, will you turtle up or go all ninja turtle on it? Will you fold and cash out or will you try to maximize the opportunity and go long to build a deeper foundation to allow for future growth?*
6. *Keep swinging hard for the fences regardless of how many times you strike out.*

CHAPTER 25

Only Salmon Swim Upstream

Choosing Supply Partners

Whenever I sit down with an aspiring entrepreneur, I can be certain that one burning question will be about where they can go to transform their homemade prototype sample into a proper commercialized product fit for retail. Securing supply partners (i.e. a contract packer and suppliers of raw material ingredients and packaging) is a critical stage that should not be hurried. Mind you, most of the time, it'll take you next to forever to find the right one so rushing isn't always an available option.

For new start-up companies without experience or industry credibility, think back to *Chapter 4: Breaking Bread*: Do your negotiations feel forced or is there a comfortable and natural spark between you and your prospect? When you ask for something basic do they make it seem like you're asking for the world, or for something that's within their wheelhouse? The easy things should come easy when choosing a supply partner: Can they reproduce your food invention relatively effortlessly or will they have to risk investing capital in special equipment or new manufacturing processes and more people or exotic ingredients? If they can produce it, do they really want to, or is your volume or margin, or both, viewed as too insignificant to fire up their machines? If they can and will run product for you, will it come at an unnecessary cost premium and with back of the bus status when it comes to scheduling pressing and important production runs?

Whenever we've had to push unnecessarily hard for a supply partner to accept our business, it eventually ends poorly (and expensively). Experience has taught us that, when basic negotiations feel unnatural or drag on for much too long, we should pack up camp and hunt elsewhere. The good news is that, if you search hard enough, there always seems to be another company out there who is more than willing to go to bat and run your modest start-up requirement with a handshake and a smile. Don't force it, your gut will tell you when you've found your match; so don't get overly excited and climb into bed with your first date—there are plenty of good fish (contract packers) in the (supply partner) sea.

When convincing a supply partner to accept your business becomes trickier, more time consuming and more stressful than selling to a chain store buyer, think about moving your business elsewhere. Typically, larger contract packers will command larger minimum production runs compared with smaller run size requirements from smaller to mid-size contract packers—e.g. approx. 750 to 1,000 cases of product versus a more eatable 200 to 400 cases, respectively. It is for this reason, despite sometimes having to pay a premium price, that building your business with a smaller to mid-size contract packer is advisable in the early going. If the economics of your business can work despite paying a premium, the chances of choking on too much idle inventory decreases, plus you'll pocket the extra margin down the road when your volume starts to build.

There are, of course, trade-offs in trusting your baby with a smaller operator. Firstly, smaller companies often operate super-lean, stretching themselves and their staff too thin. As such, the completeness and value of their responses during your courtship may not always be as structured and accommodating or as clear as that of a more staffed and organized company. However, having a bit more patience is worth the initial aggravation if your gut tells you that you've found your match.

Secondly, a smaller supply partner may not hold all the current Good Manufacturing Practice certifications (GMPs) that Canadian and US retail chains have come not only to appreciate, but to cogently demand. GMPs guarantee that the integrity of food manufacturing processes, and the traceability of ingredients and materials, complies with a strict global food safety regulation and standard. Google GS1, *HACCP, ISO 22000, ISO 9001, SQF or Kosher Certification* and you'll get a sense of how extraordinarily deep and comprehensive these certifications run. To be clear, I'm not suggesting that you hire a supply partner that works out of their garage. The company must possess the fundamental GMP practices at a level that promises both you and the retailer a product that meets or exceeds the industry standards.

If they don't hold any official GMPs, do they have a plan and timeline in place to secure one? Ask them if they have any certifications and you'll quickly see if they skirt the topic or begin to brag about their hard-earned achievements. If you're dealing with proteins (e.g. beef, pork, chicken, etc.), the plant will need to be federally licensed, registered and inspected by the Canadian Food Inspection Agency (CFIA) in Canada, or the U.S. Department of Agriculture (USDA) in the US, in order for you to sell your products to most grocery store chains. There are quite a few non-federally registered meat processing contract packers with adequate production capabilities, but they primarily exist as suppliers to either the restaurant sector or sell to the public directly.

It's been my experience that smaller to mid-size contract packers are also usually run by spirited and colourful entrepreneurs willing to engage with you directly. Larger companies will have you work with an area sales rep, most often without the authority or jurisdiction to make a call without putting your request through their company's elaborate hierarchical systems. If you can make a solid connection directly with the owner, your initial journey will usually be smoother and much more agreeable—at the very least, you'll instantly know where you stand. However, you're bound to encounter a few less accommodating, blunt and brash characters along the way.

In the end, you do have to sell your contract packer, and your supply partners on the whole, on your business plan, and of course, yourself. As I've said before, you are your own brand so you'll need to collect and carry as much goodwill as possible from one project to the next. At some point, you can bet each contract packer has been badly burned by an overly ambitious entrepreneur overpromising and radically under delivering on a forecast estimate and on their knowledge of the industry.

Years ago, I was working with a popular Chef from Hawaii. He wanted to make his unique honey pomegranate vinaigrette available to grocery retailers in the US and Canada. He made the long and costly voyage all the way from sunny Maui to visit us in Toronto on a cold December day to meet the owner of the dressing contract packer that we had sourced. As the Chef took everyone through his background credentials, recipe concept and our grocery goals, I couldn't help but notice that the manufacturing company's owner seemed displeased and irritated.

'Let me ask you this before we continue,' he said, stopping the Chef in mid-sentence. 'Are you doing this to pacify your ego? Producing thousands of bottles and then endeavouring to sell them to grocery stores isn't all fun and games. It's a very tough go, you know. And, quite frankly, I'm tired of superstar chefs assuring me that their loyal fans will run down the salad dressing aisle to buy their product. I've lost way too much money and time going down this road!'

Yikes, let's get the hell out of here, I remember thinking to myself. It's important to clearly show your supply partner that you're not green behind the ears. Bring a notepad filled with well thought out questions to create an air of credibility and comfort in the room. Here are a few questions we might have considered asking during our uncomfortable honey pomegranate vinaigrette meeting:

1. What is your typical minimum batch size and approximately how many cases is it equivalent to if expressed in the standard 250ml x 12 bottles per case? *To which he would have answered 1,600 liters per minimum run giving you approximately 500 cases. It's up to you to know how digestible this number is—can you comfortably sell 500 cases at full price well within the product's optimal shelf life? If you're charged for the full amount of cases up front, can you finance the inventory until it sells?*

2. Do you have a minimum annual case commitment? *In this case, the contract packer requested an annual volume commitment of 2,000 cases per year (one run per quarter) to ensure we weren't wasting their time; although annual commitments are much more negotiable and avoidable than minimum run sizes.*

3. Do you provide the glass bottles or do we have to source and supply them? If so, do you stock any bottle profiles that we could choose from to make it easier on us both? *They'll appreciate this approach, as bringing in custom glass means they'll have to inventory and monitor its supply—and nobody likes adding in more cost and work than is normally required. To boot, you'll have to contend with the glass bottle supplier and their outrageous minimum orders, lead times and unpredictable supply hiccups—try dealing with an Italian glass supplier during Italy's month long holiday in August, 'Ferragosto'—that being said, sometimes, a standard stock bottle just doesn't cut the mustard.*

4. What are your standard delivery lead times and will it help if we provide a preliminary monthly forecast build? *By offering this info you're indirectly telling the contract packer that you understand that they have processes in place, and a host of quickly moving parts that you'll never appreciate. Most importantly, it tells them that you hopefully won't be nagging them to pick up your order every couple of days. As frightening as it seems to expose yourself with a forecast, you won't be crucified if your numbers change ... because they always change with a new business. Forecasts are best built using relevant historical data.*

5. Can we structure our arrangement so that we buy and manage the packaging requirements instead of you buying, storing and building the cost into our price? *There's a lot to consider with this option. You don't want mortgage-sized packaging invoices coming back to haunt you if your product collects dust on the shelf. Be prepared and have an exit strategy. Conventional wisdom suggests that handing over your packaging design art files to the contract packer is easier and seemingly cheaper—i.e. they have your boxes, cartons and film, etc. printed on their account and only charge you for what's used in the production, or better still, the draw of your finished goods. But (and it's a big but), consider that they'll likely over order to get a price break and will possibly add a couple of cents per impression to what their printer has charged them. Also consider that if your product bombs, you'll be quarrelling over the invoice they mail you for the pallets of wasted packaging sitting on their (always seemingly jam-packed) warehouse floor. Incidentally, this is why you'll want to*

*have a decent co-pack agreement drawn up and signed that protects you
from packaging liabilities beyond a reasonable amount—e.g. if your
contract packer is purchasing and providing the packaging, agree to
pay for up to no more than six months of packaging equivalent to the
previous six months of sale. Take it from someone that's battled over
an invoice for over two million futile cartons of microwave popcorn
which, at the time, represented seven years of sales. Be conservative,
e.g. a decent minimum bottle label run is 20,000 to 25,000 labels—
which represents one full year's 2,000 case commitment noted above.*

Here are some additional questions and considerations when sourcing
and negotiating with a supply partner:

1. Do they have the in-house capability to accurately commercialize
   your kitchen recipe by translating it for mass production and
   ensuring shelf-stability? Or, will you need to also source a third party
   to assist with the recipe translation? Note: If the contract packer
   can provide you with this service it is usually free of charge as long
   as your agreement terms have been negotiated and are in place.
2. Can the contract packer provide you with the mandatory
   packaging declaration (i.e. ingredient panel, Nutrition Facts Table,
   allergen statements and the optional on-pack claims (no/low/
   reduced fat and calorie claims, gluten-free, No MSG added, etc.)?
   Visit inspection.gc.ca for industry guidelines and requirements. If
   you require a third party to conduct food science and safety tests
   on your recipe to determine its ingredient itemization, allergen
   exposure, nutritional analytics and shelf-stability visit Maxxam
   (maxxam.ca). It's money well spent.
3. Once your contract packer nails the commercialized recipe target,
   request that a detailed product spec sheet be created, mutually
   agreed upon and frequently referenced. This will help the quality
   from eventually dropping, your taste profile from changing, etc. It
   not only gives the operator a bull's-eye to hit each time they fire
   up the machine, it gives you a measurement instrument to wave if
   consistency drops; some slight variance in size, flavour and

appearance is to be expected—however, in many cases, a variance could wreak havoc on your brand with consumers. Remember to ask me about both over-salted and under-salted microwave popcorn, or about not enough fat in our Mr. Greek pork souvlaki.

4. What is your supply partner's declared wastage or permissible scrap factor? What are their compensation terms in the event it's exceeded? The amount can vary depending on the type of product or service provided. Certain printed film substrate or label suppliers will run up to 10 percent over or under (although, it's usually over) your order request and it's considered to be fair game in the industry—anything over 10 percent should at least be questioned. A contract packer will discard a certain amount of packaging and ingredients during the set-up of their machines—usually plus or minus 3 percent. Make it clear that you want to be compensated for any wastage above the declared and agreed to levels; at the very least, it'll keep the machine operator more honest as they'll know you're counting the pennies.

5. Does your contract packer have a manual inventory system or do they use a software tracking system? *'Mind your own business,'* keep a watchful eye on the packaging and raw materials that you buy directly and have your supply partner warehouse for you. Misplaced or miscounted boxes and bags of inventory add up in cost and will throw your ordering requirements off. Request a monthly report of any and all components that you've purchased and are recorded in your books.

6. Will the contract packer warehouse your packaging and unique raw materials in their warehouse or at third party warehouse? If it's at a third party warehouse, ask to see the rate card so that you understand the 'pallet in, pallet out and monthly storage charges'. Can you have them stored for less? They can add up and throw your cost of goods off by a significant margin. Having things stored in the supply partner's warehouse is best from a control, cost and visibility standpoint. However, smaller operators don't always have the space, especially for larger and more cumbersome items—storing flat cartons is less onerous than storing one litre glass bottles.

7. How often do you require a production forecast? Be honest with your numbers and just stretch the truth slightly, or be prepared to encounter issues down the road.

8. Once sales become more frequent and consistent, can you put a floor stock agreement in place to ensure both an uninterrupted supply and a shorter lead-time? Asking your supply partner to keep a minimum and maximum number of finished good cases on their floor, and on their dollar, can help to ensure that out-of-stocks are minimized. For example, you may decide that you only need floor stock of your bestselling skus; ask your contract packer to keep 250 cases minimum and up to 500 maximum cases at all times. It should go without saying that if your sales movement isn't predictable, don't risk putting a floor stock agreement in place as you'll eventually get the invoice and have to find an exit strategy for unused inventory.

9. What are your standard terms of payment? Can you stretch your supply partners out from their standard 30-day payment terms in order to be more creative with managing your cash flow—i.e. try to receive payment from your distributor, or in some cases, the retailer, before paying your supply partners? Albeit, many retailers will always take your cash discount terms off their payment despite making the payment weeks past the required date, so don't rely exclusively on them for creative cash flow strategies. Naturally, if you do have the cash sitting in your bank account, be sure to take advantage of cash payment terms to help improve your profit margins.

10. Are you certain that you've built in enough margin to feed from? Try to find out the gross margin percent range (**formula: sell price—cost of goods / sell price**) that the retailer and distributors command—i.e. for retailers, a decent dry-grocery product gross margin is 35%; for a produce or deli item it can climb closer to 50% because of high spoilage. A turnkey distributor that will buy, store and sell your product might ask for 15% to 30% depending on the channel(s) of service. Don't fool yourself by massaging the numbers to work in your favour. Will you be left with enough

margin per case to fund the mission, and to eventually put some money in your pocket? Is your contract packer located out of the country, or do they import certain components or key ingredients? Padding your sell price to cushion the margin blow from foreign currency exposure, and increases traced to commodities, freight or labour is also key.

There's a sweet spot when it comes to creating a truly innovative food product that has volume potential and then finding the right supply partner(s) to launch it with. It's about finding a meaningful, and hopefully breakthrough, point of difference from your competition—and then about motivating, and most often pushing, a supply partner outside their comfort zone to help you get there. In many cases, if you're not challenging your supply partner, chances are that you're perhaps comfortable with being only slightly unique on the shelf—i.e. the thrust of your point of difference is a new flavour or packaging design.

When Dave and I worked with a contract packer to commercialize our *Crazy Uncle*® culinary cocktail line, getting our bottler to agree to use real clover honey instead of high fructose corn syrup wasn't easy. It's an expensive ingredient to carry, challenging to work with and significantly slowed down production target throughputs. Despite the whining, we pushed hard to roll with pure pain in the ass honey because it met with our ultimate product vision, but only did so because we sensed it was more of an initial and palatable irritation than a longer term, and perhaps eventual, deal breaker. We were willing to pay for the honey because we had built the added cost into our pricing model and felt we could get the retail premium for it. Our vision for the brand was National, if not International, so a high fructose compromise wasn't in the cards.

We've also pushed too hard at times. When we found a supply partner to produce Mr. Greek's Moussaka exclusively for A&P / Dominion (a much smaller and limited time opportunity), we hastily gambled on having the contract packer invest in a minimum supply of fire-roasted eggplant cubes to ensure the recipe's authenticity. The contract packer had every other ingredient that we needed to produce the item; their ingredient assembly and cooking systems yielded a perfect retail product

—we just needed the eggplant. Two months after the launch and it was clear that consumers didn't take to the Moussaka as we had hoped. Six months later and we were still battling over the contract packer's seventeen-thousand-dollar tab of unused fire-roasted eggplant cubes, and dealing with the retailer's fierce deductions and mark-down invoices. We had pushed too far based on the contract packer's comfort zone and the scope of the opportunity.

When your product does take off, making certain that you have an uninterrupted supply becomes both increasingly critical and more complicated. Inevitably, Murphy's Law always seems to kick in when sales finally start flowing and you gain some consistent traction. Consumers start to repeat their purchases, retailers finally start to believe and support you ... and then boom, supply issues quickly become your central focus and you find yourself eating a thread of spaghetti from both ends. When our Kernels Popcorn Shakers started to sell at Blockbuster Video and Wal-Mart back in 2000, I spent at least three quarters of my day, and 110% of my energy, solving supply issues and assuring buyers their shelves wouldn't stay empty for too long.

How quickly will you outgrow your supply partner? Our first co-packer, *Loretta Foods*, was great for the first year or so. Our volumes were manageable and our lead times less than demanding. As our volume grew, they began to drop the ball frequently, leaving us without enough inventory as their filling-machines weren't fast enough to both satisfy our needs and also keep their own products in stock. Our next co-packer, *Newly Weds Foods*, had superior equipment, systems and capacity but we still kept getting bumped off the production schedule for better and more lucrative customers.

By this point, we had listings with most of the larger Canadian grocers so finding the right supply partner solution became paramount to our survival. This time around, we teamed up with a company called WG Pro Manufacturing who actually acquired a state of the art filling line just for our business; the thing was a veritable beast, filled an entire warehouse bay and cost them handsomely. After about a year, the pressure for us to meet and beat our forecast promises became too challenging as WG depended on our volume to make the economics of their equipment investment work. Despite being content with our growth rate and performance, our supply partner was choking on their equipment lease payments. It turns out they invested in a Ferrari when all we both needed was an entry model Honda.

After having painfully survived three failed supply partner attempts—and feeling a little like *Goldilocks* cycling through her *'much too small, much too large'* options—we found a co-packer with the help of our trusted co-packer source extraordinaire, Mr. Glen Millichamp (or as we affectionately call him, *Glenzo* ... which kind of sounds like Gonzo, my favourite Muppet). Run by the über trustworthy and industrious Ravi Thambiah, *CPI* bought the Honda and we've been doing business together ever since. Remember, you should be focusing more on creating sales and demand for your food product, not spinning out on supply challenges. As the saying goes in our office: *'Bring in the sale and the back of the house will eventually figure out how to ship it.'*

Let it Simmer ~

1. *Have you found the right supply partner match or is it time to grab the cheque and move on to the next courtship?*
2. *Have you made an effort to engage with the owner, or are you stuck in an email and voicemail match with a useless regional sales rep?*
3. *Are your simple requests being met with quick and simple answers or are you left scratching your head?*
4. *Is the sales volume opportunity size worth the clean-up risk?*
5. *Do you have a realistic exit plan if you can't move the inventory? Can you survive the financial hit if you can't move it?*
6. *Are the supply partner's minimum runs digestible? How long will depleting the inventory take based on your opportunity size and conservative volume build expectations?*
7. *Can you make enough money to keep your head above water if you decide to pay a higher cost premium to support a lower volume commitment? Do you know what the retailer's and distributor's gross margin targets are?*

8. *Does the contract packer have the necessary Good Manufacturing Practices (GMPs) in place? If not, are they at least working towards securing them?*

9. *Are you challenging and pushing the supply partners out of their manageable comfort zone to achieve a worthwhile and innovative point of difference?*

CHAPTER 26

Planting Seeds

Establishing brokers & Distributors

Debuting your newly minted masterpiece to the world can be quite the bewildering and emotional experience. It can take many months, if not years, of working in near solitude to get your invention and operating blueprint ready for business. So when it's time to emerge from the cave to share your accomplishments with the world, make sure that you fully understand and properly leverage the right sales approach and solution. With that said, the absolute best preparatory solution, hands down, is not to rely on anyone but yourself when it comes to venturing out to secure the first purchase order. You can arm the best sales person with all the fancy selling tools, slick samples and brand swag you can muster up, but it's only you, and your explosive passion, that will prevent buyers from brusquely deciding to shut their notebook long before the pitch has ended.

You are your own brand. Send in someone else to do your work and, despite their self-proclaimed exceptional relationship with the buyer, they'll ring you up from the chain store's head office parking lot after the meeting to solemnly declare that *sorry, it was a NO this time.* When it's you that's enthusiastically sitting on the other side of the negotiation table, the story always seems to advance and unfold beyond the definitive and ugly little word *'NO'*. Maybe it'll be because of your uncanny knack to paint the opportunity in a certain attractive bright light, or an ability to deflect the buyer's bullets of doubt from your chest, but I bet you hear the word *'NO'* far less than anyone else would.

And, heaven forbid that you do receive a flying 'NO' straight to the forehead. At least you know that no means no and it's not because your sales representative was more focused on selling someone else's merchandise loaded in his briefcase that morning. Listen up. Tomorrow morning, have a sip of good freshly ground coffee, take deep breath and then ride the bullet—pick up the phone and call the retailer yourself.

Once you've personally laid some decent track and have made concrete progress to share, enlisting a sales broker or a distributor will help you travel faster and further. A sales broker will be either a self-employed one-person operation, or it can be a much larger firm housing multiple sales account managers, each one overseeing either a specific set of retailers or a particular product category. A broker will only request 5% of the net sales that they rustle in for you; however, the order fulfillment requirements and costs remain with you. In which case you may also need to eventually appoint an outside warehousing company to store and ship out your goods (i.e. when your contract packer is unable or unwilling to store and stage orders out of their facility).

Plan on spending $5 to $6 per each pallet that you ship into the warehouse (in-charge), a monthly storage fee of in and around $7 per pallet, and another $5 to $6 for shipping full pallets back out, or a 25 cent per case picking fee on less than full pallet orders (out-charge). Depending on the channel(s) of sale, for 15% and up to a 30% gross margin return on your goods, a distributor will buy, warehouse and facilitate the order fulfillment. In addition to representing you and your product to the retailer, they'll also handle the multitude of individual store level sales, and via a tactical sales team, provide valuable merchandising and account maintenance services.

To be clear, contracting sales support without having first made progress on your own is actually more common. It's just my opinion that the probability of the sales company agreeing to accept your food fight, and their interest in your game, will dramatically increase if you've proven its worth. More importantly, it also helps to balance the tables and places you in a healthier negotiation position. Beware, if this is your first rodeo and you haven't any credibility, goodwill or accomplishments sitting in a store to point to, a sales company may prod you for a monthly retainer. More explicitly, they may mandate from $1,000 up to $2,500 per month for pioneering the mission up until the first billable sale comes rolling in.

By choosing to lay down a sales foundation before approaching a third party sales solution you'll cut down the requisite retainer, and if you're a decent negotiator, you might even be successful in reducing their fee against the portion of the business that you've secured and handed over. For example, ninety-five percent of the time, a sales broker in the food industry will want 5% of your invoiced sales to the retailer for their services rendered. However, if you've closed the sale yourself and have already begun to fulfill orders, one of the most challenging and time-consuming phases has already been accomplished. So in this case, you may want to offer 3% or 4%, for a specific mutually agreed to time period, and with an opportunity for the sales party to earn the full 5% based on a mutually agreed to sales growth target.

After you've appointed a sales company to help with your food fight, it's paramount to ride shotgun to every inaugural sales presentation to a key retailer account. Not only will the probability of emerging from the pitch meeting victorious increase, your sales person will witness what and how to communicate directly from watching you in action. Your presence will ensure that they know what you expect from them when you're not tagging along for the next call. It should go without saying, but it'll also aid in building a solid rapport with each sales representative responsible for the future of your company.

Before you throw down your John Hancock on a formal sales broker or distributor contract, which by the way, should be mutually cancellable in no more than 90 days, be sure that you're teaming up with a partner that's right for you personally. Going back once again to *Chapter 4: Breaking Bread*, are you getting the right vibe from the guy or does something seem uncomfortably alien? Are you fooling yourself by thinking that the awkwardness will eventually wane the closer you work and grow with the person? Do you wince when their call comes through or jump with enthusiasm to pick up the phone?

By the way, hiding behind your email is never a prudent option. The quest for space on the shelf will take time and the patience of Job, so you'll want to be über comfortable and click with whoever joins you on your culinary crusade. It has been my personal experience that there will be a heavy-duty direct correlation between the strength and ease of a relationship with a sales person and the level of effort, ultimately leading to success, that they place in selling you and your products.

Despite what you believe your sales potential is, not all product concepts are greeted with open arms and optimism by sales folk, and especially, by buyers. Where hiring someone with plenty of knowledge and skill in your product's category is perhaps more obvious, finding someone with a genuine desire to sell your product sometimes takes a backseat with respect to decision criteria. Finding someone qualified who fully wants to sell your product, however, is fortunately a key variable that you can have a hand in nurturing. The more that I can easily and freely relate with a sales person, the deeper our relationship will eventually become and, as a result, the stronger that sales person's sincere desire to see you win will be.

Looking back over the past nearly twenty years, it's extremely clear that the sales people who have contributed the most to our bottom line are also the ones that I worked to connect with the most on both a personal and professional level. They are the individuals that I enjoyed sitting down to a big glass of juicy red with, long before they dutifully faxed or emailed in their first big fat purchase order—I'm looking at you Ursini, Ciambrelli, Glusak and Lock. I knew about their families and ambitions as they knew all about mine, and I'm more than convinced that it counted when they were up to bat for me and our company.

I'm not proposing that it takes a certain degree of wining, dining and greasing to motivate someone to perform. I'm saying that investing in talented sales people you also happen to enjoy spending time with will help you to reach the finish line in a much more effective and gratifying fashion. I realize that conveniently being matched and attuned with your entire sales force is impracticable, but do make sure that there are a handful of prospective compadres in the mix who also happen to represent your largest prospective buyers.

Once you have managed to consummate a representation contract, keeping your newly adopted sales squad engaged and focused will become a weekly dance between you and them. Brokers in the food business are notorious for always wanting to sell a modified version of your product that you don't offer: if you make it with Dutch chocolate, they'll ask for French vanilla in order to secure that elusive big order. It's your duty to recognize when facilitating such requests can actually help to close a deal, and when it'll just end up wasting your time and money. But be careful, keeping a sales broker or distributor adequately interested and engaged is also critical so you'll want to bend as much as you can comfortably handle so that they don't lose interest.

Pushing hard while knowing when to step back is a balancing act that you'll learn to master over time—and no doubt, after making a few awkward mistakes. That said, the squeaky wheel gets the grease so don't expect to sit back and wait for an e-order to pop up in your starving inbox. When your sales broker or distributor does eventually forward you a buyer's offer for your review, brace yourself because they may start the negotiations by asking you for the world plus your first born. Your sales person may also be skittish and eager for you to accept the deal because they've been working for you without pay for way longer than you both had predicted.

Either way, remember that it's your business and your lint-filled pockets so do what you can to earn a space on the grocery shelf without compromising your company's wellbeing. For a start-up food enterprise, I can tell you that it's exceptionally atypical to make a return on your investment within the first eighteen to twenty-four months. It took nearly two years to make our investment back on our first few product launches. Between product development related expenses, ongoing packaging and raw material costs, listing fees, inside programs, unpredictable deductions, markdowns and freight charges, don't be startled when you're chasing your break-even target down the deli aisle.

So, where do you start searching for your army of mighty food fight warriors? It can be as simple as probing online or at one of the many industry food shows (see *Chapter 29: Poking The Yolk* for show resources) for food brokers or food distributors that are aligned with your mission. Aside from larger brokerage firms, such as well-known Acosta (acosta.ca), that cover key retail accounts from coast to coast, most smaller broker outfits operate regionally. And whereas the US marketplace can be more fragmented with respect to distributor coverage, there are a handful of very capable Canadian distributors that can represent your product on a National front—assuming that they are interested and don't carry any competitive products.

Aside from my brothers at Johnvince Foods (johnvince.com), we often use UNFl (unfi.ca) and Tree of Life Canada (treeoflife.ca) to get to market. Both these distributors also have their head office in the US, making it easier for you to travel south of the border once you have your game figured out in Canada—and take my word for it, it's better to play, win and learn the game in your own backyard before paying a visit to our American neighbours. Yes, it's a much greater and more attractive arena, but the rules of engagement are different and the consequences following failure are tougher to survive.

If your distributor does not have enough capable feet on the street to ensure that your product is both sitting in the right store location and is selling to the retailer's expectations, you'll need to consider augmenting your sales plan with a third party merchandising team. At around $20 to $30 per half hour store visit, it can get expensive quickly, but in most cases the increase in sales as a result of a properly merchandised product will help to offset a majority of the expenditure. Brand-Momentum is one of our preferred merchandising partners in this field (brandmomentum.ca).

There are also more creative means to hunt for a sales solution outside of the more traditional broker, distributor and merchandiser routes. Scan the grocery store for an established product line that can complement both your crusade and theirs. For example, a company introducing a new bruschetta seasoning might consider striking an agreement with a nationally distributed tomato company for the sale, distribution and joint-placement of their product in the produce section; or, a company launching a fish marinade might approach a fresh seafood company, and so on. In these two examples, the products also benefit from being creatively co-merchandised in a location with a higher impulse purchase intent instead of flying solo and ending up lost on the shelf in their respective overcrowded categories.

In any case, once you have your funky little food product in hand, working like mad to get an order should become your prime fixation. All too often I notice start-up businesses spending an inordinate amount of money and time on building and polishing their websites, company brochures and logo wear all at the expense of focusing on that first life-altering order. Remember, it's a waste of time to stay home heating the skillet before you're able to bring home the bacon.

Let it Simmer ~

1. *Have you tried to present your product directly to the retailer or have you been anxiously sitting back for months waiting for someone else to bring you good news?*
2. *If you have heard the word 'NO' from a retailer, has it been from your sale person's mouth or directly from the buyer?*
3. *Do you need to appoint a sales broker or a full service distributor?*
4. *Does the personal connection with your broker or distributor feel natural and productive or unnatural and strained? Does the potential exist to build a strong and long-term relationship?*
5. *Will your broker or distributor let you ride shotgun to retailer presentations so that you can help set the tone and your expectations?*
6. *In the early going, for each hour that you spend on tasks that aren't connected to securing an order, spend three hours on trying to sell your product.*

CHAPTER 27

Feeding Your Kids

Step Up, or Step Off

This next riff may come off as sounding self-indulgent—but, it may be my one and only genuine chance to tell it like it is to both those who have approached us with a *'million-dollar idea'* expecting to reap a handsome reward without investing their meaningful time and/or money; and to future partners that may play an important, albeit supporting cast role, in our production who also expect serious remuneration. Listen up, damn it! Bringing an unbelievable idea or contribution to the table and then stepping back to let others make the deadly and expensive climb [sometimes] deserves nothing more than a sincere thank you and maybe a $100 iTunes gift card. Relatedly, asking to be part of a company and to share heavily in its profits in exchange for a short-lived cameo appearance is as bizarre as getting to have a few nights of remarkable sex, getting pregnant and then handing the child off to someone else to raise.

Quickie sex is the fun and exhilarating part. Raising the child and devoting your life to its healthy upbringing and its protection is nothing short of colossally life altering—I know, I have three kids. The sleepless nights, the complete devotion, the emotional and financial investment, these are all part of the journey. I get to pay for 4 years of University education and you casually show up uninvited at their graduation to share in the credit and enjoy a piece of chocolate cake? In the words of my all-time favourite comedian, John Candy, in the classic 1985 movie *Summer Rental*, as he's smashing his crutch against the refrigerator door in pure rage after coming home to find an uninvited party of beach patrons abusing his summer home (44:28): '*Get out! Party's over! Get OUT, Get OUT, GET OUT OF MY HOUSE!!*'

I had the idea for this chapter long before I wrote it. What stirred me to start writing it was a bizarre phone call. Over fifteen years before I received this demented and irritating call, a chap by the name of Arnold initiated and facilitated the inaugural meeting between one of our more popular licensed brand partners and my partner JP at Johnvince Foods. The outcome of the meeting eventually gave rise to launching one of our most celebrated product introductions. To my knowledge, Arnold's contribution concluded after making the introductions and perhaps championing the initial follow-up period. Years later I inadvertently discovered that, for his participation, our fabulous (and generous) brand partners rewarded Arnold with a most healthy chunk of the brand license proceeds that they received from BrandFusion—considerably more than one might expect is fair for the introductions and the duties performed.

Fast forward to 2015: "*Hi Arnold, how have you been, we haven't spoken in over ten years—what's up?*" I asked. After dispensing with the pleasantries, he replies with something like: '*I'd like to pass by your office to chat about some new opportunities ... and about the product line sold under the brand I introduced you to.*' I immediately felt something awkward and curious lurking in the air. '*What about it? I'd like to understand what you're thinking about with this one right now,*' I said.

It turned out that he felt he was owed more money and was hoping that BrandFusion would consider, despite never having discussed the arrangement with us, paying him something over a decade after we had taken the reins. '*It wouldn't be that much, really,*' he promised. I felt the fucking hair on the back of my neck stand up as my temperature rose to a '*snapping*' level. Am I dreaming or is this guy actually calling me out of the blue fifteen years after our business was built asking for a goodhearted handout of our hard-earned money? Maybe I should swing by the walk-up window fast food resto at Blue Mountain, or ring up the *TV network* that borrowed our food show idea to ask for some lunch money. Um ... '*Get out! Party's over! Get OUT, Get OUT, GET OUT OF MY HOUSE!!*'

Setting your party's role and expectations early on in the game, and then working to hold them in check throughout your mission will greatly help to keep unnecessary external pressures and distractions at bay. Proceed with extreme restraint when providing an important player in your game (e.g. brand owners, new business partners, supply partners, brokers, the bank) an estimate (e.g. revenue, profits, case volumes). Learn to skilfully squeeze out their expectations early on in the game to make sure you're on the same page, and then get it in writing. Newcomers will always lock into the first number you slide across the table—even if they don't admit it, they'll measure success by your initial guesstimate. Don't blurt out an aggressive number unless you're willing to repeatedly waste time and patience to defend yourself down the road. It's tempting to embellish the story to keep the group interested and engaged, but if you must provide a number, think about a super conservative outcome and then divide it in half!

When Dave and I sat down with Crazy Uncle's first recipe contributing master mixologist (Frankie Solarik) and the agency that represents him, we were new to the alcohol business. At some point in the conversation, after understandably being probed for volume estimates a few times, we carelessly mentioned that sales could be upwards of 20,000 cases in the first year. It was the only number offered during our lengthy conversation which was meant to be centred more around how connecting with our project would serve to build both our brand and his own; not to say that financial reward wasn't part of the offer's allure, but we were open and honest about the chances of failure and the less than desirable volumes.

By the time we put Crazy Uncle® on the map, well over a year had passed. We had spent the better part of each week, invested well over six figures, and overcame many setbacks getting there. Based on how the opportunity ended up coming together (i.e. our first sku was positioned as a one-time seasonal buy, sold in stores over a 10-week period), we sold less than 2,000 cases into the LCBO—less than 10% of what we had told the guys in our inaugural meeting. Despite the lacklustre sales, we were content with our accomplishment given that the odds were stacked heavily against us. We had successfully broken into the difficult alcohol market, had achieved nearly a 100% sell through at retail of the inventory we sold in and, via a fruitful PR campaign, had begun to develop a devoted and growing fan base.

It takes time and a load of patience to properly raise a child, and for the first year of its life, our precious little boy had grown into a crawling toddler trying to find its way out of the crib. Nonetheless, our relationship and the good vibes with Frankie's agency became mutually awkward at best. While we celebrated our accomplishment and readied ourselves, both mentally and financially, to navigate the next section of the steep climb, Frankie's camp seemed faintly deflated and disillusioned with the mission. Aside from providing the, albeit beautifully brilliant, recipes and initially posting some props on social media, the love seemed to grow dim on both sides of the bar. Maybe it was our fault?

Looking back, we should never have offered such an aggressive case volume estimate. I understand that now. I also believe that, despite the positive Crazy Uncle PR Frankie received from a handful of major newspapers, online blogs and even local television interviews, the gap between the size of our royalty cheques versus the number we speculated about in our first meeting contributed to preventing our relationship from progressing. I imagine both sides were left thinking the same thing: *'They don't appreciate what we've contributed and accomplished here?'* I'm convinced that, just as with Arnold's point of view, Frankie's agency felt eligible for a much greater reward. Perhaps, in someone else's hands, with a more established partner in the alcohol sector, more money could've been made. Sure, maybe. Then again, perhaps a more empathic understanding on everyone's part of what it took to achieve the final results could've taken the business to a healthier level. Or maybe it was our distorted paradigm and overly exposed nerve that served to sober up our relationship buzz. That said, in the case of Frankie Solarik himself, setting our likely differences in financial suppositions aside, I deeply respect his contributions to our cocktail crusade and still think he's *the* grandmaster flavour-wizard.

Either way, it'll be your money, your titanic time investment and exposed neck. Make sure you're at ease with everyone's expectations and motives. If you know that you'll only need someone's participation for a limited time, or only for a particular phase to make progress, choose your words (and numbers) very wisely—if it feels awkward and unnatural, despite getting what you want in the short-term, chances are you'll have to field an unwanted call ten years down the road from a forgotten someone looking for a sizeable charitable handout?

Let it Simmer ~

1. *At what level, financially or otherwise, should you involve a third party based on what they might provide to your mission over the long run?*
2. *Have you clearly set the roles and expectations, or have you unnecessarily embellished the storyline to keep the party engaged and involved? If so, can you weather and stomach the possible repercussions down the road?*
3. *What does an acceptable outcome look like to you? Is it also acceptable to your third party or will only the very best outcome be good enough for them?*
4. *Are the numbers you've provided reflective of half of the conservative outcome, or did you stretch the truth to a point where you'll be constantly backpedalling?*
5. *Do you really need the third party, or should you save the money and risk and go it alone despite the trickier road?*

CHAPTER 28

Fruit Pulp Clouds & Chocolate Bloom

The Mysteries of Food Science

Whether it's pesky flocculating fruit pulp clouds or unexpected chalky-white chocolate bloom, the science of food, the biochemistry of intermingling ingredients, can show up uninvited to your grocery get-together just when things are starting to move and groove. If comprehensive shelf-life testing isn't a possibility because of pressing launch deadlines, or simply because of limited funds and resources, keep a sharp lookout for this irritating and destructive party-crasher.

It wasn't easy, but we were able to team up with a first-class contract packer to replicate Great Canadian Bagel's® gourmet cream cheeses. It took us eight months or so to nail down the recipes to our liking, but we managed to pull it off. In the process, we dutifully scarfed down more than our fair share of double toasted multigrain bagels generously smeared with the famously yummy Zesty Cheddar, Vegetable, and Feta & Spinach cream cheeses. The product was good, very good.

You could imagine my frustration then, when I slid into my local Food Basics store to check on our newly christened product line a few weeks after we had shipped the first order only to discover that the Vegetable cream cheese sku had transformed from an appetizing creamy white colour into an unsightly and unappetizing blush red. It turns out that the pieces of fresh radish had slowly seeped into the product. I ended up buying all twenty units on the shelf to help clean the slate in that particular store. Unfortunately, I couldn't visit and attend to the other 116 Food Basics locations so a costlier and unfortunate recall was in order.

The bright red cream escapade was bad, but not as befuddling as the cloudy white and milky mass that grew in the centre of our Crazy Uncle® Blood Orange and Rosemary Maple Punch. Admittedly, during our many smaller lab test runs, as well as the inaugural production run, we did notice a very faint cloud floating in the bottle, but it looked more than reasonably natural and normal. After a couple of weeks of sitting on the shelf, however, we noticed that the cloud increased in size, density and colour. We knew the product was safe for consumption as our lab tests and continuous weekly pH checks were all in order. We purchased, cracked open and drank a few bottles and found the flavour profile also to be in accordance with our taste targets—(at 14% alc. vol., we also found that catching a warm buzz was a little too easy).

It turns out that the unsightly flocculation was triggered by our natural red colouring (made from purple carrot, beet and elderberry juices), unpredictably mingling with the fleshy pulp from the unfiltered lime juice. Our competitor's cocktails used inexpensive artificial gums and stabilizers to create a more homogeneous product and to avoid product settling. We had intentionally spent more money to source and incorporate all natural and premium ingredients and it nearly ended up backfiring on us—go figure that one out. Needless to say, we drove around the city for a couple of weeks visiting more stores to shake more bottles than I care to remember.

There's no doubt that the funky flocculation in our craft cocktail kept us awake at night for a few weeks, but at least in the end the product sold through at retail—97.7% of it to be exact. We made our money. I wish I could say the same for our dollar-store-focused popcorn seasoning gamble. It was 2005 and our Kernels Extraordinary Popcorn® Shakers had gained decent national distribution and popularity amongst consumers and retailers alike. But when Canada's largest dollar store chain came knocking and asked us for a smaller and more affordable version of our product, we were reluctant to offer one in fear of damaging our premium brand by making it available in a discount retail environment.

Not wanting to let the opportunity go, we developed a similar product offering and created a new brand called Flavour Station® Popcorn

Shakers. The savoury chip-inspired seasonings were packed in cylindrical shaped composite (cardboard) containers that were less than half the size and fill weight of our flagship Kernels Shakers, sold in a more attractively shaped polypropylene (plastic) container. They would retail for an even $1.00 compared with $2.99 for the Kernels product line sold in grocery stores.

In order to seal the new composite containers, we gambled and purchased a special machine for slightly north of $50,000 called the Angelus 10P Seamer. It wasn't necessarily a cheap or easy capital investment decision, but the projected conservative sales estimates more than justified our return on investment. Within a year or so, the machine should have paid for itself. With the 10P and the mini canisters on order, we hit the streets and began to peddle our new product to not only dollar stores, but to any bargain-hunting retailer that we had initially passed over for our Kernels line.

By the time the mighty Angelus 10P Seamer was installed, we had a couple of truckloads of purchase orders to fill and ship out. Following a few fits and starts with the new equipment, we managed to build the orders. As we were loading the maiden order onto the truck, a few canisters tumbled out of the retail-ready floor-stand we had packed them in, and made an unexpected solid 'ka-thunk' sound as they hit the concrete warehouse floor. 'That sounds peculiar,' I thought. I picked the product up off the floor and gave the little container a firm shake. 'Oh. My. God!' I murmured through my clenched teeth. 'It's rock solid!' I was stunned. We had tested the product earlier and didn't experience any sticking or hardening. I recall having a sample for the initial 10P trial sitting on my desk for a couple of months, and it was still fine. What the hell happened?

I'll tell you. It turned out the composite material that the canisters were made from didn't prevent humidity from creeping in as well as our Kernels polypropylene containers. Although the same composite canisters were used universally for other types of seasoning, such as salt or pepper, our product was designed to be more susceptible to retaining moisture so that it could adhere to hot popcorn. The damp warehouse environment was just enough to trigger a hydroscopic reaction that caused the seasoning to absorb moisture from the air. Despite a futile attempt to rework the product, the entire smorgasbord was deemed pure garbage. The real kick in the composite container was trying to return the Angelus 10P Seamer. By the way, if you're getting sick of hearing this name, then welcome to the party. We eventually got rid of the 10P all right, but it sat idle for nearly two long years and only sold for a meagre $6,453.08! Talk about rubbing a little seasoning salt into an open wound.

The rock solid seasoning shakers damaged our pocketbook and pride, but it's not the only time pesky hydroscopic ingredient problems have wreaked havoc on our little business. Before we decided to close down our Snack Brands popcorn plant in Ottawa, Ontario (see *Chapter 32: Family Table*), we created an over-the-top indulgent popcorn-based masterpiece called Crème de la Crème. We had four crazy innovative flavours—Black Forest Cake, Ultimate Chocolate Chip Cookie Dough, Banana Cream Pie, and Maple Pralines with Toasted Oatmeal.

The stuff was diabolically off the snack-charts compared with the status quo popcorn concepts on the grocery shelf. For example, our Black Forest Cake recipe was made using decadent caramel popcorn prepared in three different ways (coated in chocolate, coated in yogurt and flavoured with dark cherry essence), then mixed together with plump real dried cherries and buttery chocolate cookie buttons.

Given the product's indulgent positioning, and premium SRP, we decided to sell it in a Häagen-Dazs style pint-sized container. To pull this off, we had to invest in yet another unique sealing machine so that consumers would have to peel off a protective film to get to the product in the same fashion as a container of ice cream. Needless to say, this popcorn snack wasn't on the Weight Watchers® approved list. We're talking heavy-duty delicious here. What made this mission heavier than the cream cheese escapade, the funky cocktail flocculation and the rock hard seasoning blowout was that we had everything riding on the line with this sucker. We had recently purchased part ownership in the struggling popcorn Ottawa plant in hopes that we could turn it around. A year later it was still hurting badly and we were about ready to call it a day. We were up to bat in the bottom of the ninth, with two out, two strikes, no one on base and trailing by one run. An epic World Series homerun was needed to tie things up and to stay alive in the game. Instead of gunning for a base hit with another boring bag of butter or cheese popcorn, we decided to swing for the fences with something the likes of which consumers had never seen. It was an easy sale.

Our first pitch was to Shoppers Drug Mart—who is also one of the leading Canadian retail pharmacy chains when it comes to offering unique seasonal confections. The buyer took one look and one taste and it was a done deal.

Before the product left our facility, it looked and tasted tremendous —the popcorn and the cookies were fresh and snappy, the cherries were chewy and the chocolate was creamy. Although we shipped the orders on time, Shoppers Drug Mart ran into a few floor space logistical issues, which is common for all retailers during key seasonal periods, and wasn't able to display our product until a few weeks after they had received it.

When Crème de la Crème eventually emerged from the crowded stock rooms and made its way on to the busy store floor, it was rock-hard déjà vu. We started to receive the typical unfiltered phone calls and emails from irate consumers. *'Who do I speak with to complain about being ripped off! I just bought my son's teacher one of your $8 popcorn tubs and it's inedible! I'm embarrassed. You should be embarrassed!'* As a side note, the consumer is always right, no matter how much you'll want to reach through the phone to honk their nose a la Mr. Miyagi style. That's not to say that you can't scream in frustration into the rear-view mirror at your reflection on the drive home.

We ran across the street to the nearest Shoppers Drug Mart to buy a few popcorn pints. The popcorn and the cookies were soggy, the dried cherries were stiff, but at least the chocolate was still creamy! Fluctuations in temperature and humidity had, yet again, triggered moisture in the dried cherries. The contents in the package had morphed into one hydroscopic sweet and sticky ... lump. *'Perfecto,'* I lamented as I muttered *'Crème de la Crap'* under my breath. Batter swings; strike three. Game over. Plant closes. Baah!

After nearly two historic decades of ingredient related misfires, we've honed our ability to recognize early warning signs of any bleaching, cracking, burning, hardening, softening or blooming. Having said this, as the old proverb goes, only the spoon knows what's stirring in the pot. For each failure on the public stage, we've had twice as many food science related saves behind the office-curtain. One of the more recent averted incidents was with our newest brand partner, Beaver-Tails®. A Canadian-based chain of pastry stands, its namesake product is a fried dough pastry that resembles a beaver's tail; for my American friends, it's more or less like the fried 'elephant ears' you'll find at carnivals (mmm, carnie treats).

The company, run by the super sharp and stylish Di Ioia bros, had been toying around with creating a CPG retail product concept for grocery using the brand's unique proprietary cracked wheat base-mix and distinct oval shape. They had come up short in partnering with a handful of other interested grocery concept developers because of either an inability to create a product that translated the brand's essence successfully for retail, or simply because they just didn't feel like the right fit. Pino Di Ioia and I hit it off immediately like Italian second cousins chatting at the Sunday lunch table over a plate of fresh pasta. We seemed to instinctively land on precisely the same page each time we chatted about his brand, our business or our opinions of the industry at large. We respected one another to the point where I didn't push to have a contract commitment in place before we began the quest together—which is rare for us and for good reason.

We began to court donut manufacturers with the capability to hand stretch and fry the trademark cracked wheat dough. By way of our COO at Johnvince Foods, the resourceful Luis Deviveiros, we were introduced to Tony Lam, a veteran in the donut business—a master deep fryer if you will. Standing at the end of his massive industrial fryer to catch fresh and hot donuts off the line and then pop them directly into my mouth was one of the many fat guy highlights of my career —and hopefully not the last one. Tony was super patient and super helpful when we commissioned him to provide sample after sample of various recipe tweaks and shape iterations of the product.

At one point, our office fridge and backup freezer chest were both crammed full of nearly eight months' worth of fried and failed attempts. We like to retain samples from each trial run to measure our progress and to gauge changes that occur to the product over set periods of time. As a side note, it's very common for the recipe fine-tuning stage to drag on for so long that your contract packer begins to lose interest and faith in both you and your mission. Be aware and be prepared. Try to keep your finger on their pulse and do what you must to keep them engaged in the project by sharing your progress, package design concepts, etc.

Just days before I bit the bullet investing in a second back-up freezer chest to house the ever-growing number of fried dough rejects, Tony showed up at reception with a smile and a carton of fresh samples still warm from the fryer. This time, their shape, texture and taste were in the pocket. So much so that Dave and I jumped in the car a few days later and drove five and half hours to Montreal to hand deliver the samples to the BeaverTails gang. As we quietly sat around the boardroom table in their ultra-funky Canadiana-themed office, marvellously munching on the latest submission, everyone grinned at one another with a similar *'you know what, I think that this is the one'* look.

Fast forward a few weeks after our meeting in Montreal and we had already designed a slick pastry box and pieced together a launch strategy worthy of the brand's potential. Just a month or so after that, we presented our program to a key grocery retail chain who was not only immediately on board, they wanted an exclusivity on our product for nothing less than a three-year term. The stage was set. We were given an aggressive launch date expectation and hit the ground running to prepare.

Upon completion of the packaging design, we couriered a mock-up of our pastry box filled with samples to our buyer for review by her peers. A few days later, we received a disparaging email asking us why the product was now so dry compared with the moist samples we had tried together in her office a couple of months back. We ran to our freezer chest and slacked-off a few of the samples we had sent her. Note: As with many goods sold in the bakery department, the product was designed to be shipped frozen into grocery stores, and would be stored frozen until it was time to thaw and display in the bakery section with a four-day window best before date.

'Doh!'—literally. The buyer was right; the texture had changed dramatically in under two months. The expectation was that the product would last for at least six months when frozen. It was much too dry and had lost its just-fried texture and allure. Upon closer investigation and inquiry, we were told that incorporating a common bakery industry preservative called calcium propionate would extend the product's shelf life, but we decided that the ingredient didn't jive with the brand's mission to use ingredients that consumers could relate with—it wasn't a guaranteed fix either.

Despite both the retailer and our brand partner encouraging us to work on a solution, we decided to deep-fry the idea. Had we not survived the Flavour Station seasoning and the Crème de la Crème product texture fiasco we might have given into the temptation to press on. After all, we had been developing and chasing the product concept for nearly a year and now had a willing contract packer, slick packaging, launch plans and a serious retail chain lined up. The drawback is that you only get one good first shot when bringing a well-loved brand into grocery with established consumer expectations. Not to mention, it's our money that's at stake.

Thanks to our coloured past, it was actually surprising how very easy it was to let go and to shift gears. Within a few weeks of deciding not to pursue the concept we had worked so hard to sell everyone on, Dave established a relationship with yet another contract packer specializing in a completely different type of bakery product capability. He's deep into developing a completely new pastry concept. If we end up keeping this one on the tracks, it'll make the previous concept look less than mediocre. Everything happens for a reason. As long as they don't ask us to buy an Angelus 10P Seamer, I think we'll be game. But then again, let's see what happens.

I've always considered cooking and baking to be two very distinct culinary activities. Most notably, where cooking doesn't always require a calculated hand, only loose interpretation and inspiration of a recipe, baking is much more about precise steps, science and measurements. Metaphorically speaking, you'll need to bring both your cooking and your baking game to the table when designing your label, bag, box or bottle. It's about making your product look original, creative and innovative, but it's also about ensuring that you carefully comply with the necessary government regulations tied to your ingredient declarations, allergen statements and any product claims. The minutiae in which you declare your ingredients on the back of your package, and showcase certain choice ingredients front and centre, deserves nothing less than a well-measured quadruple cross-check.

If it's your first kick at the can, consider searching on-line for a *nutrition labelling* or *food label consultant* in your area. For a palatable $100 or so per sku, a food label consultant will review your design to guarantee that it's in full compliance with either the CFIA or FDA legal requirements. In today's world of food allergen hyper-paranoia, miscommunicate or leave out just one word, and your company risks becoming more vulnerable than Mr. Peanut® making a surprise appearance in a school cafeteria bursting with EpiPen® armed Moms.

A few years back, a single unnamed consumer called into the CFIA to advise them that her child experienced an allergic reaction after having eaten our Kernels Salt & Vinegar popcorn seasoning. The severity of the reaction was never shared with us so I can't tell you how minor or major it actually was. I do hope that is was nothing serious. I have kids, so I obviously can understand and sympathize with how this Mom reacted. We declared *lactose* on our product's ingredient statement that, at the time, we had considered was sufficient to forewarn consumers with a dairy allergen. It turns out that we were dead wrong.

Despite having sold millions of bottles of this particular seasoning flavour well over a ten-year span and having never encountered a consumer dairy allergen inquiry on the product, let alone an actual allergen related incident, the CFIA rang us up to let us know that they were sounding the red alarm and commencing with the highest level of product recall communication to the general public that also ensured all product was immediately removed from grocery shelves from coast to coast, and was quarantined in our warehouses.

The only decision we were given was to either go public with the news ourselves or to have the CFIA make the announcement of their own accord. We quickly appointed a public relations specialist to help craft an appropriate response, and within less than twenty-four hours of circulating the news we were drowned with calls from worried retailers, distributors, brokers, consumers, CFIA plant auditors and, to a slightly lesser extent, my concerned Father. Within forty-eight hours, we were brought to our knees and gasping for air as the hammer continued to fall and the associated recall costs continued to mount.

When the dust settled (or should I say when the seasoning settled), the episode had cleared our bank account of nearly $250,000 in related penalties and charges. You know how much blood, sweat and tears it took to save that much money in this game of nickels and dimes! You see, it's much more than the cost of your product being pitched in the trash that comes into play here—setting aside the fact that you're charged back for product at the retailer's purchase price, it's also the cost that they incur to have the product physically pulled from the shelves and then thrown into the trash. To boot, many larger retail chains tack on a sizable five-digit fine. This isn't to mention the cost of lost sales, PR agency assistance, discarded packaging, re-worked product and brand humiliation.

For our size and stature of company, the recall was a mighty and massive blow to the head and chest that we barely survived. In some cases, we asked for the opportunity to reclaim and re-label the product since there was technically nothing wrong with the seasoning inside the bottle, but the majority of retailers discarded the product immediately upon receiving CFIA's broadcast. In one case, our largest retail chain account erroneously deducted the recall-related fine twice from their outstanding payments and then it took us four months to get the money back into our account. In another case, a retailer wanted to play it safe and made the aggressive call to throw out inventory of all the Kernels flavours they carried. Before the recall, Salt & Vinegar was the third best seller out of eight flavours. It was a real workhorse product for us. It's been years since the catastrophe and we're still being punished with weaker than normal sales on this particular sku. Lesson well learned. Never estimate! Calculate by using a measuring cup when it comes to nutritional labelling nitty gritty. Dot those tiny little 'i's and cross those godforsaken 't's.

Let It Simmer ~

1. *Collecting and understanding data on the chemical and physical fluctuations of your new product over time are required before you launch. How extensively have you tested your product to understand both how it will behave over time, and what you can safely declare on your packaging as the official shelf-life or best-before date?*

2. *Can your contract packer and/or ingredient supplier provide you with the necessary test results and formal shelf-life validation? If not, can they help connect you with the right company. For example, we often use a third party company called **Maxxam** (maxxam.ca) which provides analytical services when our contract packers cannot. It may cost us a couple of thousand dollars, but it's well worth the investment.*

3. *If time isn't on your side, ask your contract packer to conduct an accelerated shelf-life test (ASLT)—a cost effective method used to determine a new product's shelf life in a fraction of the time that it would normally take. It's not as dependable as leaving the product on your desk for six months or a year and watching to see what unfolds, but it's better than nothing.*

4. *Have a look at the ingredient deck of other similar products in the grocery store. Do they have preservatives that you do not? Why haven't they attempted to sell their products without these preservatives? Is it because of the risk?*

5. *If you're at a crossroads between either holding up a new launch or pushing things through without getting your hands on shelf-life data, consider delaying the launch until you have peace of mind. That is, unless you can use a fridge full of bright red cream cheese.*

6. *Hire a nutrition labelling or food label consultant to ensure that your packaging design is thoroughly compliant with government regulation standards so that you're not at risk with misleading or confusing the consumer.*

CHAPTER 29

Poking The Yolk

Moving to Action
With Calculated Risk

I t's time to gently poke the fragile membrane to let all that trapped goodness come oozing out. Onward! That's what I'd say to all of the hopeful food entrepreneurs deliberating over whether it's time to make their move into the wonderful world of grocery retail. I'm picturing the conga line of foodies and wannabe CPG (consumer packaged goods) moguls that I've had the pleasure of sitting across from, armed with their tasting sample in one hand and a skeletal business plan in the other. From the muesli-multigrain pancake mix maiden to the navy bean-based-butter-tart baron, I can still clearly see their expressions of determination mixed with a crumb of trepidation.

After dispensing with pleasantries, the barrage of routine and foundational industry questions begins to roll in. Questions like: Where and how do I begin? Do you think that my product has what it takes? How much money can I make? How much money will I need to bankroll the launch, and how long will it typically take to make my investment back? What should I expect to be on the hook for if it doesn't work? With whom can I speak to commercialize my recipe and have it mass-produced?

These questions, steeped in both enthusiasm and suspicion, are about the path and probability of transforming a leisurely cooking pursuit into a moneymaking food enterprise. Despite the unlikely probability of a positive from-play-to-profit transformation, I make it a personal goal to never smother or douse someone's craving for wanting something more. I'm sure that, before they've come in to chat, they have had to endure their fair share of killjoys.

The logical solution to quenching a thirst is to drink something, and take it all in. So, in my view, moving to action is always the best prescription. Move wisely and move slowly with a calculated risk and an acknowledgement that the likelihood of failure is lurking around the corner. Remember, scalability is vital. Start small, start local and move to poke the yolk and break the membrane to get the process rolling.

One of two scenarios will ensue: Either you'll find that the mission is going to take much more time, investment and nerve than you have to offer; or, you'll eventually trip and stumble into a manageable rhythm and make it to the finish line. Regrettably, the former scenario is the more prevalent outcome. However, even if the launch is disastrous, I'll bet the person who moves to exercise the following steps will be more satisfied, and will have achieved proper closure with how they arrived at the outcome compared with the person who places their concept on the back burner and ends up living with *"what if?"* regrets.

Okay, let's run through a few useful and inexpensive tricks of the trade to get you out of the kitchen and into The Hunger Games. But first things first. It should go without saying: Have you recently conducted a comprehensive store audit within each of your targeted retailers? Have you searched deep online to see if any similar products have recently popped up? If it has been more than two months since you've strolled down the grocery aisles to check out your competition, get into your car and double back to ensure that the coast is still clear. I can't tell you how many times Murphy's Law will spoil the broth when you turn your back for a split second. If I had a cucumber for each time we had a cool food concept, took too long to launch it, only to discover that another company marginally beat us in the race to the shelf, I'd have a full barrel of pickles by now.

Assuming that the cluttered grocery landscape still appears fertile and hospitable after conducting your store audits and extensive web-searching, there are a number of relatively inexpensive steps that you can take to start preheating the oven:

Food Shows

Visit Agriculture and Agri-Food Canada's website (agr.gc.ca/eng/industry-markets-and-trade/agriculture-and-food-trade-show-service/canada), or Food Reference's website (foodreference.com/html/us-food-festivals.html) in the US, for a comprehensive list of both consumer and trade events in your local area and abroad. Most of the shows are open to the general public for a nominal on-site entry fee. Aside from aisle after red-carpeted aisle packed with a wealth of free tasting samples, it's hands down *the* best venue to get a quick and conveniently itemized snap shot of new players, new product trends, enthusiastic supply partners and likeminded food entrepreneurs. You'll be able to rub elbows with more food industry folk in a chatty mood that can help you with your business in one afternoon, than you could travelling the country for months.

On any other day, it would be next to impossible to get a return phone call from that artisan contract packer in New Orleans that produces the killer Andouille sausage you want for your frozen gumbo entrée line. But at the show, you get to chat up the company's President and exchange stories, pork recipes and business cards so that when you ring him up a few weeks later, he'll probably call you back. You also get to toss a couple of fresh sausage links into your free tote bag so that you can try them in your recipe over the weekend.

Trade shows can also serve as a sobering eye-opener. You'll quickly notice how many new and remarkably interesting and attractive products are introduced; products that sadly won't graduate into grocery stores, or at least, won't stay there long enough for you to see and taste again. Perhaps more discouragingly, you'll also smell an air of desperation wafting out from behind the rows of vendor booths that haven't been able to draw interest from the hungry crowds.

Midway through a trade show walk, I'll take a rest across from a struggling booth to sip a free espresso sample while I try to appreciate the long road that's led them there. After having invested, and put faith in similar food events from Halifax to Vancouver, and from Florida to California, I can empathize with their situation. I'll ask myself questions like: Has their journey thus far been relatively stress-free? Or did they have to borrow start-up money from a relative or mortgage their home to finance the first production run?

Taking a closer look at their product, I'm asking myself why the heck they decided to go with a clear pressure sensitive label over a shrink-sleeve collar that could've helped to hide the offensive liquid separation in the bottle? I'm wondering if they've seen the uncannily similar beverage that's on display in the crowded booth a few aisles over. I'm hoping they sell enough cases and bank enough margin to be able to continue to fund the never ending battle that lies ahead.

Having said all this, please don't feel dejected. Instead, soak it all in because it might be you on the other side of the black-skirted foldable table next year. One of the most valuable items that you can grab at a food show, aside from the free prosciutto di Parma, is a show guide, which will have a complete list of exhibitor company profiles and their detailed contact information. It's typically crammed with contract packers and packaging suppliers.

Looking for something cheese related? From international artisanal cheese makers to extruded cheesie snack contract packers to spray-cheese-in-can companies, you'll find them in the book. If you decide to only hit one event, The Fancy Food Show (specialtyfood.com) is a safe, fun and tasty bet. There's one in San Francisco during the winter, and another in New York City during the summer. For the mother of all food events, jump on a plane to Cologne, Germany in October of every second year to visit the Anuga Food Fair (anuga.com). With over 280,000 square meters of exhibition area, you're bound to fly back home with a luggage full of promise.

Packaging Design

Unless you're an Adobe Illustrator design pro, investing in a praise-worthy package design is an investment I suggest that you may want to consider. Take my word for it. It'll be challenging for most folks to see, understand and believe in your vision unless you show them, more or less, precisely what the product will look and feel like when it's perched up on the shelf. An impressive napkin sketch, or a poor attempt at using Keynote or PowerPoint can end up creating more confusion, questions and doubt than interest and praise. What's more, unless your packaging design complies with the necessary CFIA (Canadian Food Inspection Agency) or US FDA (Food and Drug Administration) labelling guidelines, a retailer cannot legally retail your product—e.g. ingredients, allergens, nutrition facts, weight declaration and domicile statements all with a very specific font size, orientation and placement requirement.

Find a young and aspiring freelance graphic artist who's looking to add relevant CPG projects to their up-and-coming design portfolio and you might be able to dodge a very costly design bullet and spend practically nothing up to only a few hundred dollars. If not, budget around sixty to seventy-five dollars per hour, or a couple of thousand dollars per sku for a proper design. Search on-line or visit the local graphic design colleges in your area to begin your quest for a packaging Picasso. If you do opt for a more established and reputable design firm, consider appointing a smaller, boutique-sized company as opposed to enlisting a larger and potentially overly-structured one. You'll most likely find their services to be markedly cheaper, faster, flexible and less fastidious.

Once you find a willing and capable candidate, be sure to arm them with a clear, well-written and succinct packaging design brief. A packaging design brief document will aid both you and your designer, or marketing agency, in arriving at the target without wasting more time and money than is needed. If your direction is unclear, unfinished and uncertain, there will inevitably be frustration between you and the designer brought about by multiple design attempts that miss the mark and unnecessarily rack up the bill. A poorly thought out design brief and strategy will also eventually suck the fun out of the process. Try to operate under the mantra *'garbage in, garbage out'* instead of hoping that the designer can read your mind.

I suggest sharing the relevant project background info (who, what, why, when, where, how, how much), a snapshot of the current grocery landscape and the hierarchy of messaging you'd like to incorporate. It's not necessary, but I find it both fun and useful to name a well-known person or character who best embodies the essence of your brand. For example, Bill Murray is a great specimen for our Crazy Uncle® brand as he represents the loveable quirkiness and straight-up delivery that we shoot for. When I was at Quaker Oats, we wanted our Crispy Minis® rice chips to personify Meg Ryan (although, it was the late nineties, and was probably because I had a thing for her). It's also a good barometer for the designer to measure their work against.

Be sure to bring along packaging examples and tasting samples of other brands that capture the look, feel and vibe of what you're hoping to create. Always include a UPC (universal product code) in your design to ensure that you can officially sell your product should it graduate to the big leagues. Visit GS1 Canada (gs1ca.org) to register and secure a 6-digit company prefix license. It's well worth the initiation set-up charge and annual license fee. Once you have a kick-ass design, roll up your sleeves and mock up a sample, using glue guns, Avery labels or the like so that your prototype looks as legitimate and genuine as possible. Perfecto. Now you're more suitably armed and one full-size step closer to going live. It's also a prudent point in time to begin (cautiously) showing your product concept around. Share it with would-be consumers and visit prospective supplier partners (contract packers and suppliers of raw material ingredients and packaging) to gauge unbiased interest and to collect value feedback.

Genuine, Unfiltered Input.

It's time to develop a monster-thick and bulletproof skin. Presenting your masterpiece to friends and family at first, and then deliberately moving to show supplier partners, and yes, even prospective retailers, is an indispensable piece of the process. But beware, most comments, especially in the early goings before you've had a chance to tinker and tweak, will be painful pinches more than congratulatory pats on the back. Everyone's a seasoned critic and an industry expert when it comes to providing feedback. It'll be mondo uncomfortable, but keep the wincing down to a bare minimum and work to develop an aptitude for sifting the gold nuggets out from the wet sand. Consider the alternative of shutting out worthwhile feedback only to learn that you should've listened and made an adjustment to the recipe or packaging after the product hits the shelf. It's free to listen to and filter feedback, but it can cost you dearly to ignore it.

Gathering opinions can be as simple as staging a basic qualitative taste test among a handful of family and friends who best fit your targeted demographic profile. Your objective is to better understand the obvious and the underlying purchase intents of both your product and of the food category you'll be selling it in. If you want to structure a larger, more quantitative test, to help quantify preferences using numerical data, there are a number of turnkey online survey tools to help you out (e.g. visit surveymonkey.com). Either way, don't become too proud or fearful to open yourself up to criticism.

Connecting with Supply Partners

Even if you're not prepared to make a binding commitment to launching your product concept, simply knowing that you have a willing and capable supply partner network (contract packers and suppliers of raw material ingredients and packaging) waiting in the wings is advisable. More importantly, you'll be able to zero in on the associated start-up costs, nail down a realistic COGS (cost of goods) range, understand minimum production run requirements and plan ahead using their lead times.

This type of information is indispensable if you're to appreciate and accurately gauge your mission's financials and the feasibility of having your product manufactured as you continue to probe the market for interest and opportunities. Consider that, if you begin to see encouraging results, or receive interest from a retailer, making important decisions with unsubstantiated financial estimates will most likely backfire. What if it costs you double than what you expected to have your product made? What if the minimum run is more than you can comfortably sell within nine months and you end up sitting on a mountain of expired inventory? What if your recipe or packaging format has to change dramatically in order for the contract packer to produce it on a large scale?

A clear understanding of what you're working towards will also allow you to plan for a smoother evolution on the road to market. It will also minimize the amount of backpedalling if what you've been hoping to bring to market isn't possible to recreate from a contract packer's capability standpoint. To boot, it's free to speak with supply partners, source samples and secure quotes; just be sure to get any third parties to sign a basic NDA (Non-Disclosure Agreement) so that you protect your concept from being copied should your discussions end abruptly. Search the web for local manufacturing associations who might be able to pair you with the right sized outfit. For example, the City of Toronto has a food and beverage program that focuses on assisting local contract packers to build and promote their businesses. Our contact at the city, Michael Wolfson (a.k.a. *'The Fonz'* in our office) is always ready and willing to hear about our newest product mission so that he can introduce us to the appropriate local manufacturing partner.

Full disclosure: It can be a delicate and awkward dance to court and carry conversations with a supply partner, particularly a contract packer, too far in advance of your launch for fear of being copycatted. It is, however, well worth the fancy footwork and stomaching the slight feelings of uncertainty as it'll help push to authenticate your mission and to radically improve your aim once it's time to pull the trigger.

Kitchen Co-ops

There's a deep and scary chasm between having to carefully whip up small batches of goodness in your home or office kitchen versus commissioning someone else to having your product mass-produced. Setting aside the risks and demanding obligations that come along with hiring a company to run your product, building orders out of a non-sanctioned kitchen comes with a serious accountability for food safety—not to mention that most big retail chains will require a facility audit before giving you a ticket to ride. In order to preserve foods using acidity, regulation requires the pH to be 4.6 or below. Sell just one improperly pasteurized mason jar of your wicked chimichurri marinade or use too little citric acid or potassium sorbate, and the Canadian Food Inspection Agency can shut you down like a culinary outlaw on the most wanted list.

Do yourself a big flavour, Google '**communal kitchens**' or '**kitchen incubators**' or '**kitchen co-ops**' in your area. There's a fantastic, fully decked out facility in Toronto, operated by a non-for-profit board, called Food Starter (foodstarter.ca). A relatively new, but quickly growing service, these useful establishments provide a proper food-regulated manufacturing space, complete with professional equipment, ingredient and finished goods warehousing, experienced production staff and savvy industry pros to help your budding business connect the necessary dots until you can become self-sufficient.

Producing your product out of a food-licensed communal kitchen may be prohibitive to making decent profit margins, but consider that your cash outlay and overall financial accountability will be dramatically more digestible. And, if your mission goes sideways, there's very little aftermath clean-up to concern yourself with. More crucially, if you can build a workable financial model using temporarily inflated COGs, you'll be laughing all the way to the bank once you graduate to using a more traditional, permanent and cost effective manufacturing set-up.

Before establishing your SRP (suggested retail price) range, visit the retailers on your target list to determine what the realistic SRP ceiling is. Also try to find out what the retailer's targeted profit margin range is by asking a willing department manager, or more conveniently, by asking the contract packer you have standing by. **Gross profit** is calculated by subtracting the COGs from the selling price. To calculate **profit margin**, divide the gross profit number by the selling price (e.g. a product with a $3.99 SRP and a COGs of $2.79 will have a gross profit of $1.20; divide the $1.20 by the selling price of $3.99 to get your profit margin, which in this scenario would be 30% for the retailer).

Tattoo this formula on your forearm, as this will be your equation to calculate both the retailer's financial objectives as well as your distributor's (and / or wholesaler's) and of course your own. For example, if the SRP ceiling for your product is $3.99 and the retailer requires a thirty percent profit margin, you'll need to charge them $2.79 if they are buying from you directly. If you're going to market using a traditional turnkey distributor with DSD (direct-to-store) shipment capabilities—who will purchase, warehouse, re-sell and ship your product for the $2.79 in the above example directly to retailers, they'll want anywhere from 17% up to a more likely 30% profit margin which suggests that you'll now be required to sell your product for as low as $1.95 to the distributor versus selling it directly to the retailer for $2.79. Note, for certain retailers (i.e. food service, convenience and gas stations), more often than not, you'll sell your product via wholesalers, who will require a more affordable 12% to 15% profit margin.

Can you make money selling your product for $1.95 based on the COGs associated with producing product out of a communal kitchen, or do the numbers only jive when you plug in the reduced COGs scenario associated with running product out of a more traditional manufacturing facility? Don't fret, remember that we're moving to poke the yolk and to move wisely and slowly until we're ready to take on more.

For your first legitimate selling adventure, consider selling directly to the consumer and cut out the retailer's, distributor's and/or wholesaler's profit margin. To start, consider selling your product in smaller, more flexible venues that will allow you to squeeze a dollar or two more out of the SRP to temporarily buff up your gross profit. Look for an intermediary selling-step that will allow you to watch, learn and to stay afloat financially until you can graduate to the big leagues. Use this phase to get a manageable and firm grasp on consumer interest and challenges, potential volume and profit, product issues, and most importantly, your comfort level. Use the opportunity to tweak, tinker and modify your product and your sales pitch.

Having already courted a contract packer prospect, you're now ready to advance out of the communal kitchen incubator and to start fulfilling the growing customer orders with your longer-term supply partners. Remember, with each step up, you'll need to generate and bank more profit margin to feed the growing number of hungry mouths at the supply chain table. Although, as your operations, capabilities and the economies of scale improve over time (we're talking a few years here), you'll likely tire of feeding too many mouths, double back and restructure to sell retailers directly in order to maximize your profits. But until such time, plan on setting and serving a crowded dinner table.

Preparing for the Big Leagues

There are quite a few meaningful and more manageable food venues to begin selling your product in than with a traditional grocery retailer. To test the waters and validate your concept's potential, before breaking the bank and your back on investments linked to gearing up for larger production runs, consider offering a single, medium-sized, regional retail chain a short-term exclusivity. For a start-up food enterprise, aside from the perhaps more common B-to-C on-line store opportunities, consider cutting your teeth at local farmers' markets and food fairs. My personal favourite is the Evergreen Brick Works in Toronto (evergreen. ca). To boot, the larger the retailer, the longer it will take to get a return phone call or email, let alone a meeting to pitch your product. Without a buyer relationship to lean on, you might end up watching the snow fall in December and then melt away in April before you get an ambiguous, one sentence voicemail or email reply.

A few years ago I had the privilege to work with Covenant House Toronto—an incredible organization that provides much needed 24/7 crisis care to homeless youth, aged 16 to 24—on a food-driven social enterprise concept. The catalyst for the program was The Covenant House's successful and well established 'Cooking for Life' program which teaches their kids the necessary culinary skills required to build a career in the food service industry. The program operated out of an onsite training kitchen armed with essential restaurant equipment. The social enterprise initiative was centred on utilizing the kitchen facility to support a food business that would manufacture a few choice homemade hot sauces that the kids had created. TAXI, the well-respected Toronto marketing agency that also happened to have fashioned our Crazy Uncle® cocktail brand, had created an exciting brand for the project that conveyed the mission's powerful message and unique point of difference.

As the project evolved, and particularly because I was the only participant with grocery industry experience, I felt a mounting sense of obligation to ensure that a foray into grocery wasn't viewed through rose-coloured glasses. Deep down I knew that, despite our product's admirable and influential social cause, we'd be primarily measured by the product's quality and efficacy, our ability to fill a category need, our packaging design impact, and ultimately, our ability to fulfill orders and generate a profit.

As much as I love a wickedly good hot sauce, there isn't a shortage of mind and mouth blowing options in the market. And, despite instantly falling in love with TAXI's clever brand name, narrative and design approach, I felt that grocers would be quick to accept a first order because of the charitable intent, but then hang us out to dry once the sales fell short. What type of destructive message would that send to the kids?

Instead, we decided to set up shop at local farmers' markets and food fairs. The scaled-down approach would allow the team the opportunity to engage with consumers first hand. It would allow them to learn and to tweak their recipes, packaging format, packaging design, and pricing before investing to print large minimum runs of labels and running too much inventory—you tend to think and operate differently with the pressure of having to stare at a warehouse full of impatient product. I was also banking on the farmer's market experience to temper the team's lofty sales volume ambitions.

Given that we hadn't performed proper shelf-life tests, these smaller venues would also allow us to understand how our recipe aged and reacted over time: Would the colour and flavour hold up, or would it brown and the flavour impact fade after only a couple of months? In the end, if your mission proves to be too complicated and costly to bring to grocery, or if consumers just don't respond as you had hoped, you'll know before you've bet the farm.

Walking food shows, investing in a proper packaging design, listening to consumer feedback, investigating supply partners, and setting up shop in a local market will not only help you cultivate your business safely and organically, it'll aid you in writing a compelling story and in mastering your one-minute-sales-pitch. You'll build a convincing case for the larger retail chains who will then be more apt to hold your hand and to collaborate when you bring them concrete in-market results. This scalable approach isn't only for newbie start-up companies. It's how we've carefully approached many of our more questionable product launches in the effort to learn before leaping, to avoid wasting money, and to keep the fire stoked when we're just not entirely sure how things will go on the big stage. Go on now, grab that fork and poke the yolk.

Let it Simmer ~

1. *Have you recently conducted a detailed store audit to ensure that another company hasn't begun to eat your lunch?*
2. *Have you visited a food trade show? If so, were you able to connect with any contract packers, distributors or brokers relevant to your mission? Did you find any product concepts similar to your own? If so, what's your takeaway on their brand, packaging, messaging, ingredients and retail price point? How does your product compare?*
3. *Have you taken the time to write a proper, clear and concise packaging design brief before collaborating with a designer?*
4. *Are you opening your mind to the feedback of others, or are you too proud and anxious to actively listen to what they have to say?*
5. *Do you have suitable supply partners waiting in the wings? Do you know how much they'll charge you per unit, what their minimum run is and what the overall start-up charges will be? Are they willing to amortize the start-up costs into the unit price over a period of time to make the leap more financially digestible for you?*
6. *Where can you start selling your product to gain momentum, to learn more and to iron out any kinks before you step up to the big leagues?*
7. *Is your business model scalable? How fast can you go from zero to a hundred if a large retail chain throws a purchase order in your lap?*

CHAPTER 30

The Candy Man (Almost) Can

Brand Promotion & Awareness

I n the summer of 1998 I was a brand manager for a confections company called Beta Brands (you remember, when I slept in the makeshift bedroom made of office dividers in the living room of our company frat house). Blair Neuss and I were searching for a persuasive and affordable marketing strategy to make LifeSavers® hard rolled candy relevant to tweens and teens again. The candy, originally invented in 1912 as a 'summer candy' that could withstand heat better than chocolate, had become more of a grandma's candy-bowl treat amidst the competitive sea of much hipper chewy, ultra sour and funky confections of the day.

Around the same time, I received an invite from a marketing firm named Big Bang which was promoting and licensing a DreamWorks' theatrical release called *Small Soldiers*. The media event looked interesting enough, and it was a Friday afternoon out of the office, so I went. Although we didn't end up buying into the Small Soldiers property, I did click with the firm's magnificently energetic owner, Scotty Stevenson. I loved spending time with Scotty as he had full access to the music and film industry, was an exceedingly creative and ambitious thinker and, above all, we got along instantly. Aside from working on some pretty cool campaigns together, I spent some great time with him and his lovely wife Lucy. It was long before I was married to Lisa so they tried to set me up more than a few times. (Thanks guys.)

*NSYNC was an upcoming boy band in the era of boy bands. They had not yet reached superstar status, but Scotty and Co. felt they were destined for great fame. He also believed that he could get the band to put on a private LifeSavers concert, complete with a meet-and-greet for 500 contest winners at Toronto's The Guvernment bar. He was right. The campaign was aptly named '*LifeSaver's Sweet Sounds of Summer.*' The connection between the candy to the band and to music was simple but on point—colourful, pleasurable, five flavours for five diverse band members, etc.

At the time, I was in my mid 20s (and as I just pointed out, still single) so the whole thing was right in my wheelhouse and I loved it. The secondary prize was a giant groovy LifeSavers jukebox. We had an extra one made for the office, and we still use it at BrandFusion. A few weeks after we signed on the band, their career started to blast off ... crazy fast. Throngs of young and painfully-screechy teenage girl groupies started to obsess over Justin Timberlake, Joey Fatone and the boys.

A few of the diehard groupies somehow found out about the private LifeSavers concert and that I was helping to organize it. They would ring me up and literally cry with intense excitement and raging hormones begging me to dish out a couple of free tickets. Two girls actually built and devoted an entire website to asking me for tickets. It shouldn't go without mentioning that this was 1998, so homespun teenager-developed websites weren't a normal occurrence. In the end, we did have two extra tickets so I called everyone into my office to witness the congratulations call to the two web-o-gram gals. My coffee mug nearly shattered into pieces with all the high-pitched screams and jubilant wailing blasting through the speakerphone.

The day of the concert arrived after what seemed like an eternity of build up and calls from everyone and their sister looking for tickets and backstage passes. I stood next to the band's beefy bodyguard a few feet from the stage to watch the warm-up set— '*It's tearin' up my heart when I'm with you, but when we are apart, I feel it too*'—catchy stuff. The magnitude of the event hit home when I stepped out of The Guvernment's back door to assess the line-up. I was stupefied. It was huge and ... they were all female. The two girls I had awarded the free tickets to actually made a large picket sign that said something like '*Thank You,*

Bruno! We Love You' ... or at least that's the way I remember it and tell the story.

As the people crammed in, the energy peaked uncontrollably. A funny side note was that, unbeknownst to me, my future wife Lisa was in attendance as a chaperone for her younger cousins who scored tickets. And then it all went very wrong—not the event, but my time in the glorious sun as the ultra cool guy with direct access to the band. Turns out that JT and the boys couldn't get through all 500 meet-and-greets because of tight timing. It also turned out that the girls to whom I promised the meet-and-greet—the ones that probably didn't sleep for weeks because of their bottled excitement—were the ones that got stiffed. They slowly sauntered towards me like angry teenage zombies forming a tight mob-like circle. The words '*Why? You promised*' were mournfully barked at me, over and over. At one point (and this is the truth) one of the girls started madly pounding on my chest while wistfully sobbing. '*My God,*' I thought. '*It wasn't supposed to be like this.*' Needless to say, I watched the entire concert from the very back of the room peeking out from behind a pole.

The final results of the campaign were far more prosperous than my one night as a music mogul. LifeSavers sales rocketed up by triple digits for a few months and retailers were once again interested in what the brand had to say. Tethering the tired and unconnected brand to a fresh and new anchor in a meaningful and relevant way gave it the relevance it desperately needed. If the plan was for the forgotten candy to find its way into the back pocket of a few ripped and torn Levi's instead of buried under a change-purse in Grandma's handbag, well then mission accomplished.

To be clear, there was a host of sales tools (i.e. displays, posters, entry pads, concert tickets for store managers' kids, etc.) and volume targets that built up to the private concert finale. It wasn't just a case of let's throw a rock concert to get people liking the candy again. Of course, I realize this was really just basic marketing tactics. (I can just hear brand managers out there reading this last paragraph and saying: '*Tell me something I don't know.*')

For an aspiring company looking to rapidly build brand value, the real morsel to pull out of the *NSYNC story is about gaining meaning-ful credibility through a creative and relevant association with an es-tablished and desirable third party brand. It's about tapping into some-one or something that will elevate your launch and street cred. In the case of *NSYNC, the timing was somewhat of a fluke as Big Bang was able to sign on the band right before they became literally untouchable.

When launching a product, we always ask ourselves, would it be better to build credibility from the ground up or is it worth it to pay a fee to an established and respected third party entity (via a license fee or a one-time amount) to help carry our heavy cart up the hill? [Cau-tion: Hitching your trailer to another brand's goodwill to help build your own brand doesn't suggest that you should be willing to sacrifice control or ownership in your mission—for me, that's a big no-no.] *'Might sound crazy, but it ain't no lie. Baby, bye, bye, bye.'*

Let it Simmer ~

1. *Can you think of another brand, company or entity to associate with that will elevate your product launch, strengthen and validate your brand's narrative, and improve the chances of success? If so, can you enter into the agreement without giving up any ownership or strategic control?*

2. *If you choose not to associate or promote your product with another well-known and accepted entity, how much longer will it take to achieve the same level of awareness and success (i.e. product trial, media coverage, consumer / retailer / distributor interest, etc.)?*

3. *How long do you need to associate your product with another entity? Is it just for the initial launch period or for the entire life of the product? If so, have you clearly set expectations via a written contract before going too far down the road?*

CHAPTER 31

Milk Money

Spend Your Marketing
Money Wisely

B ack in 1983, like most rebellious ten-year-old kids, I rarely used my milk money allowance to purchase a plain old boring carton of 2% milk from the school cafeteria. Instead, on the way home from Mill Valley Public school, I'd duck into this small gem of a tuck shop inconveniently located at the back of a residential apartment building. My hot handful of quarters were often used to purchase a Mr. Freeze® banana freeze-pop, a sack of Gold Rush® bubble gum and the occasional lucky rabbit's foot keychain. (Remember those fuzzy things?) Sure, the milk was a considerably healthier choice and would've prevented many lingering stomach aches, but I just didn't have enough coin to afford both luxuries. I had to choose between making a sensible purchase or a much more entertaining and colourful one.

When I landed my first job at the local Red & White grocery store, I was so elated to pocket a whopping $3.81 per hour that each shift I spent the entire day's earnings on a hefty meal during my breaks and lunch, complete with a 650g container of Astro® Cappuccino yogurt and, of course, a small carton of milk. On the long walk home I'd hit the neighbouring tuck shop to grab a banana freeze-pop or a couple of jumbo ice cream sandwiches. I finally had enough coin to blow, but somehow always managed to arrive home with empty pockets.

Fast forward thirty or so years, and I'm still toiling over making the same sorts of decisions in the quest to have something left in my hot little hands when the day is done. This time around, however, it's all about whether to spend our modest marketing budgets on colourful and flashy agency-inspired out-of-store consumer advertising temptations, or on the safer and perhaps more staple in-store trade promotional tactics. Note: In-store promotions are generally account management activities arranged between you and the retailer, whereas out-of-store advertising deals with activities and communication directly between you and the consumer. In the ad agency world, they also refer to the distinction between advertising to consumers at the point of sale as **below the line** (BTL) and advertising to consumers via mass media as **above the line** (ATL).

In an effort to simplify things from here on in, with an omission of the eCommerce sector, let's categorize and compare these two disciplines as **in-store** vs. **out-of-store** marketing. And if in-store marketing is your milk, then out-of-store marketing is your banana freeze-pop and Gold Rush bubble gum. Either way, you're going to have to reach into your pocket further than you might think if you want a buy a ticket to properly play the game. Consider that, while a sexy and mind-blowing packaging design can be your greatest and most inexpensive asset in stimulating consumers to toss one of your products into their cart, you can't expect it to do all the heavy lifting. With only a few seconds on the clock to convince passing shoppers, you'll need to cover off all of your bases to get the job done.

For smaller start-up companies, I believe that until you earn more cash to play with (hopefully it works out to more than $3.81 per hour), it should be more about investing in uncomplicated in-store promotional marketing tools that will elicit more measureable and immediate trial, separate your product from the competition, and help to strengthen your relationship with the retailer; for example: aggressive temporary price reductions (TPRs), flyer ads, air mile contributions, off-shelf point-of-purchase (POP) displays, sweepstakes and contests, rebates, product sampling, etc.

While it will eventually become increasingly vital to invest in building product awareness and in shaping your brand's narrative via engaging out-of-store advertising campaigns that live beyond the retailer's four walls, be on guard with how much of your money you initially allocate; for example: television, newspapers, magazines, radio, outdoor ads, direct mail and (to some extent) online efforts.

The results of pure out-of-store advertising efforts, and their positive financial impact on your bottom line, are just too difficult to measure compared with the more traditional in-store promotional marketing efforts that can drive measureable sales volume; and unfortunately, a difficulty to quantify results often leads to growing disappointment, doubt and a resentment to reinvest in marketing programs. To clarify, allocating less of your budget on advertising doesn't also imply that you should spend less energy and time on out-of-store communication. Inversely, we probably spend much more effort and time managing our consumer advertising efforts because we have to be more creative and resourceful when operating with an insignificant budget.

As your pockets become heavier with earnings, shifting more of your budget to imaginative out-of-store advertising efforts will become possible, but it shouldn't be at the expense of the in-store promotional marketing side. Albeit, the dawn of social media and the proliferation of its available platforms, save for your time, has created the ability to balance and, better still, tie both disciplines together with integrated closed-loop marketing programs without adding much more cost.

Yet, if this is your first time around the block, know that before it becomes about making money, it will be more about keeping your company afloat and alive—and hopefully without having to endure a constant stomach ache brought about by misspending what few funds you have on the wrong marketing persuasions. Remember, your business will have an undying and insatiable appetite for rapidly chewing up all the cash you can feed it. Knowing how and when to feed your little growing monster, without having to take on more debt and paralyzing stress, can be the big difference between making it home with or without a few crumpled bills in your back pocket.

So, what's on the marketing menu? Where can you afford to dine? Which goodies can you afford to open your wallet for? Will they meet with your strict expectations and keep you from feeding your hungry business more than it actually needs to scoff down? In the early going, from an out-of-store advertising spend perspective, we typically try to find or create affordable brand building opportunities that we can mount and manage in-house ourselves. Sure, it's much easier and even more fun to hand the creative reins over to a hip boutique marketing agency to dream up an imaginative concept, but unless you have a worthwhile budget, and can still sleep soundly should their execution fall short, you're better off sticking with a home-grown plan.

The magic is coming up with an advertising campaign that will make your already-stretched-too-far $10,000 investment look more like a cool $100,000 to both retailers and the consumer. Squeeze as much blood from the stone as you can. When our Kernels Popcorn Shakers started to become more omnipresent on the grocery scene, we managed to store a few big nuts in the tree and then decided that it was time to up the ante in our food fight by investing more into our advertising efforts.

We ended up working with the tween television station YTV to invent a silly, Emmett Lathrop "Doc" Brown, Ph.D. inspired cartoon character we called *Marty the Mad Flavour Scientist* that YTV starred in a series of animated short promotional commercials. Marty's *'mix it up'* message was designed to inspire kids to come up with, and then share, their very own wacky recipes by mixing together our popcorn seasonings. The idea was playful and relevant. The production values of the cartoon were impressive and ended up looking very credible when aired alongside commercials for other more established brands.

It was the first, and regrettably, the last time that we dished out $120,000 big clams at one time on an advertising campaign. Like many of our other out-of-store marketing attempts, our sales didn't seem to spike whatsoever as a result of the significant expense. And, of course, we lost sleep because it was a lot of bread for our company to dish out.

Look, I've worked in the marketing department at larger CPG companies and was charged with the responsibility of allocating significant multimillion dollar budgets. I've sat and collaborated with the agency gurus on numerous occasions so I can appreciate and still subscribe to the importance of building product and brand awareness sustainably over time via integrated campaigns that weave both marketing disciplines together. The gravity of misfiring when it's your budding company and half-inch deep pockets however, is nothing short of life-altering and somewhat vomit inducing.

If you're able to raise the generous capital required to fund a properly weighted and integrated marketing campaign, then God bless you. But know that you represent the minority of crusading entrepreneurs. I can't tell you how many companies and hopeful brands that we've been offered up for pennies on the dollar because the owners ended up broke by overfeeding their cause with half-baked out-of-store marketing spend. There's no room for big and costly mistakes when you're feeding the monster from hand-to-mouth.

Consider investing in a marketing plan that focuses on leveraging an affordable out-of-store advertising effort to drive a more tangible, and most importantly, measureable sales impact. For the last few years, for example, we've teamed up with Sony Pictures to help them promote their theatrical movie releases by selling a limited edition Kernels Popcorn shaker which incorporates both a main character from the movie as well as a sweepstakes offering on the packaging.

Aside from the obvious and natural partnering of movies and popcorn, the program is remarkably affordable and also serves to leave our retailers with the impression that we've invested far more than we actually have. Think special edition packaging designs with Optimus Prime, Gru from *Despicable Me*, etc. In this particular example, we're also indirectly leveraging Sony's out-of-store advertising campaign to bolster our in-store promotional program.

Unlike our YTV media ad spend remorse, we also know that this program consistently yields a 10% to 12% direct lift on our sales because we can measure the lift by controlling the printing and distributing of the specially marked product. The affordability has also allowed us to comfortably repeat the program for a number of consecutive years, so over time, we've also been able to nail the forecasting requirement down to a science to ensure maximum sell through and minimal unsold product wastage.

If we're feeling ambitious, we'll use the movie partnership campaign as an instrument to venture out to try and secure new distribution by preselling point-of-purchase in-store displays filled with the limited edition product to new, untapped retailer prospects. If we're successful, we'll have generated additional incremental volume (i.e. beyond the 12% lift), and because we've presold the inventory before pulling the expensive trigger on building more production, there's little risk as we only need to build against the order commitments in hand. The real beauty is that, if you can sell enough incremental volume, you may not only completely cover the entire marketing costs associated with the program, you're actually in a position where you've made money—a marketing investment strategy I like to call reversed-cost-marketing.

As discussed in the previous chapter, synergizing with a complementary product or brand partner, that lives either in or out of your product category, can also be a resourceful technique to aid you in providing a major concrete value offering to retailers and consumers. For example, part of our strategy when licensing a well-known restaurant brand for a grocery retail product is to include a hefty on-pack bounce back offer from the restaurant partner—for instance, with a $3.79 purchase of our Pizza Pizza® Dips in grocery stores, consumers receive an on-pack coupon for a free small box of potato wedges at Pizza Pizza restaurants.

Our restaurant partners love the ability and the unconventional access to be able to provide an offer and an awareness for their brand in grocery stores. Considering that consumers are traditionally used to receiving 50¢ to $1 off deals that will only last for a week or so, we love that our partners can provide us with deals valued up to $5 that will last considerably longer because they are printed directly on our packaging. Oh, and by the way, given that we're providing both the canvass and the unique distribution for their offer, there's usually no charge to us! But then again, maybe it's just my lucky rabbit's foot finally starting to do its thing.

As your volume grows from a struggling few hundred cases per year to a more desirable few thousand, it's prudent to start assigning a fixed dollar amount per case towards your out-of-store advertising marketing efforts. Depending on how poor or rich your net margin is—the percentage of revenue left in your hands after subtracting all operating expenses, interest, and taxes from your total revenue, consider delegating from $5 up to $10 per case to play with.

Be forewarned. Periodic margin dilution is written in the stars irrespective of the game that you decide to play. If you're not making enough profit to contribute at least a few dollars per case, you should probably be very concerned. Consider raising your prices or find a way to chop away at your COGS. To quote Stephen R. Covey from his ubiquitous self-help book, *The 7 Habits of Highly Effective People*: '*No margin, no mission!*' I'd also suggest baking the in-store promotional marketing funds directly into the sell price from the get go so that you're not tempted to zip your pockets shut when it really should be time to support the retailer by investing with them more aggressively. By the way, funding in-store promotions isn't cheap either so be sure that you're baking enough quality dough into your sell price.

When you build the muscle to financially step up and start playing with marketing agencies to create and execute your out-of-store advertising campaigns, don't rest on your laurels by expecting that whatever ultra-imaginative idea they formulate will result in pushing you further up the climb. It can take a few failed attempts for both you and them to discover what the best direction and narrative for your product and brand should be. Keep some poker chips up your sleeve and avoid doubling down until you see some success and can measure the results.

Despite the sometimes awkward breakup aftermath, don't be afraid to cut bait and hook into another agency should the understanding of your mission and their position begin to dramatically differ from your own. If you can invest more manageable chunks of money at a time, and both parties can continue to agree with and lean on the postgame learnings, staying the course together is more probable. Conversely, overspending and an inability to agree on the takeaway lessons from a botched campaign will end with an '*it's not you, it's me*' heart-to-heart chat.

The danger, however, in expecting an agency to work miracles with a starving budget is that you're tying their hands on being able to integrate and deploy the mechanisms required to win. Remember, they too must make money and live under their own '*no margin, no mission*' rule of law. So, that big investment that you're so proud to finally be able to offer up as your entire budget might end up being burned up solely by agency fees and in turn leave very little for a proper execution of the plan.

The other caution is that it can take a few months and numerous brand-questing exercises with the agency to better understand what your product's narrative should sound like and what direction your company should travel in. It's never an overnight process. Lately, I'm finding that presenting an agency with a limited budget recurrently leads to a plan that relies too heavily on social media tools. And, more often than not, I can tell you that you'll feel cozy and satisfied at first simply because you've at least made a concerted effort to work with a third party to understand your business and have taken a step towards promoting your product at a deeper level.

The trouble is, after weighing the results against the economics generated by your in-store promotional marketing efforts, especially if the out-of-store ad campaign hasn't been able to drive quantifiable sales, you begin to better appreciate where your delicate investments will work harder for you. There are always exceptions to the rule, for example if your product is truly newsworthy there's always the chance that your message and mission will go viral and drive consumers into the store, but such luck is not easy to come by.

Despite my marketing training and experience, it's unfortunately difficult for me not to sound pessimistic about serious out-of-store advertising expenditures in the early goings of building sales for your product simply because I've been thwarted by our return on investment more times than I can count. With that said, this book was inspired by and written for the starting entrepreneur with restricted funds at their disposal. The lessons were meant more for the would-be company and brand that has to continue hitting the mark in order to keep their product from ending up in the clear-out bin. I'm thinking more about your sustainability and your ability to responsibly scale up marketing spend over time.

Spending beyond your means with aggressive out-of-store advertising too early in the game could cause you to fall into a deeper financial and emotional hole. Spend your milk money wisely by focusing the lion's share of your marketing budget in-store so that you can stick and move before your banana freeze-pop completely melts and you have nothing left to show for your hard work.

Let it Simmer ~

1. Are you relying too heavily on your packaging design to do all of the heavy lifting with respect to creating interest and awareness for your product?

2. What's on the marketing menu? Are you ordering the Wagyu beef when all you can afford is a burger and fries? Can you make every $10 of marketing budget work for you like it was $100 or more?

3. How much money can you comfortably afford to risk investing in an out-of-store advertising campaign without causing irreparable damage to your mission?

4. Are you applying more of your already-inadequate budget to lofty agency driven out-of-store advertising efforts than to more functional and measureable in-store promotional marketing programs? If so, make sure that it's for the right reasons and that the strategy will work before your well runs dry.

5. Can you synergize with a complementary product or brand partner to create cross promotions, joint sampling efforts, alternate distribution opportunities and valuable bounce back offers?

6. Are there opportunities for reversed-cost marketing campaigns that serve to cover your costs by creating incremental selling opportunities?

7. Are you ready to afford the luxuries that come along with hiring a marketing agency, or should you continue to mount and manage your out-of-store campaigns in-house? If you are ready to appoint an agency, how much money can you comfortably afford? Is it enough money for the agency to work their magic?

CHAPTER 32

Family Table

Blood Before Money

Aside from eating out with clients or supplier partners, I haven't paid for my lunch in over fifteen years. Much more importantly, I eat like a bloody King. Here's a snapshot of this past week's menu:

- **Monday:** Niçoise salad (with each ingredient carefully prepared and served in separate glass containers to ensure a fresh assembly)
- **Tuesday:** cherry wood smoked Tilapia tacos with fresh Pico de Gallo and pickled red cabbage
- Wednesday: red wine-braised short ribs and sweet potato wedges with homemade hot antipasto spread—washed down with an icy glass of Crazy Uncle® Whisky, Cider & Chai Tea Cocktail
- **Thursday:** lightly charred Calabrese bread topped with ricotta from the corner bakery, juicy tomatoes and basil from my wife's vegetable garden, and my barber Kam's hometown olive oil from Lebanon.

It's currently Friday morning and I can't wait to see what's waiting for me in the office refrigerator—forget about it! Ready for this, my brother and Dad prepared everything from scratch—everything. To boot, if my brother can't bring lunch to the office for us because he's away, Pop makes it a point to drop off lunch so that I won't starve. (Yes, I'm 43 years old, but don't hate me.) Both are tremendous home chefs.

My Mum passed away at the tender and tragic age of twenty-eight when I was only eight years old. Consequently, my Dad completely amped up his game in the kitchen and found that he had both a love and talent for good cooking. Growing up, Dave and I would sock-slide into the kitchen before school to see what was waiting for us in the oven—seafood crêpes with a side of oven roasted paprika and rosemary potatoes (the man is crazy for potatoes) were but one of his typical 7 a.m. breakfast specialties.

Today, Dad loves to visit the BrandFusion office two or three times a week for a decent cappuccino and one of Dave's homemade chickpea-based biscotti. Note: We respect and handle the preparation of our morning cappuccino very religiously—whole milk at 140° to 160° degrees only, please and thanks. The staff and surrounding companies, courier delivery guys, etc. all affectionately refer to him as 'Papa Joe.'

For the record, I'll add in that my wife Lisa is also an inspired and fabulous home cook with a set of magic green thumbs. The woman will cheerfully pop into the kitchen at 6 a.m. to bake homemade focaccia bread with freshly picked herbs for the kid's school lunches. During the first year of our marriage, Lisa would make it a point to whip up more than she figured we could both eat for dinner so that I could bring the leftovers to work for lunch. After eventually realizing that I was programmed to inhale every last morsel placed on the table, regardless of the stupid amount, she half-heartedly surrendered my insane lunch provisions to her father-in-law.

As those of you who work with family and friends know, it's not all sunshine and seafood crêpes. Working with family and close friends can be, without a doubt, complicated at the best of times. Like a successful marriage, it's about responsibilities and mutual respect—ignore this and your tasty lil' business, and more seriously, your relationships, will painfully suffer bringing the ship down with them. Practice and embrace the basics, and your good ship lollipop will enjoy a layer of strength and protection that others can only dream of.

Some of the largest food companies have either been built on the broad shoulders of family power, or have crumbled because of it. To me, the greatest leg-up that working with your parent, sibling, or spouse 'should' offer you is untiring and abundant trust. My brother always has my back, and puts my needs and goals right alongside his own, if not above his own most of the time, and vice versa. It allows us to focus on making the demanding climb without worrying about how and when we'll push one another off the cliff. Equally imperative, we never go after the same bone. We rely on one another for counsel, but we're more aware that we both need to entirely own, lead and contribute something different to the mission. It helps that we have distinctive skill sets, but work with the same set of core values and a similar paradigm. Going after the same bone will eventually lead to silent competition, acrimony and one or both persons feeling undervalued.

For example, I look after most of the company's sales, but Dave is also responsible for a set of key retail chain accounts so that he can keep a firm finger on our customers' rhythm. He also governs the finances and supply partner relationships. We both tackle product development, but we each have our own brands and product concepts to flush out and to build. Be aware that roles and responsibilities also have best before dates—and because your relationship is always hanging in the balance, be honest about shaking things up before they get stale.

In the first ten years of building the business together, Dave and I found that tackling retailer and supply partner meetings together worked best—people seemed to like the 'brothers in arms' show. After a while, we felt that each meeting ended with either one of us unintentionally stealing the show causing the other to feel dejected and undervalued. As soon as I felt this problem bleeding into our time together out of the office, I became obsessed with restructuring the business so that we both felt re-energized and inspired. A couple years or so ago, we went so far as to hand the BrandFusion Presidential reins over to Dave. He was more than ready and capable to lead, and I'm ready to help contribute to our family's future via other initiatives.

Would you be okay with losing a small fortune if it meant keeping peace in the family? My family would, and here's a story—about popcorn, of course—to prove it. My younger cousin Chris (think back to the Pope corn escapade) worked with me during BrandFusion's primary years—we grew up as close as brothers. During that time, he worked with, and got to know, both the popcorn business and our partners over at Kernels Popcorn. As he grew older and gained industry experience, and an insatiable appetite for his own entrepreneurial adventures, it became clear that BrandFusion wasn't large enough to provide both a career path and the financial compensation, both of which Chris deserved.

After some time, he ventured out on his own to pursue a number of related and remarkably creative opportunities (and has been very successful since). One such opportunity was partnering with an existing small popcorn manufacturing facility out of Ottawa, Ontario called Snack Brands. His partners, Mike and Todd, built the business on producing bagged popcorn for Kernels' fundraising division that sold product to schools for kids to resell and generate funds for sports programs.

When Chris (and Kernels) asked for my opinion about his role and involvement, I somewhat hastily gave them my blessing either believing or, perhaps miscalculating, that his Kernels branded fundraising business wouldn't clash with BrandFusion's Kernels grocery initiatives—knowing that if our worlds did end up colliding it would lead to conflicting agendas and retailer confusion. Besides, at the end of the day, who'd want to deny family a chance to advance if their mission seems realistic.

Chris rolled up his sleeves, and invested a serious six-digit amount into the company to buy equipment, packaging and to improve the facility on the whole. Early in the game, it became apparent that, in order for his new company to sustainably grow, pay back his investment and turn a profit, the potential volume that we could generate in grocery would count the most. In the early going, we felt only a slight and manageable pressure to come up with ideas and concepts that could drive meaningful volume into his bourgeoning company. The issue was, and still is, that selling popped popcorn is a difficult and frustrating game—the cost of entry is laughable ($60,000 in listing fees per sku with certain National retail chains!), the margins are dangerously low, the competition is too stiff, the product's shelf life is gravely short, and the aftermath clean-up of a failed grocery launch can be financially crippling.

Unfortunately, or perhaps inevitably, we just couldn't come up with a breakthrough item that could stick. As the pressure to produce in order to survive mounted, Chris was put in a precarious, and obvious, position. If BrandFusion couldn't find a concept winner, he had to do what he could without us in order for his company to live. And yes, I would've totally done the same thing if the cross was mine to carry. The drawback was that BrandFusion's most coveted asset was, and quite frankly still is, its licensing agreement with Kernels that grants it the right of first refusal to represent the brand's pre-packaged retail products outside of its normal channels of operation (i.e. kiosks in shopping malls and fundraising related activity).

It was only later that we all realized that Snack Brands had inadvertently succeeded in getting Kernels to sign a somewhat similar, and regrettably conflicting, agreement allowing them to produce and sell its namesake popped popcorn directly to retailers. To explain, although we had no immediate plans to sink our teeth into creating and selling popped popcorn into grocery stores pre Snack Brands, the decision of when, how and why rested exclusively with us. What's more, should we have decided to launch a popcorn product, Snack Brand's agreement prohibited us from shopping our concept around to other contract packers, irrespective of unfavourable pricing and manufacturing capability differences. Under the new arrangement, we'd be shoved into launching a product for the wrong reasons, at an inopportune time, and potentially with an ugly balance sheet. Suffice it to say, neither Chris or I had duly thought through the potential complications before pulling the trigger. In any case, the seeds were sown.

We shook our head in disbelief: *'How could this have happened?'* Rest assured, Chris, Dave and I lost many nights sleep over this one. Feeling the gravity of the situation, I started to bring the burden home which, for me, is rare. My Grandmother taught me at an early age to *'hang your problems on the problem-tree outside the house before you walk in the door'*—which, incidentally, sounds much cooler in her Sicilian dialect —*'they'll be waiting for you to claim the next morning.'*

It began to get ugly as Chris and I tried to navigate our respective companies through the murky waters knowing full well that, if we weren't dealing with a close family member, we'd both take a much more forceful position. It got well beyond the point of being able to sit restfully at the family table together—a ritual we practiced often since birth and both respected immensely. It was agreed that we had to nip things in the bud before someone took a more regrettable and irreparable route. Despite not being able to drum up consistent and worthwhile volume for Snack Brands, we half-heartedly decided to buy Chris's share of the company. Chris half-heartedly agreed to sell it to us knowing full well that if it was anyone else he would've dropped the Sicilian hammer. We all realized that it was imperative in order to regain family balance, control of the wheel and our sanity.

Aside from a handful of heated debates and empty disparaging threats, we settled on a number—a large number that resulted in a very serious six-digit hoof to the family jewels for both sides. The purchase felt more like we had bought a money pit cottage when we should've been focusing on making mortgage payments on our principal residence. Our new partners Mike and Todd proved to be hard working, agreeable confidants in the battle to see the company triumph. Despite our best efforts, serious additional cash infusions, and fifty percent of our time (backed by no salary, of course), we eventually closed the corporation down a year or so later. Our accountants used the losses as best as they could to minimize the throbbing financial sting.

In the end, we justified our actions on two critical fronts. We managed to uphold our exclusive sales and distribution rights, unshackling my cousin from the peculiar predicament he was unfairly placed in; and, much more importantly for Chris, Dave and I, we still can enjoy sitting at the family table with one another. Actually, my relationship with Chris is stronger today than it ever was. To be frank, he's developed into quite the unshakable and formidable warrior. He's the one dude you want at the helm should you go into battle, not the guy you want to see coming through your binoculars. For those of you still cross-examining our actions, you haven't met Chris's father (my Mum's big brother, my second father, and our family's undisputable moral compass)—having disappointed him by choosing power and money over family would've stung way, way more.

The moral here isn't that losing small food fortunes is okay if it means saving Easter lunch with your next of kin. It's about reminding yourself to challenge your logic before making your lil' sis the social media marketing guru of your company, or partnering with Pops to launch his legendary sweet potato home fries. Cousin Chris and I have a uniquely staunch relationship that implored us to go Dutch on our wild and crazy-expensive outing and then eventually call it a day. If you were parked in a similar predicament with your blood, could you call it a day and move forward? Before you start handing out jobs or commitment letters to your family make sure you're partnering with, or hiring them because they have the right talent and aptitude, or at least potential talent. Think about what type and size of impending conflict tomorrow might bring, and ask yourself if you'll be emotionally equipped to navigate through it. Have no doubt, on the road to profit, conflict is inescapable and with it comes the responsibility to govern your emotions.

Make sure that your company is, or can become, large enough to adequately support you and your posse. We work closely with two very well respected, prominent and successful family-owned food companies. One generates enough volume and opportunity to employ and sufficiently reward parents, siblings, spouses, children, cousins and even neighbours—but, each has a key role in the company that reflects their specific talent and temperament. The other is run by three equally sharp brothers and their larger-than-life and lovable father. Before their collective eleven children were old enough to need a career, the family agreed that treating everyone equal was the mission; and given that the company tree wasn't large enough for each of the children to suitably harvest from, it was decided none of them would be given a career opportunity. That's not to say that each of the brother's children didn't work at the company during a few summers to earn money and valuable experience—in fact, I imagine slugging it in the factory was a mandatory rite of passage. And, most importantly, the intent of this chapter was to rightfully brag about the insane calibre of my office lunches.

Let it Simmer ~

1. *Are you partnering with a close friend or family member because you make a strong team together, or because it's comfortably convenient and could be exciting?*

2. *Do you unintentionally upstage friends or family at the negotiation table? If so, do you know when to take a backseat to let them shine and to maintain balance in your more important relationship outside the office?*

3. *If you're in a position where involving a close friend or family member feels inescapable, have you documented the difficult discussion about expectations, boundaries and consequences?*

4. *Is your company large enough to permanently support the friends and family members currently working there? Would it be healthier to provide them with a clearly defined contract opportunity so that you both can assess a longer-term fit?*

5. *What's in your office lunchbox?*

CHAPTER 33

Putter or Butter?

Networking

I'm a ghastly golfer so despite the chance to forge a deeper relationship with my supply partners and retailers, I don't attend too many—well, actually not any—of the many golf tournaments I'm invited to. I don't mind playing sports, especially with my own three kids, but for me, playing or worse yet, watching most sports is like watching the apartment lobby camera channel—it's fun and exciting for about 5 minutes. Cooking, eating, watching and learning about food, however, is pure pleasure for me.

I'd trade a primo set of TaylorMade® golf clubs for a set of Wüsthof® Chef knives any day. So when JP, my Uncle El, Milan, Just-a-Pinch (Gourmet Salt) Mario and my brother formed a Brotherhood dedicated to 24-hour food excursions, I knew I'd discovered front row season tickets worth investing in. The bi-monthly outings look something like this: We pick a showcase, occasionally rare, ingredient (à la *Iron Chef*)—something like white truffles or Kobe beef. Each person submits an ambitious dish contribution to Dave one week before the outing so that he can organize a structured full day's gorging where gluttony becomes a sport.

At 2 p.m. on a Friday, we leave the office and rendezvous at one of two hush-hush locations, both an hour out of the city. Copious amounts of gorgeous Italian wines, a giant leg of Iberico ham, a hand-forged-iron stone pizza oven and monogrammed cutlery are indispensable essentials. We cook, eat and drink until around midnight. We then dust off a bottle of Brother Milan's homemade plum brandy and then finally re-tire to bed. By 6 a.m. the premises are cleaned, and we're back on the road and home to our families by breakfast. We usually have a new pledge each time—typically a supply partner or a customer from the food biz. It's my chance to forge a deeper relationship, but over a glass of wine and a leg of imported pork instead of over a hot dog at the half-way house. Hey hey, now that's more my speed.

CHAPTER 34

Chew Your Food

Tale of the Triple Pants

Onward and upward. It's high time to take a solid crack and bust open any crusty hesitations that are holding you back from moving forward with your quest. Protect yourself. Move sensibly by defining and then playing within your risk tolerance threshold, but move forward. Carefully structure your game-plan so that, if you should nose-dive, you'll easily be able survive the fall. If and when you do fall, take time to let the situation simmer and then apply the learnings and try again—and again. Create and embrace the self-pressure that comes along with involving supply partners and prospective retailers in your mission. If nothing else, consider that a little well-placed stress is both healthy and necessary to keep you travelling in the right direction.

I started this book by confessing that your fight will be about surprising, and sometimes unplanned, successes as well as carefully planned product launches ending in agonizing failure. Full disclosure: I'll be the first one to admit that I've had more food fiascos than tasty triumphs. For clarity's sake, let's call it five to one, respectively. And believe you me, I'm still sitting on a colourful cornucopia of more untold whoppers that I haven't shared for either legal or future tactical motives—remind me to tell you about the popular 80s seltzer that we struggled to resurrect. But hey, to the quote the Chairman of the Board: 'Regrets I've had a few, but then again too few to mention.'

The flip side of the coin is that, for every five or six letdowns, we've had one hell of a sweet ride. Consider that most everyone you know has secretly had a viable idea at some point in his or her life. It's startling then to recognize just how very few folks choose to act on their burning ambitions. To breakaway from this pack of overly-cautious nonstarters, you'll need to flush the idea out of your system and be cleansed of that nagging blueprint that you've been telling people about for longer than you care to remember. Go for it. Be all in. Sound the bell. Strap on a pair of mitts, step into the hot and sticky ring and throw the first punch to instigate your food fight.

'*Son, please chew your food! Breathe in between bites. Slow down, no one is chasing you!*'

I can't tell you how many times I've heard these cautionary words in my life. But damn it, I'm hopelessly addicted to the flavour rush too damn much despite the imminent risk of passing indigestion. Want proof? I'll let you in on my top-secret triple-pant-size strategy to prove just how much I love to food, can unleash my appetite and just flat-out go for it. When I travel on vacation, I'm always prepared to accommodate my culinary curiosity and ravenous appetite. I'll pack three different waist sizes of pants because I know what to expect. After years of practice, I'm all too familiar with the rapid transformation and damage that I'll wreak on my waistline, so deploying what I call the *34-6-8* routine is mandatory if I'm to function comfortably.

Hold your judgment and give me the chance to explain. Six or so weeks leading up to my travel, it's all about the pregame training. You see, I know I'm about to be all in at the all-inclusive buffet so doubling down on trips to the gym and cutting serious calories will be my fleeting obsession. When it's time to go, I'm dialled in. I'll step off the plane in my 34" Levi's feeling like an Olympian. Halfway into the voyage, after having put back one too many beachside cervezas and hot chicken wings, I'll slip on a pair of 36" khakis to let the belly breathe a bit better. By the end of the week, after having totally invested myself into the experience, I'll need to strap on my emergency 38s to survive the flight home.

However, the very moment that I touchdown on Canadian soil, it becomes all about the control of knowing it's time to unplug, step away and to rebalance. Within a week, I'm sporting my Levi 511's again and looking back on the adventure with a nod and a smirk. I suppose you can call it eating in extreme moderation. Or you can just call me un-controllably crazy. Either way, it's how I'm built.

When an opportunity to create and launch a food product comes my way, I attack the situation with the same ferocious appetite and veracity. I'm all in, baby. Look, don't over-think the jump too much—think of it more as a well-organized expedition than as a blind leap of faith. If you want it, go for it with a purpose and without regret. Avoid the energy-vortex that comes from analysis-paralysis. Assess the situation as you go without waiting around for every light between your starting point and the finish line to turn green. Otherwise, you're bound to grow weary and then leave your car parked in your driveway. Go for it with a sharp aware-ness and the responsibility of knowing when to put your fork down, get up from the table and then properly digest until it's time to dig in again.

It's a common characteristic and philosophy that serves to separate the corporate soldiers from the entrepreneurial warriors. Learn to think quickly and to operate freely with no reservations. Relish in the last minute magic and the exhilaration that comes as a result of string-ing together a clever and imaginative opportunity with only a few uten-sils at your disposal—this is the mark of a genuine entrepreneur's spirit and ultimate ability.

My most memorable and prized meals were never associated with scoring a rare reservation at the hottest and hippest restaurants. Whether it was barbecuing short ribs on the beach in Maui while watching surfers carve up the waves, or brown-bagging a silky Pinot Noir while enjoying a fresh focaccia on a vineyard bench in Napa, it was never about over-thinking the menu options. Nah, it's all about embra-cing the last minute opening and then totally giving into the experi-ence. Imagine being able to dream up a product idea in the morning, and then have it become your reality to pursue by dinner.

When obsessing over your work comes naturally, onlookers will de-scribe it as passion. For me, if it's about food, I'm instantly excitable. Food is my medicinal marijuana. These days, I've slowed down a touch because I've had to as my stomach isn't ironclad anymore. Dramatic binging followed by erratic weight fluctuation have thankfully also slowed. Admittedly, I'm also a tad more responsible when I operate, but still take on more challenges than most. I've finally dropped the danger 38" waist zone from my arsenal and can now proudly travel with only a couple pairs of 34s—and, of course, a pair of emergency 36s. But I guess that comes with a little experience and one too many generous slices of humble pie à la mode.

As with any recipe, there are numerous interpretations and techniques that can be used to prepare a successful dish, but it's the final product that matters most. Whichever industry you're attempting to conquer, be sure to lean heavily on the fundamentals. Let my lemons help to serve as a careful reminder that it takes more than one attempt to pull off a perfect dish. Add your own flair. Mix it up in your own way, but don't change or challenge the basic ingredients. Like every pizza dough, a product launch plan will demand a lot of kneading before the final pie presents itself. Keep battling and know that you may have to survive ten unwelcomed flops before busting the game wide open with your eleventh swing. Play hard, but play smart. If you're new to the product launch game, try to resist up and quitting your day job until that triumphant eleventh wallop comes through. Play the game on the side until there's enough traction to transfer all of your energy and effort into the same pot. Keep your head down, keep your cash burn rate way down, and keep chopping away. Have faith, it's not a matter of if it'll happen, it's much more about when it'll happen and then ensuring that you're properly suited up for battle.

To be completely honest with you, what keeps me going is the fear and discomfort of not being able to repeat the process, for that would mean I'd have to actually find a job for a living. Ugh! Nope, not me. I'm hopelessly addicted to three tasty vices: chocolate, coffee and napkin sketches.

Let it all Simmer ;)

Acknowledgements

To my wife Lisa (fresh pasta fanatic) for her unwavering enthusiasm & encouragement for every new road I unexpectedly decide to travel; to my little meatballs Gabriel (steak hunter), Eliana (bacon addict) & Lea (salmon sashimi ninja); to my Mother (lemon meringue mama) for her unforgettable spirit; to my Father (hot pepper maniac) and Brother (master pizzaiolo) for the nearly 3,000 superb homemade office lunches, complete with a daily helping of integrity; to my Nonna Iole (arancini artist) for her endless nourishment; to Uncles El (burnt & butterflied sausage Baron) and Lou (pecan pie specialist) for fueling my appetite for something more; to my Mother-in-Law Marisa (queen of brunch) for entertaining my unpredictable appetite; to my childhood friend Christine (poutine predator) for her commitment to seeing this book completed; to BrandFusion warriors Febe Ann (chocolate dreamer) and Archie (popcorn Picasso); and to my business partner Joe (King of Alaskan King crabs) for the bottomless cups of vino and wisdom.

About the Author

Bruno Codispoti is Founding Partner at BrandFusion Ltd., and Co-founder at Crazy Uncle Cocktails. Over the past twenty years, he has crafted and launched over one hundred unique retail food products into the Canadian and US marketplace. He lives in Vaughan, Ontario with his wife Lisa and their three children.

Printed in December 2016
by Gauvin Press,
Gatineau, Québec